15V

SHIP WELDING
HANDBOOK

Ship
Welding
HANDBOOK

MARTIN J. COEN
Welding Engineer
Navy Department

New York - 1943

CORNELL MARITIME PRESS

Printed in the United States of America

Preface

The purpose of this book is to present in a simple, understandable manner some of the fundamentals of direct-current, metallic arc welding in ship construction. While many welding books attempt to cover the entire field of welding, this one is designed to deal with only one branch of welding, but to do so in detail.

The main idea is to lay a groundwork of some of the many things that enter into shipyard welding and so prepare the reader for books of a more technical nature. If this book will help show the uninitiated welder that welding consists of more than merely melting an electrode, then its purpose is accomplished.

Acknowledgments are made to Miss Elsa W. Stone of the Newton High School, Newton, Massachusetts, for reading and criticizing the manuscript; to Miss Elizabeth Deans of the School Administration Staff, Newton, Massachusetts, for many helpful suggestions; to Mr. Nicholas F. DeGaetano, Associate Principal Inspector, Hull Construction, U.S.N., for reviewing some sections; and to the following companies for photographs, tables, and other materials:

Lincoln Electric Company, Cleveland, Ohio

General Electric Company, Schenectady, New York

Westinghouse Electric and Manufacturing Company, Pittsburgh, Pennsylvania

Air Reduction Sales Company, New York, New York

Society of American Shipbuilders and Designers

The American Welding Society

The American Society of Mechanical Engineers

Table of Contents

SHIP WELDING
HANDBOOK

Part 1

Introduction to Welding

Welding may be defined as a consolidation of metals by heat and pressure or by heat alone.

There are at least thirty-three methods of welding in use to-day. All of these methods may be listed under the following main divisions:

      1. Non-Pressure Processes
      2. Pressure Processes
      3. Brazing Processes

Non-Pressure Processes have three subdivisions, one of which is Arc Welding. Metallic Arc Welding, the particular method with which we deal in this book, is one of the seven methods listed under Arc Welding.

The fact that welding involves more of the different sciences than any other trade or process has two opposite effects upon many people. To some it opens up a life work with unlimited possibilities; for others, there is too much to learn and, there-fore, after learning the mechanical manipulation of the elec-trode, they neglect the "how and why" and feel that theory belongs only to the engineers and supervisors. The welder should realize that welding in a practical way cannot progress very far without the proper understanding of such things as electricity, the effects produced by welding, metallurgy, radio-graphic work, chemistry, and mathematics, to mention only some of the things that seem farfetched to the practical welder.

If a welder has a basic knowledge of electricity he will realize the necessity of proper care of the welding machine. With a knowledge of the welding effects on a metal structure, he will realize the necessity of such things as welding sequences and heat treatment, and will know how to overcome possibilities of undesirable stresses and distortion. A knowledge of the other subjects connected with welding will also show him that certain things must be welded a certain way and help him distinguish the right procedure from the wrong.

The first practical experiments with welding took place seventy or eighty years ago, but little if anything was accomplished at that time. The real development of metallic arc welding has taken place within the last fifteen years. It is during this time that covered electrodes have been efficiently manufactured, and generators for welding so highly developed. Even with all the experiment and research that has taken place, welding is still in its infancy and has a long way to go.

The benefits of the progress already made have been proven by the enormous amount of war production made possible through the use of welding. Ships are now built in terms of days instead of months; the production of tanks, pipe lines, locomotives, as well as all other types of metal products, has been speeded up so that it is done in a fraction of the time it would take without welding.

The developments of recent years open up wide vistas of future possibilities to men of vision who wish to devote themselves to experimentation and research in this field.

Part 2
Electricity

Before attempting to go into any detail concerning electricity, it is first necessary to have a general idea of how electricity acts. For purposes of illustration, the action of electricity may be compared with the action of water, because in many cases, particularly in simple electric circuits, electricity will act in the same manner as water under similar conditions. In order to appreciate this type of comparison, the electricity must be thought of as water, and the cables through which the electricity flows must be thought of as pipes. When water flows through a system of pipes, it follows a path determined by the pipes. The cables carrying electricity likewise determine the path of the electricity. This electrical path is referred to as a circuit.

When a water pipe is cracked or broken, it is only common sense to conclude that water will leak out of the pipe. If the insulation of a cable is broken or damaged, it is possible to have an electrical leak. This leak of electricity is referred to as a ground, or short circuit. If the leak takes place from the cable to the side of the ship or the earth, it is called a ground. If it takes place across two cables, it is called a short circuit—the current in either case does not flow through its complete path.

It is also logical to say that more water can flow through a pipe of large cross-sectional area in a given time than can flow through a pipe of small cross-sectional area in the same time. For one thing, a small pipe will offer more resistance to the flow of water than a large one will. Therefore, more pressure will

3

have to be used to overcome the resistance of the small pipe; and because there is very little resistance in the large pipe, only a small pressure will be required to overcome its resistance. These same conditions also hold in the electric circuit. The larger the cross-sectional area of the cable carrying the electricity, the easier it is for the electricity to flow; and the smaller the cable is in cross-sectional area, the greater will be the electrical pressure required to force the electricity through the cable.

FLOW OF ELECTRICITY

Suppose water is being pumped through a pipe line made up of various sizes of pipes, as in Figure 1. Due to the fact that

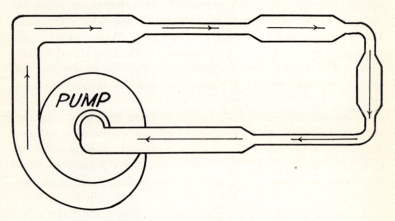

Figure 1: Water pump analogy of electrical resistance.

some pipes are large and some are small in cross-sectional area, it can be seen that there will be different resistances offered to the flow of the water. The smaller sections of pipe will offer the greater resistance, and will tend to slow down the flow of water. In order to overcome this slowing-down effect, more pressure must be supplied by the pump. This additional pressure will represent the loss in original pressure due to the pipe resistance.

If the pump is of such design that it can give only a constant value of pressure, it will be unable to supply the needed additional pressure, and the water will flow at a lower pressure after passing through the narrow sections of pipe. The result of this condition, then, is that the water will return to the pump at a lower pressure than it left the pump. The difference between the pressure at which the water left the pump and the pressure at which it returns is known as the total pressure drop of the system. This total pressure drop will, of course, be equal to the sum of the individual pressure drops of each section of pipe, the greater pressure drops being caused by the smaller pipes.

In an electric circuit, such as shown in Figure 2, the resist-

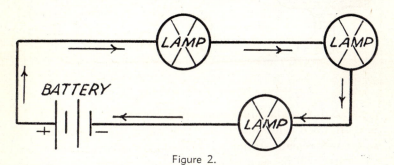

Figure 2.

ance of the lamps is greater than the resistance of the cables connecting the lamps. In this case, then, the lamps may be compared with the narrow sections of pipe. That is, they offer more resistance to the flow of current than do the cables and, therefore, cause a larger drop of electrical pressure.

The term used to designate electrical pressure is **voltage.** It can, then, be said that each lamp and each section of cable causes a voltage drop and the sum of these voltage drops is equal to the voltage drop of the entire circuit.

Direction of Flow. To illustrate the direction of flow of electric current, consider Figure 3. Here are two glass tanks

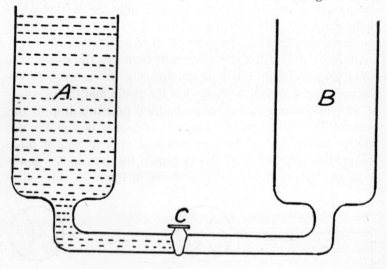

Figure 3.

connected by a glass tube containing a shut-off valve C. If one tank is filled with water and the valve is turned "off," the water will remain stationary. When the valve is turned "on," the water will be seen to flow from tank A into tank B. The water will again remain stationary when the water in both tanks reaches exactly the same level. This may be explained by saying that the water in tank A is under pressure, and as soon as the valve is opened, the water will flow into tank B because there is no pressure to oppose its flow. In other words, the water flows from a high-pressure point to a low-pressure point. As the water continues to flow into tank B, it will start to build up a pressure in such a way as to oppose any more water flowing into this tank. When the water in tank B has reached the same level as the water in tank A, the pressure in each tank will be equal and opposite to the pressure in the other.

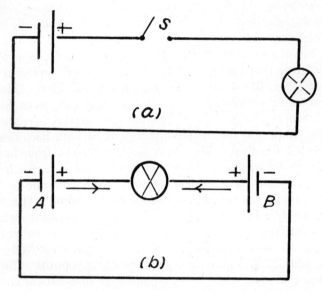

Figure 4.

To compare the action of electricity with that of the water in the tanks, consider Figure 4 (top). Here is a lamp connected to a battery, but the switch S is in the "off" position so current cannot flow. The current, like the water in the tanks, is there and ready to flow; but because the switch is "off" the circuit is broken, since the current must have a continuous path or circuit through which to flow. It can be seen that when the switch is closed there will be a continuous path through which the current may flow. This path will be from the positive terminal of the battery, through the lamp, and back to the battery by way of the negative terminal. When the switch is closed, the lamp will light, indicating the flow of current—just as, in Figure 3, when the valve C was turned "on" the flow of water could be seen. The point to note in both cases is that the path of flow is from a point of high pressure to a point of low pressure, the high-pressure point in the battery circuit being the positive terminal and the low-pressure point the negative terminal.

If two batteries of equal electrical pressure are connected in such a way that the flow of current of one is opposite to that of the other, the result is that no current will flow. This can be shown by connecting a lamp to two batteries, as in Figure 4 (bottom). The positive terminal of each battery is connected to the lamp, and the negative terminals of both batteries are connected together. The result is that current from battery A is opposed by current from battery B, and as both currents have the same voltage, neither current can continue to flow. The water in the tanks also illustrates this point. The water flowed only when there was a difference of pressure between the point from which it was flowing and the point to which it flowed. As soon as the difference in pressure was removed—that is, as soon as both pressures were equal and opposite—the flow of water stopped. This principle holds in all electrical circuits. In order to have a flow of current, there must be a difference of electrical pressure. In electrical terms, this condition is referred to as a difference of potential or a difference of voltage.

There are two distinct parts to any electrical circuit, namely, the internal circuit and the external circuit. This idea may be seen if the circuit is compared to a system of pipes through which water is being pumped. The water will flow from the pump at a high pressure and return at a low pressure. After the water returns to the pump, it is brought up to its original pressure by the pump and flows through the pipes again. The internal path of the water is that within the pump, or from the low pressure point to the high pressure point. The external path is that outside of the pump, and is always from the high-pressure point to the low-pressure point. The flow of electricity is, for the purpose of illustration, the same as that just described for the water. That is, outside the generator, battery, or whatever the source of supply may be, the current will always flow from a positive, or high pressure point, to a negative, or low-pressure point. Inside the source of supply, the flow will be from a negative to a positive point.

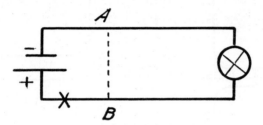

Figure 5: Current flows across AB.

Electricity will always follow the line of least resistance, and it is because of this fact that short circuits occur. An example of this tendency to follow the line of least resistance may be illustrated by Figure 5. Here is a lamp connected in a battery circuit by two pieces of cable. The cables may be insulated or they may be two pieces of bare wire. In either case, under proper conditions the current will flow through the circuit, causing the lamp to light. If both these cables should be connected by another cable or piece of metal (in the case of insulated cables, the insulation would have to be damaged), as at AB in the figure, the lamp would immediately go out. There would not be enough current flowing through the lamp to keep it illuminated, because the greater amount of current would be flowing through the connection AB.

There would, however, be a very small amount of current flowing through the lamp. The relative amount of current flowing through AB and through the lamp may be understood by Figure 6, which shows a water tank with two outlets. One outlet is very small, offering a great deal of resistance to the flow of water; the other outlet is very large, offering practically

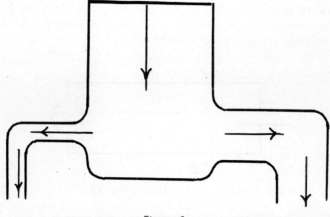

Figure 6.

no resistance. The lamp in Figure 5, because of its high resistance to the flow of current, may be compared to the small outlet of the tank in Figure 6. The connection AB in Figure 5 may be compared to the large outlet because both allow an excessively large flow due to absence of resistance. When a condition is encountered whereby an excessively large amount of current flows, as in Figure 5, it is known as a short circuit.

If a fuse were placed in the circuit at point X in Figure 5, the excessive amount of current would cause the fuse to "blow," breaking the circuit and preventing any further flow of current.

OHM'S LAW

All of the conditions so far considered may be shown mathematically by what is known as Ohm's Law. This law is the basis for all electrical calculations, and should be thoroughly understood.

The three basic terms used in electricity are:

1) **Current—Ampere.** The unit of electric current per second is the ampere, and is the rate of flow of electricity through a circuit, just as the rate of flow of water is gallons per minute through a pipe.

2) **Pressure Voltage—Volt.** The unit of electrical pressure is the volt. The total voltage developed at the generator is known as the **electromotive force** (e.m.f.) of the circuit. The amount of voltage necessary to cause current to flow through any particular resistance is the voltage drop of that resistance. The difference of electrical pressure between the positive and negative terminal of a complete circuit is known as the **potential difference.** This difference of potential is expressed in terms of volts.

3) **Resistance—Ohm.** A cable, lamp, motor, or anything else through which current may flow, offers a resistance to this flow of current. The unit of resistance is the ohm, and may be defined as that resistance which will allow one ampere to flow when one volt is impressed across its terminals.

In any electrical circuit there are three factors to be considered: the current (in amperes) or rate of flow of electricity; the resistance (in ohms) of the material through which the current flows; and the e.m.f. (in volts) which causes the current to flow. If we know any two of these factors, we can easily calculate the third by means of Ohm's Law. This law states that the current is equal to the e.m.f. divided by the resistance. The formula for this statement is:

$$I = \frac{E}{R} \qquad \text{(Formula 1)}$$

Where I represents the current in amperes, E represents the e.m.f. in volts, and R represents the resistance in ohms.

Problem 1

An electric motor has a resistance of 10 ohms and is connected across 100-volt mains. What current will flow through the circuit?

Using the formula $I = \dfrac{E}{R}$ $I = \dfrac{100}{10} = 10$ amps.

From the above formula it follows that if R, the resistance of the circuit, is increased and the voltage remains the same, the current will be smaller. In other words, as the resistance increases, the current decreases in direct proportion, which means that the current is inversely proportional to the resistance.

Problem 2

If we connect to the same source of supply a motor having twice as much resistance as in Problem 1, we still have the same e.m.f., which makes the calculations as follows:

$$I = \frac{100}{20} = 5 \text{ amps.}$$

Thus we find the current half of what it was in Problem 1.

If the voltage of the circuit is increased, the current will increase in direct proportion to the voltage.

Problem 3

Connecting the same motor as used in Problem 1 to 200 volt mains, we find that:

$$I = \frac{200}{10} = 20 \text{ amps.}$$

In this problem we doubled the voltage and therefore caused twice the amount of current to flow.

Summing this up it is seen that:

Rule I. The flow of electric current is directly proportional to the voltage of the circuit and inversely proportional to the resistance of the circuit.

If the values for I and R of the circuit are known, Formula 1 may be transposed to solve for E directly as:

$$E = I\,R \qquad \text{(Formula 2)}$$

Here it is shown that the voltage of the circuit is the product of the current and resistance. If either the current or resistance increases, the voltage will increase in direct proportion.

Problem 4

A piece of electrical apparatus draws 10 amps. and has a resistance of 10 ohms. What voltage is necessary to cause the current to flow through this circuit? From Formula 2 we have:

$$E = 10 \times 10 = 100 \text{ volts}$$

Problem 5

What voltage is necessary if the resistance of Problem 4 is doubled?

$$E = 10 \times 20 = 200 \text{ volts}$$

It can be seen from the last two problems that when the resistance of a circuit is increased, the voltage must be increased in direct proportion if the same amount of current is to flow, therefore:

Rule II. With a constant current flow, the voltage will increase or decrease in direct proportion to the resistance.

Rule III. With a constant resistance, the voltage will increase or decrease in direct proportion to the amount of current flowing.

Problem 6

A circuit has a resistance of 10 ohms and draws 2 amps. What voltage must be impressed on this circuit?

$$E = 2 \times 10 = 20 \text{ volts}$$

Problem 7

If the circuit of Problem 6 should draw only one-half as much current, what voltage would be necessary?

$$E = 1 \times 10 = 10 \text{ volts}$$

If the resistance is the unknown factor in a problem concerning Ohm's Law, we may solve for it directly by:

$$R = \frac{E}{I} \qquad \text{(Formula 3)}$$

Here it is seen that the resistance is the quotient obtained by dividing the voltage E by the current I, and that if I remains constant, both R and E increase or decrease in direct proportion to each other.

Problem 8

A certain circuit has 100 volts across its terminals and draws 50 amps. What is the resistance of this circuit? From Formula 3:

$$R = \frac{100}{50} = 2 \text{ ohms}$$

Problem 9

Double the current of Problem 8 and find the resistance of a circuit requiring the same e.m.f.

$$R = \frac{100}{100} = 1 \text{ ohm}$$

In other words, if the circuit in Problem 9 will allow twice as much current to flow through it without the help of additional voltage, it must be that the resistance is only one-half of that in Problem 8.

Rule IV. With a constant voltage the current is inversely proportional to the resistance.

SERIES CIRCUIT

It was said in regard to Figure 2 that each lamp in the circuit offered a certain resistance to the flow of current, and that the sum of these resistances was equal to the total resistance of the current. It will be noticed that in this circuit it is necessary for the current to flow through each lamp in turn in order to flow through the complete circuit. Now, if the flow of current is to be maintained, it can be seen that as the number of lamps (the resistance) increases, the voltage of the circuit must also increase. As far as the current is concerned, it will not increase in value regardless of how many lamps are inserted in this circuit, because it is the same current that flows through each resistance and there is no loss of current.

This may be seen by going back to Figure 1, where there are a number of sections of pipe connected in such a way that the water leaving the pump flows through each section. While there is a drop of pressure through the system, the amount of water flowing back to the pump is equal to that which flowed out of the pump. In other words, there is no loss of water in the system. If the current is thought of as being water, it can be seen that, although there is a drop of potential through the circuit of Figure 2, the current will remain the same. This type of circuit is known as a series circuit. The same reasoning and results would apply if, instead of a battery supplying current to a number of lamps, a generator was used to supply current to electric motors.

If an electric motor is connected as shown in Figure 7a, and it has a resistance of 5 ohms and requires 10 amps., voltage must be (using Formula 2): 10×5 or 50 volts.

If another identical motor is added, as in Figure 7b, both motors are said to be connected in series, and the resistance of the circuit in Figure 7b is twice that in Figure 7a.

From Formula 2, the voltage necessary for the circuit of Figure 7b is: 10×10 or 100 volts. .

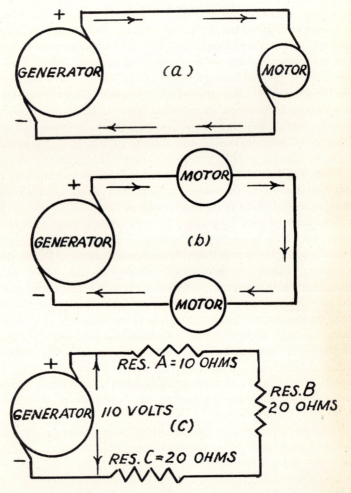

Figure 7.

It is possible to go on continually adding motors of the same current rating, provided the source of supply, the generator, has enough voltage available to supply the voltage drop across each motor. From calculations of Figure 7a it is seen that each individual motor of this type will cause a potential drop of 50 volts. The circuit of Figure 7b has a total drop of 100 volts. If a third motor were inserted, there would be a drop of 150 volts, but the total current flowing would be only 10 amps., which is all that was required for the single motor in Figure 7a. This can be shown by Formula 1:

$$I = \frac{E}{R}, \text{ when } E = 150 \text{ and } R = 15; \ I \text{ will be 10 amps.}$$

Rule V. In any series circuit the current is the same in all parts of the circuit, but there is a potential drop through each resistance in the circuit. This may be illustrated further by the following problems:

Problem 10

Figure 7c shows three resistances connected in series across 100 volt mains. What current flows through the circuit?

The total resistance of the circuit is 10 + 20 + 20, or a total of 50 ohms. According to Ohm's Law we then have:

$$I = \frac{100}{50} = 2 \text{ amps.}$$

Problem 11

What is the voltage drop through each resistance in the circuit of Problem 7c?

1) Through resistance A there is a voltage drop E which is equal to $I\,R$.

$$I = 2 \text{ amps.}, R = 10 \text{ ohms, therefore,}$$
$$E = 2 \times 10 = 20 \text{ volts}$$

2) Through resistance B, by the same reasoning, the drop is:

$$2 \times 20 = 40 \text{ volts}$$

3) The resistance in C is equal to B, therefore, the drop will be the same or 40 volts. The total voltage drops, then, 20 + 40 + 40 = 100 volts, which is the total voltage impressed across the mains.

Rule VI. In any series circuit the total resistance is the sum of the individual resistances.

PARALLEL CIRCUIT

If, instead of connecting a number of lamps to a battery in series, they are connected as in Figure 8, the circuit is known

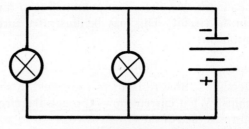

Figure 8.

as a parallel circuit. The result of connecting the lamps in parallel will be a great deal different from connecting them in series. A parallel circuit may be illustrated by Figure 9, where water is being pumped into a large main and is flowing back to the pump through two smaller pipes A and B. Each pipe offers a certain resistance to the water as it flows from C around to D, but twice as much water will flow through A and B as will flow through A or B alone. Therefore, the total resistance of A and B combined must be only one-half of A or B alone. Another way of considering this is to think of a tank of water having one outlet. Through this one outlet a certain amount of water may flow, but if there are two outlets, twice as much water will flow. Therefore, although each outlet does offer a certain resistance to the flow of water, the combined resistance of both outlets is less than the resistance of either outlet.

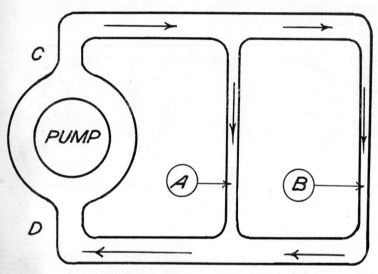

Figure 9: Water analogy of parallel circuit.

Going back to Figure 9, it can be seen that each pipe will take a certain amount of water. If more pipes were used to connect the mains, the same as A and B, then each additional pipe would also take part of the water, with the result that the more pipes that were added the smaller would be the total resistance offered to the flow of water and the greater would be the amount of water that could flow through the system at a given pressure. In order to maintain this pressure, the amount of water must increase as the number of pipes connecting the mains increases.

The same reasoning holds true in electricity when resistances are connected in parallel. Each resistance offers a path through which the current can flow, as in Figure 8. The greater the number of such paths, the more the current that will flow through the circuit, and the total resistance of the circuit will be smaller. In a parallel circuit each resistance will draw its own current, but the voltage of the circuit will be the same in all parts of the circuit.

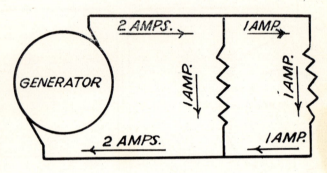

Figure 10.

Figure 10 shows how the total current from a battery will divide between two equal resistances when connected in parallel. Each resistance draws 1 amp.; therefore the generator must supply 1 amp. to each resistance, or a total current of 2 amps. The voltage, however, will be the same in each resistance.

If the resistances are not equal, the current will not divide equally. The larger part of the current will flow through the smaller resistance, while the smaller part of the current will flow through the lamp or motor, offering the greater resistance. This may also be illustrated by a water condition. If the pipe A, in Figure 9, were twice as large as pipe B, it is logical to assume that twice as much water would flow through it as through pipe B, because the resistance of pipe A is only half the resistance of pipe B.

Rule VII. In any parallel circuit the voltage will be the same in all parts of the circuit, but the current may vary through each resistance in the circuit.

In figuring the total resistance of a parallel circuit, it must be borne in mind that the larger the number of resistances in the circuit, the greater will be the total conductance of the circuit. **Conductance** is the opposite or reciprocal of resistance. That is, the greater the conductance of a circuit, the smaller will be the total resistance to the flow of current in the circuit. The larger the number of resistances connected in parallel, the greater will be the conductance of the circuit, because each resistance allows another path for current flow.

To find conductance of the circuit, we can use the formula:

$$C = \frac{1}{R}$$ (Formula 4)

where C is the total conductance of the circuit and R is the total resistance of the circuit.

If two resistances, one of 2 ohms and one of 4 ohms, are connected in parallel, the total conductance will be:

$$C = \frac{1}{2} + \frac{1}{4} = \frac{3}{4} \text{ mho}$$

The term "mho" is used to designate conductance. It will be noticed that this word is ohm spelled backward. C being the reciprocal of resistance, we may obtain the resistance of a parallel circuit by simply inverting the value of C. In the above problem, the total resistance of the circuit is ⁴⁄₃ or 1⅓ ohms.

This may be shown by the following:

$$\frac{1}{R} = \frac{3}{4}, \quad R = \frac{4}{3}, R = 1\frac{1}{3} \text{ ohms}$$

In Figure 11 are shown two conductances connected in parallel. It is obvious that the conductance of B is five times as

great as A, because five times as much current can flow throug͏̲
it. On the other hand, the resistance of A is five times as gre͏̲
as the resistance of B.

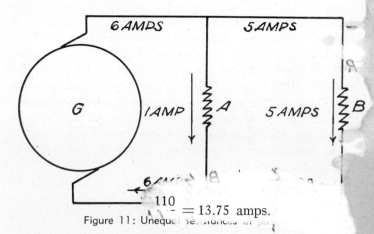

$$\frac{110}{\ldots} = 13.75 \text{ amps.}$$

Figure 11: Unequ͏̲ ͏̲e͏̲s͏̲i͏̲s͏̲t͏̲a͏̲n͏̲c͏̲e͏̲s͏̲ ͏̲i͏̲n͏̲

To find the total conductance of a parallel circuit, Fo͏̲
4 may be used, always keeping in mind that R refers t͏̲
total resistance of the circuit.

Figure 12a shows a parallel circuit containing two resis͏̲
—one of 5 ohms and one of 15 ohms. The total condu͏̲
would be:

$$C = \frac{1}{5} + \frac{1}{15} = \frac{4}{15} \text{ mho}$$

The total resistance would be the reciprocal of
$^{15}\!/_4$, which is equal to $3\frac{3}{4}$ ohms.

Rule VIII. The total conductance of a parallel circu͏̲
the sum of the separate conductances. (Compare this w͏̲
Rule VI.)

The total resistance of a parallel circuit is the recipr͏̲
the total conductance of the circuit.

2) Each resistance causes a voltage drop.

3) The total resistance is the sum of the individual resistances.

4) The current is the same in all parts of the circuit.

2) Each resistance draws its own current.

3) The total conductance is equal to the sum of the separate conductances.

4) The total current is the sum of the currents in the individual resistances.

SERIES-PARALLEL CIRCUIT

Figure 13 shows a combination of a series and a parallel circuit.

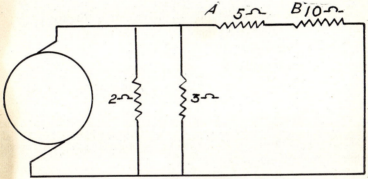

Figure 13: Series-parallel circuit.

In order to find the total resistance of this circuit, first find the resistance of the parallel group, and consider this as being in series with those resistances which are in series.

Consider Figure 13. There are two resistances in parallel— one of 2 ohms and one of 3 ohms; and two resistances in series —one of 5 ohms and one of 10 ohms.

Problem 15

What is the series equivalent resistance of the parallel resistances?

From Formula 5:

$$\frac{1}{R} = \frac{1}{2} + \frac{1}{3} = \frac{3}{6} + \frac{2}{6} = \frac{5}{6}$$

$$R = \frac{6}{5} = 1.2 \text{ ohms}$$

This resistance, then, of $1\frac{1}{5}$ ohms is the series equivalent of the resistances connected in parallel.

Problem 16

What is the total resistance of the circuit in Figure 13?

Parallel resistances	=	1.2 ohms
Resistance A	=	5
Resistance B	=	10
Total resistance		16.2 ohms

Problem 17

If the generator of Problem 16 is operating at 110 volts, what is the current of the circuit?

$$I = \frac{110}{16.2} = 6.79 \text{ amps.}$$

Problem 18

What is the voltage drop through resistance A, through B, through the parallel resistances? Using the formula $E = I\,R$:

$E = 6.79 \times 5 \quad = 33.95$ volts across A
$E = 6.79 \times 10 \quad = 67.9 \quad$ volts across B
$E = 6.79 \times 1.2 = 8.15 \quad$ volts across C and D

The total voltage drop = 110 volts, which is the total voltage drop across the entire circuit.

VOLTMETERS

The voltmeter is an instrument used to measure the voltage drop across an entire circuit, or across any particular part of a circuit. In any type of circuit and under all conditions, it is extremely important to remember the rule given below.

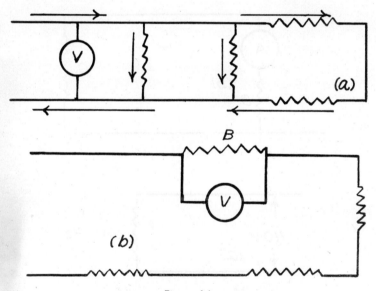

Figure 14.

Rule X. A voltmeter must always be connected in parallel.

If Rule X is not obeyed, and the voltmeter is placed in series with the circuit, the voltmeter will be destroyed. The reason for this is that a voltmeter is designed in such a way that it can

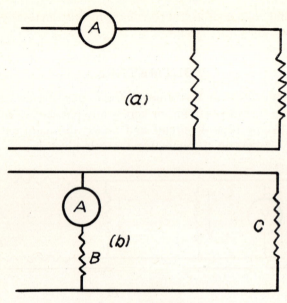

Figure 15.

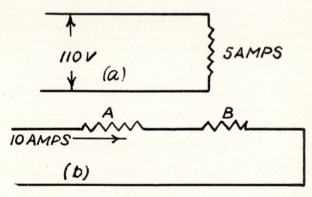

Figure 16.

carry only a very small amount of current, but when placed in parallel it will draw only that amount of current which it is capable of handling. Check No. 2 under Summary of Parallel Circuits.

Figure 14a shows the proper way to connect a voltmeter to measure the voltage across the generator terminals.

Figure 14b shows the correct method of measuring the voltage drop across an individual resistance.

In Figure 14b the voltmeter will measure the voltage drop across resistance B only.

AMMETERS

An ammeter is an instrument used to measure the current in a complete circuit, or the current flowing through any individual resistance.

Rule XI. An ammeter must always be placed in series.

If Rule XI is not obeyed, the result will be a short circuit, because an ammeter is made with a very low resistance, which means, if it is placed in parallel, it will draw an excessively large current.

Figure 15a shows the correct method of inserting an ammeter in a circuit to measure all the current flowing through the circuit.

Figure 15b shows the correct method to measure the current flowing through an individual resistance in the circuit.

In Figure 15b the ammeter will measure the current through resistance B only.

ELECTRIC POWER

Electric power is the product of current and voltage. The unit of electric power is the watt, just as the unit of power of an automobile is the horsepower.

If, then, there is a circuit drawing 10 amps. on a 110-volt line, the power used in that circuit is 10×110 or 1100 watts.

Problem 19

What is the power consumed in Figure 16a?

$$W = I \, E = 5 \times 110 = 550 \text{ watts} \quad \text{(Formula 6)}$$

Where W represents the watts or power of the circuit.

Problem 20

If in Figure 16b, A has a voltage drop of 40 volts, and B has a drop of 60 volts, and there is a current of 10 amps. flowing through the circuit, what is the total power consumed?

The total voltage drop is 100 volts; the current is 10 amps. Therefore, from Formula 6 the power is:

$$W = 10 \times 100 = 1000 \text{ watts}$$

If the voltage in a circuit, or any part of a circuit, is unknown, and it is desired to find the power of the circuit, or any part of it, another formula may be used.

$$W = I^2 R \qquad \text{(Formula 7)}$$

The derivation of this formula may be shown as follows:

It has already been shown that $E = I \, R$

It has also been shown that $W = I \, E$

If we substitute $I \, R$ for E, we can say that $W = I \times I \, R$, and this is the same as writing $I^2 R$

Here the power is the product of the square of the current and the resistance of the circuit.

Problem 21

In Figure 17a, the resistance and current are shown. Find the power necessary to operate this circuit.

From Formula 7:

$$W = 10^2 \times 5 \text{ or } 100 \times 5 = 500 \text{ watts}$$

Problem 22

What power is necessary to operate the circuit shown in Figure 17b?

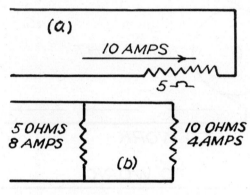

Figure 17.

If the solution is attempted by using Formula 7, it can be seen that the total resistance of the circuit must first be found. To find this total resistance use Formula 5, which is:

$$\frac{1}{R} = \frac{1}{5} + \frac{1}{10} = \frac{2}{10} + \frac{1}{10} = \frac{3}{10}$$

$$R = \frac{10}{3} = 3\frac{1}{3} \text{ ohms}$$

And from Rule IX, it can be seen that the current flowing is 12 amps. Therefore, by Formula 7:

$$W = 12^2 \times 3\frac{1}{3}$$
$$W = 144 \times 3\frac{1}{3} = 480 \text{ watts}$$

THE WELDING CIRCUIT

Polarity. Polarity may be defined as the direction of current flow. In direct-current arc welding, it is particularly important

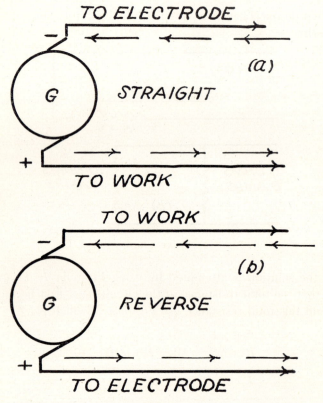

Figure 18: (a) Straight polarity. (b) Reverse polarity.

to understand the meaning and application of polarity. With bare electrodes, straight polarity is generally used. For heavy-coated all-purpose electrodes, reversed polarity is used. For electrodes of the free-flowing type, such as the type used exclusively for fillet welding, straight polarity is also used.*

To distinguish between straight and reversed polarity, consider Figures 18a and 18b. When using straight polarity, the current flows from the positive terminal of the generator, through the cable attached to the work, through the work piece being welded, across the arc gap, into and through the electrode, through the electrode holder, and back through the negative cable to the negative terminal of the generator. In other words, when using straight polarity, the electrode holder is attached to the negative terminal of the generator and the current flows from the work into the electrode.

Reversed polarity, as the name implies, is the reverse of straight polarity as far as the direction of current flow across the arc is concerned. The current leaves the positive terminal of the generator, flows to the electrode, and across the arc gap into the work, and from the work through the cable back to the negative terminal of the generator. When using reversed polarity, the electrode is connected to the positive terminal of the generator and the current flows from electrode into work.

All modern machines are equipped with a polarity switch for changing polarity. On the older types of welding machines it was necessary to change the cable connections at the generator terminals.

Welding Cables. In actual practice the ground cable may not run directly from the generator terminal to the piece being worked on, but might be as in Figure 19, which shows the ground cable running to the work bench. In this case, the metal bench acts as a continuation of the ground cable; or the circuit may be as in the case of ship construction (Figure 20). In this case the ship acts as a continuation of the ground cable.

All connections should be tight and clean. If the connection at any point is loose or dirty, the resistance to the flow of cur-

* See Part 4 for description of electrodes.

rent might be enough to interfere with the job to the extent that only a fraction of the welding power would reach the point being welded; the rest being used to overcome the resistance of the loose or dirty connection. Refer to problems under

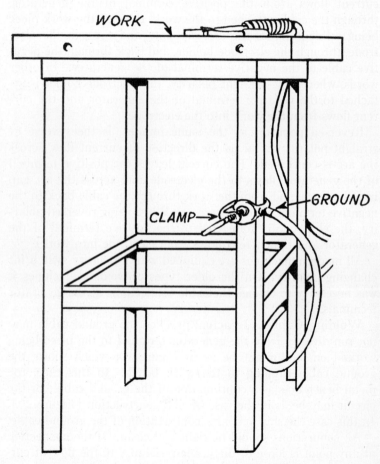

Figure 19: Table acts as part of welding circuit.

Figure 20: Ship acts as part of welding circuit.

Ohm's Law for comparative loss due to resistance. It is, therefore, important for the welder to check all connections of his cables before starting a job. The insulation of the electrode side should always be in perfect condition. If the insulation on this cable is broken, it is likely to short-circuit the source of power, with the result of burning out the cable at the point of the broken insulation. While a short circuit of this type will cause the power source to overheat, it is not likely to cause any permanent damage, as most modern welding outfits are equipped with protective devices to cope with a situation of this kind.

The resistance of a cable will vary directly with the length and inversely as the cross-sectional area. So, the resistance of 100′ of cable will be just twice that of 50′ of cable, with the same cross-sectional area. Having twice the resistance, the longer cable will also have twice the voltage drop. If this voltage drop is excessively large—that is, if the cable has a size too small for its length—it will interfere with the welding operation, because there will not be enough voltage to maintain the proper arc. It should be remembered that the arc is in series with the machine, and, as shown under "Series Circuits," the voltage drops are additive. If the 100′ of cable referred to above has twice the cross-sectional area of the 50′ cable, the total resistance of both cables would be the same. Therefore, as the distance increases from the welding machine to the job, the cross section of the conducting cables must increase also. This applies to the return cable as well as the electrode cable.

In ship welding the return cable may be attached to one point of the ship, and the welding may be carried out at another point. In a case of this type, the ship itself is an actual part of the ground, and a good one, providing the cable is securely fastened and the connection is clean. The same method of ground connection may be used on all other steel structures, providing the return cable makes a clean, tight connection.

When cables are coupled together, the couplings should be of such nature that they, too, provide a clean, tight connection.

It is necessary to figure the size of the cable and know that it is not going to offer too much resistance to the welding circuit.

Table 1 shows the voltage drop per 100′ used.

TABLE 1

Amps.	Size of Wire	Voltage Drop
100	9	8.1
200	6	8.1
300	5	9.6
400	4	10.
500	3	10.
600	2	9.6

A 10-volt drop should be the maximum total through both ground and electrode cables.

The cable used for welding should be rubber-covered, flexible, multistrand copper. The greater the stranding the more flexible it will be, easier and more convenient to handle.

Sources of Current. There are two general sources of welding current in use today. The first one to consider is the single-operator generator. In this case, the welding generator is used to supply current to just one welding line. If the job does not require a full one-half of the total current available, the generator may be used to supply current to two welding lines. This is accomplished through the use of grids, which are simply resistance units, as shown in Figure 21. Let us suppose there is a 400-amp. generator available and the job requires only 150 amps. There is, then, 250 amps. available but not being used. Instead of purchasing another machine, two grids may be connected in parallel to supply 150 amps. to two welders. This results in two men working off the same generator. The reason for connecting the grids in parallel is to divide the current but at the same time keep the voltage in each welding line up to the proper welding voltage.

Figure 21: Resistor arc welder, type WAR, DL. 4382174G1. Top and right side, oblique front view, front cover raised. (General Electric Co.)

In shops, shipyards, and other places where many welding operators work in the same locality with electrodes of the same polarity, the use of this type of equipment to supply arc-welding current to a group of operators simultaneously (instead of using a single-operator welder for each) results in a considerable reduction in the original investment as well as a saving in subsequent maintenance. The possible reduction of installed capacity depends largely on the welding duty—that is, the average percentage of time each operator is actually welding. The lower the average welding duty, the greater are the possible savings obtainable with multiple-operator equipment. For instance, in shipyard work, where the average welding duty is in the neighborhood of 25%, it is common practice to supply 30 operators, using 150 to 200 amps. each, from a single 1500-amp. machine. In contrast, it would require 30 welders with a total capacity of 6000 to 9000 amps. to supply this current with single-operator equipment.

It should be noticed that each grid has its own individual current switches to control the amount of welding current; also, that there is no voltage control on a grid. The voltage is controlled at the main generator, and is theoretically the same in all the grids. The grid is made up of a number of different-size resistances, with a number of switches to change the effect of these resistances to the point where the desired current is available.

THE ARC

The working part of the welding circuit is that between the end of the electrode and the work, or the arc. When the end of the electrode is struck against a piece of grounded work, the welding source is short-circuited, causing a heavy current to flow. The available voltage tends to keep the current flowing as the electrode is withdrawn from the work, and so the current is forced across the air gap. The result is that this air gap becomes ionized. Ordinary atmosphere is an insulator as far as electricity is concerned, but when it is ionized it becomes a conductor of electricity. When this ionizing, or breaking down of air into electrically-charged particles, occurs, an arc is established. A small amount of metallic vapor is now present also, facilitating current flow. The arc, being a part of the electric circuit, is subject to electrical laws the same as any other part of the circuit. That is, the voltage, current and resistance will vary, and upon these variations depends the power which, in turn, will govern the quantity of heat in the arc. The arc may be varied in length, depending upon the voltage available.

The intensity of the heat of the arc has been estimated at from 5000° to 10,000° F. The quantity of the heat of the arc will depend upon the amount of power being consumed. The intensity and quantity of the heat should not be confused. Intensity is the temperature of the arc, and quantity is the amount of heat at this temperature.

Example: A small piece of wood will have a flame of the same intensity as a huge bonfire, but the quantity of heat will be greater in the bonfire. The heat produced by the arc is concentrated in a very small area, and because of this fact the area beneath the electrode and the electrode itself are rapidly brought to fusion temperature, allowing a speedy method of welding. As the electrode reaches welding temperature, which is almost instantaneous upon striking the arc, the metal of the electrode melts and is transferred across the arc, from the electrode to the work, which is likewise molten, and the two metals readily flow together.

This transfer takes place partly in the form of minute globules, and partly in the form of vapor of the electrode metal. The coating is likewise vaporized and forms the protective shield of gas around the arc. At the same time, the arc is melting the workpiece and digging into it, making a place for the electrode metal to lie. The transfer of metal takes place within

he confines of the gaseous shield. The shape of the arc and
shield is roughly that of an inverted V. The further the electrode is from the work, the wider is that part of the arc in contact with the work. The wider it is at the work, the more area
it covers, thereby heating up a larger area than if held close to
the work. This means, then, that instead of the heat being all
concentrated at one particular point, a great deal of it is being
wasted. Because of this, a long arc gives poor penetration.

Individual machines are advantageous in many respects,
particularly so in the matter of individual control. With the
individual or single-operator machine, the welder has complete
control of both voltage and current. He may vary the characteristics of the welding arc to suit the particular job. At one
time, the only thing considered as far as the arc was concerned,
was to have enough heat in the arc to melt the electrode and
fuse the work. However, the advantages of controlling the arc
characteristics to suit the job have become of such importance
that the manufacturers of welding generators take considerable
pains to design their machines in such a way that both voltage
and current can be controlled to very fine limits.

Volt-Ampere Combinations. It is understood that only
when a welder is using a single-operator machine can he control both the current and voltage. Therefore, this does not
apply to a grid system, because the whole system is working
with the same voltage, and the only control the individual
welder has is that of current.

It was previously shown that when the resistance of a circuit
is increased, the voltage carrying the current through the circuit must also increase. If, then, the arc is lengthened, thus
increasing the resistance of the welding circuit, the voltage drop
across the arc is greater. This is equivalent to saying that the
more voltage available, the longer the arc may be drawn. If
no voltage were available, it would be impossible to produce
an arc.

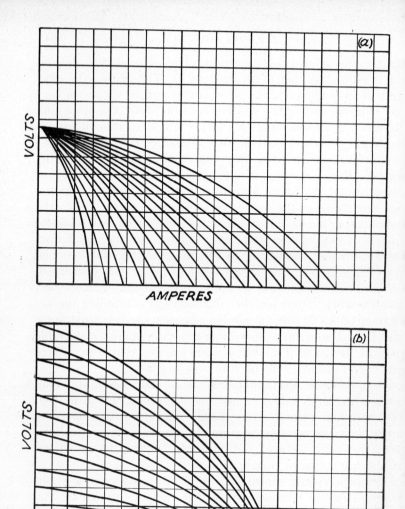

Figure 22.

42

On any individual machine having voltage control, the voltage is available in any desired strength. It may be varied by what is known as the "voltage control," which is really a rheostat.

If, when the machine is started, the rheostat is adjusted to read 70 volts, it is said that the machine is operating on an open-circuit voltage of 70 volts. If the rheostat is varied so as to vary the reading of the voltmeter, the open-circuit voltage is changed accordingly. The term "open-circuit" means the voltage available at the machine terminals before an arc is struck; or in other words, before the circuit is completed. If, when welding is started, the voltmeter on the machine is observed, it will be seen that the reading will drop immediately almost to zero when the electrode contacts the work. That is because the machine is short-circuited and almost no resistance is offered to the flow of current. Therefore, very little voltage is necessary to force the current through the circuit. When the electrode is drawn away from the work and the arc becomes established, the reading of this meter will go up again, showing the voltage through the circuit. If the arc is increased in length, the reading on the voltmeter will increase; while, if the arc is shortened, the reading will decrease. This shows, then, that the arc may be controlled to some extent by simply varying the arc length.

If the ammeter is observed, it will be seen that, as the arc is shortened, the current will increase and as the arc is lengthened the current will decrease.

The amount of control it is possible to obtain by simply varying the arc length is not sufficient to weld different types of jobs where different voltage and current values are necessary. If a welding generator were built in such a way that only current could be varied and the voltage remained constant at all times, control range would, of course, be larger than where the only control offered is by the varying of the arc; and if various cur-

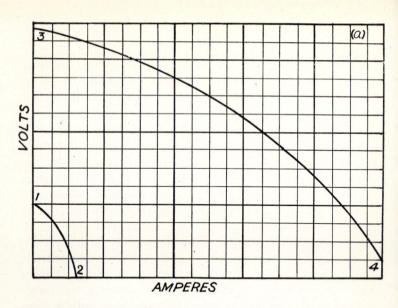

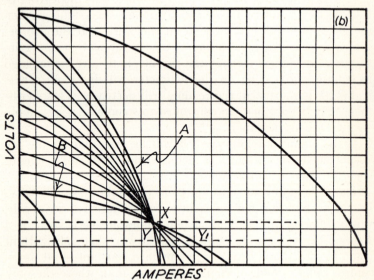

Figure 23.

44

rent readings were plotted, the graph would appear as in Figure 22a. In this case, only one of the two factors that are being used can be controlled, giving only one-half control.

If the machine were of a constant-current type, and only voltage could be controlled, the plotted graph would be as shown by Figure 22b. This method would also give only one-half control. In order fully to control the machine to suit any particular job, there must be control of both voltage and current.

Before going further on arc control, it might be well to explain the difference between arc voltage and open-circuit voltage. **Arc voltage** is the voltage drop across the arc. That is, the amount of voltage necessary to maintain the arc between the electrode and the work. **Open-circuit voltage** is that which is shown on the voltmeter of the welder while the machine is running, but before welding is started. Increasing the open-circuit voltage with any given current rating will increase the total amount of arc voltage available.

In order to obtain control of the arc over any and all ranges, it is necessary, then, to control open-circuit voltage and current. If the voltage and current of a machine, with full control, is plotted, the graph will be as in Figure 23a. Here any desired volt-ampere curve may be obtained between the lowest open-circuit voltage and minimum current curve (1, 2) and the highest voltage and current curve (3, 4). These two curves represent the extremes, but any combination such as a high voltage and low current curve, or a low voltage and maximum current curve, may be obtained.

The arc characteristics due to open-circuit voltage may be better understood by studying Figure 23b. Here are shown two curves, A and B. The curve A is a high open-circuit voltage curve; while B is a low open-circuit voltage curve. Now, for a certain arc length there will be a corresponding voltage drop across the arc. That is, when the arc is increased in

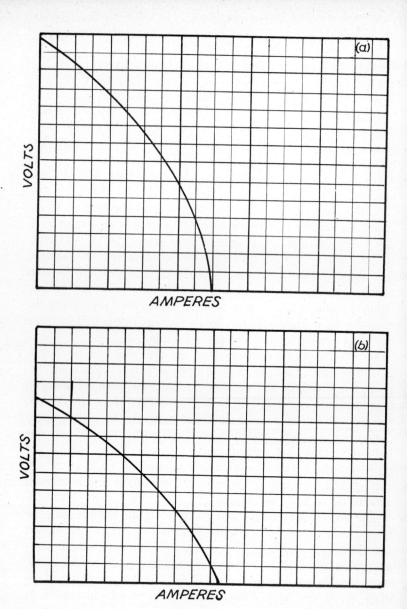

Figure 24: (a) Rubber arc. (b) Short forceful arc.

length, the voltage will also increase, and when the arc is shortened, the voltage will decrease. Going back to Figure 23b, consider X as the voltage drop across the arc of both curves, A and B. Now, if the arc is shortened, the voltage drop across the arc will be decreased to Y, Y_1. It can be seen that the current increase of the high voltage curve has gone up very little, while the current increase of the low voltage curve has become quite large. The arc of curve B, then, is one which has a large current increase as the arc length is shortened; while the current of curve A will remain nearly constant as the arc length varies.

Following are six types of volt-ampere combinations and the type of arc produced by each.

Rubber Arc. A high open-circuit voltage arc, the current of which remains nearly constant whether arc length is increased or decreased. It is ideal for out-of-door work, particularly during windy weather. (Figure 24a)

Short Forceful Arc. This curve has a more gradual slope than the previous one. The current will increase quite rapidly as the arc length decreases. In other words, when the arc is held close, it will dig into the parent metal. It is ideally suited for overhead weaving on fairly heavy stock. (Figure 24b)

Depositing Arc. This curve gives a fast deposit rate and can be used advantageously where deep penetration is not necessary. Where heavy plates are bevelled, there is sufficient penetration obtained with this type of curve. The feature of the depositing arc is speed of depositing metal. (Figure 25a)

Digging Arc. The curve of the arc is more gradual than that of the depositing arc. It is for use where deep penetration is essential, such as butt welding heavy stock that is not bevelled. (Figure 25b)

Tiny Arc. A steep, low-current curve giving a light penetration arc. Particularly useful on light-gauge metal. (Figure 26a)

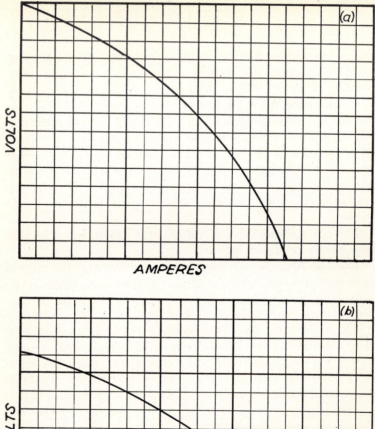

Figure 25: (a) Depositing arc. (b) Digging arc.

48

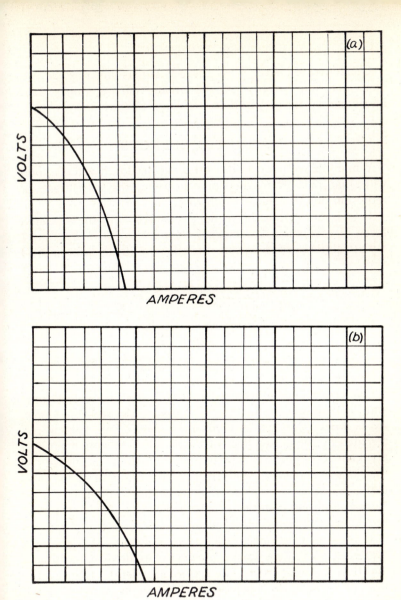

Figure 26: (a) Tiny arc. (b) Concentrated arc.

Concentrated Arc. This curve is not as steep as the previous one, but covers a slightly greater current range. It is ideally suited for cast-iron arc welding. (Figure 26b)

MAGNETIC EFFECTS

While this section is to deal with magnetism, it will deal only with that part of magnetism concerning the attraction and repulsion due to magnetic influence.

It is assumed that the reader is familiar with the attractive force of a common bar magnet such as shown in Figure 27. By attractive force is meant its ability to attract iron or steel.

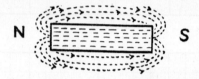

Figure 27: Magnetic field around a bar magnet.

One end of such a magnet is known as the N, or north pole, and the other end as the S, or south pole. Between these poles exists what is known as a magnetic field. This field is represented by the dotted lines of Figure 27. The individual lines are known as lines of induction. The greater the density of the lines of induction, the greater is the strength of the magnetic field. It is considered that these lines emerge from the N pole and enter at the S pole, forming a number of loops in and around the magnet.

Here we can see some similarity to electricity. It was shown that electricity must have a complete circuit to flow through, and that it flowed from a point of high potential to a point of low potential. With magnetic lines the circuit is from a N pole to a S pole, so the N pole of the magnet may be compared to the point of high potential from which electricity leaves the generator. The S pole may be compared to the low potential point through which the electricity returns to the generator.

It was also shown that if two batteries of equal potential were connected in such a way that the positive side of one was

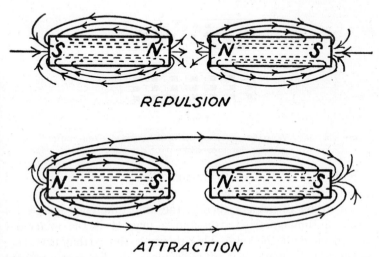

REPULSION

ATTRACTION

Figure 28: Repelling action of like poles; attraction between unlike poles.

connected to the positive side of another, the currents would oppose one another. If two magnets are so placed that the N pole of one is placed very close to the N pole of another, the magnets also will oppose one another. (In speaking of magnets it is common to use the word "repel" rather than "oppose.") Likewise, the S pole of one magnet, when placed very close to the S pole of another magnet, will cause repulsion between the two magnets. On the other hand, the N pole of one magnet will cause attraction between the magnets when placed close to the S pole of another magnet. The attraction and repulsion are illustrated in Figure 28.

Rule XII. Unlike poles attract, like poles repel.

If a magnet is placed near a piece of unmagnetized iron, this piece of iron will be attracted by the magnet. This attractive force of the magnet will be exerted whether the iron is placed near one pole of the magnet or the other.

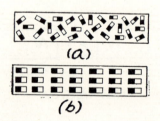

Figure 29: (a) Molecular arrangement of unmagnetized material. (b) Molecular arrangement of a magnet.

Rule XIII. A piece of unmagnetized iron will be attracted by either pole of a magnet.

According to present theory, the only difference between a piece of unmagnetized iron and a magnet is the molecular arrangement of the two. This theory assumes that iron, like all matter, is composed of molecules. It also compares the molecules of iron or steel to minute magnets and, before the metal is magnetized, it is assumed that these molecules are arranged in a haphazard manner as shown in Figure 29a. When the iron or steel is subjected to a magnetic influence, these molecules supposedly arrange themselves in the manner shown in Figure 29b.

Considering the individual molecules as magnets, each with an N pole and S pole, this would seem to be a logical possibility. In Figure 29a, where the molecules are arranged in a haphazard manner, the forces of attraction and repulsion between the S and N poles being in contact, each offsets the other and the net force is zero. In Figure 29b, all the S poles exert their influence in one direction, while all the N poles exert their influence in the opposite direction, giving evidence of a net total force at either pole.

If the magnet shown in Figure 27 were broken at a point halfway between the two poles, each piece would be a magnet with N and S poles. If both of these pieces were also broken in half, four magnets would be had. Regardless of how many pieces a magnet is broken into, or how small the pieces are, each piece will be a magnet with an N and an S pole. This is considered as proof of the molecular theory of magnetism. It is considered that a piece of iron or steel is a magnet, regardless of how small the piece may be, as long as its molecular arrangement is like that shown in Figure 29b.

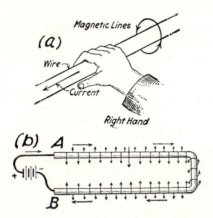

Figure 30: (a) Illustration of Rule XIV. (b) Direction of current through conductor and direction of magnetic field around conductor.

Any conductor carrying an electric current has a magnetic field formed around it. The strength of the magnetic field will increase as the strength of the current flowing through the conductor increases. There is a definite relation between the direction of current flow and the direction of the magnetic field.

The direction of this field may be determined, if the direction of current flow is known, by the following rule, which is known as the Right-Hand Rule:

Rule XIV. If a conductor is grasped in the right hand with the thumb pointing in the direction of current flow, the fingers will point in the direction of the magnetic field.

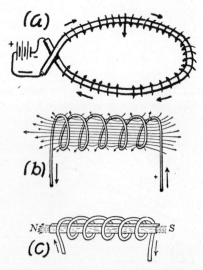

Figure 31: (a) Direction of current through loop and direction of magnetic field around loop. (b) Direction of field through coil. (c) Method of magnetizing iron bar.

This rule is illustrated in Figure 30a, where the curved line represents the direction of the magnetic field. Figure 30b shows the above rule for a complete circuit. It should be noted that the field around the section of the circuit on side A is in a direction opposite to that of side B. The reason for this is that the current through side A is flowing in a direction opposite to that of side B. Check the direction of the field around both sides with Rule XIV.

Figure 31a illustrates the Right-Hand Rule for a conductor

in the form of a single loop, while Figure 31b shows the resultant magnetic field when a current flows through a coil. The magnetic fields around the individual coils are all acting in the same general direction to form one strong magnetic field. If a bar of unmagnetized iron or steel were placed within such a coil as in Figure 31b, it would be in the magnetic field, which consequently would magnetize it. Figure 31c shows a bar of iron in such a field.

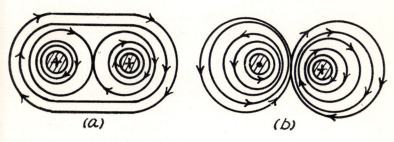

Figure 32: (a) Magnetic fields around conductors carrying current in same direction. (b) Magnetic fields around conductors carrying current in opposite directions.

Another result caused by the magnetic fields surrounding a conductor that is carrying current is shown in Figure 32a. Here are two conductors carrying equal current in the same direction. The conductors are parallel and close to one another. Both fields have the same direction and, because of this, there will be a tendency for the conductors to be drawn together. If the current in these conductors were flowing in opposite directions, the fields would be opposing one another, as in Figure 32b. In this case, there would be a tendency for the conductors to be pushed apart from each other.

It can be seen in Figure 32a that the resultant field envelops both conductors, causing attraction between these conductors. In Figure 32b, where both fields are in opposition, the result is a crowding of the lines between the conductors. This crowding effect causes a repelling action to exist between the conductors.

Rule XV. An attractive force exists between conductors carrying current in the same direction. A repelling force exists between conductor carrying current in opposite directions.

The attractive and repelling actions between conductors increase as the strength of the current flowing through these conductors increases.

MAGNETIC BLOW

Magnetic blow, or as it is sometimes called, **arc blow,** is a condition where the arc is disturbed by magnetic influence. The result is that the arc will jump around and run wild. While there are ways to eliminate this arc blow, the method of this elimination will depend on the specific job being done. There is no one method which can be considered as a cure-all for every job.

While every welder at some time or another has experienced the bother and inconvenience of arc blow, very few, if any, have bothered to find out what causes it. Some welders believe it to be the fault of the machine. While, with some machines having unusually long arc characteristics, magnetic disturbances have less noticeable effect on the arc than machines lacking this ability, the welding machine should not be blamed for magnetic blow.

The real cause of the magnetic disturbance is due to the magnetic fields in the work and not to the design or construction of the machine. In an attempt to overcome magnetic blow, some welders will use an excessively long arc. This remedy is as bad or worse than the blow because of the poor characteristics of the finished weld. Therefore, there is no point in trying to overcome arc blow by pulling a long arc. It should be remembered that while, as a general rule, arc blow is a hindrance, it is, at times, beneficial if the welder knows how to make use of it. One example of its benefits is when welding heavy bevelled plate. If the blow is such that the arc is slightly ahead in the direction of welding, the metal will receive a small amount of preheating which will prevent sticking and give better fusion at the root of the bevel. The benefits, however, are so small that it would be better, if it were possible, to eliminate arc blow entirely.

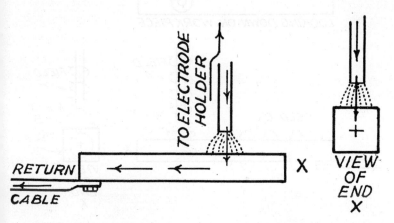

Figure 33: Path of welding current between electrode and return cable.

To get an idea of the cause and effect of arc blow, consider Figure 33. Here is shown the path of the welding current as it passes through the electrode, across the arc into and through the piece of work being welded. The work is a piece of 1″ square bar, an end view of which is shown at the right in Figure 33. Since this is a view of end X, the current would be flowing in a direction away from the reader, or "into" the page, and may be represented by the tail of an arrow.

In a previous section it was shown that every conductor carrying an electric current is surrounded by a magnetic field. The larger the current, the stronger and more effective is the magnetic field. The magnetic fields of Figure 33 may be represented by Figure 34. Here are shown the paths of travel of the current and the three magnetic fields caused by the current. In Figure 34 the magnetic field around the electrode is shown

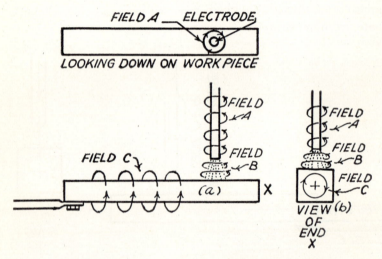

Figure 34: Magnetic fields produced by welding current of Figure 33.

as travelling from the right-hand side of the electrode, across the front and around to the back of the electrode. Looking down at this field, it would appear as in the top view of Figure 34. Check this direction with the Right-Hand Rule previously discussed. This field will be considered as Field A. Field B is shown directly beneath the electrode and travelling in the same direction as Field A. Field C is caused by the current as it travels through the work, and is shown as travelling in and around the work.

From observation of the figures it can be seen that Fields B and C are travelling at right angles to one another. The result is that the arc is attracted by these fields. The amount of attraction and resultant direction of attraction seems to depend to some extent on the distance between the ground connection and the spot where the welding is being done. From practical experiments the following was observed:

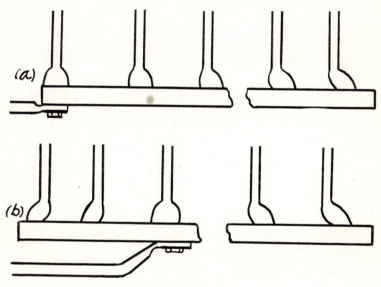

Figure 35.

In Figure 35a is a piece of work 2″ wide by ⅜″ thick and 10′ long, with the ground connection at one end. The arc showed a tendency to veer away from the grounded end for a time, but as the weld proceeded toward the grounded end, this tendency became less. When the arc was directly over the ground cable, the arc ran straight out from the electrode with no tendency to veer one way or the other.

When the ground connection on this piece of work was changed (Figure 35b) from the end to the center of the piece, a different effect was noticed. The weld was started at one end and was run the complete length of the piece. At the starting end, the arc veered away from the ground connection. As the ground connection was approached, the tendency of the arc to blow in a direction away from the ground connection became less until, directly over the ground connection, the arc had no tendency to blow either way. After the ground connection had been passed, the arc showed a tendency to again blow in a direction away from the ground connection.

In both instances there was no arc blow when the electrode was directly over the ground connection. It can be seen that when the electrode is directly over the ground connection the field C (Figure 34), which is caused by the current travelling through the work, is eliminated. At this point, also, the path of current travel is the shortest. When the electrode is directly over the ground, and field C is eliminated, there are left only two fields, A and B. These two fields are in reality only one, because B is a continuation of A. If, then, by eliminating field C it is possible to eliminate this magnetic blow, it is logical to assume that field C is the force which attracts and disturbs the arc.

Working on this theory, a movable ground connection was attached in such a way that as welding progressed the ground connection moved along. The ground was always directly beneath the arc. The field C was eliminated by this method and the arc blow was also eliminated. The arc was direct from the electrode to the work at all times without veering to either side.

In Figure 36 is a frame used in such a way that the path of the current after going through the workpiece C must travel beneath the workpiece through E in order to reach the return cable of the generator. A cross-sectional view from A of the magnetic fields around C and E would be as shown at the right.

Here the field around C is equal and opposite to the field around E. It should be noted that the field around C is caused by the current travelling in a direction perpendicular to the electrode, and is the same as field C in Figure 34, end view. It should also be noted that the field around E is caused by the same current flowing in an opposite direction. From the Right-Hand Rule of magnetic fields it can be seen that the

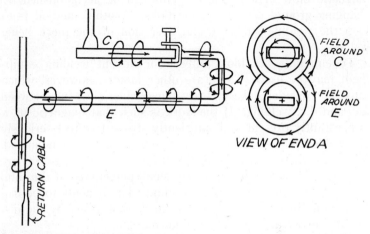

Figure 36: Magnetic field between electrode and ground connection.

fields around C and E are opposing one another. It can also be seen that both these fields are of equal strength because they are caused by the same current.

While the work was being welded in this frame, there was no evidence of magnetic blow. This fact would seem to show that the net effect of the two magnetic fields was zero as far as disturbing the arc was concerned. That is, the magnetic field around E which was purposely made, offset the effects of the magnetic field around C which would ordinarily have caused arc blow. So far this shows that when the field caused by current flowing perpendicular to the electrode, such as field C in Figure 34, is eliminated by a movable ground, or when its effects are eliminated by a counter field, magnetic blow is also eliminated.

While it is usually impossible to impose magnetic fields to offset the effects of the disturbing fields or to eliminate them entirely on every welding job, it is possible at least to reduce magnetic blow in most cases. This can be accomplished by changing ground connection locations. Another method is to loop the welding cable around a section of the piece being welded.

To eliminate arc blow, alternating-current welding equipment may be used. There are other factors, however, which must be considered besides arc blow, when choosing between a.c. and d.c. welding. If the work is such that magnetic blow is constantly present and sufficiently strong to affect seriously the welded job, then a.c. welding equipment is recommended. The jobs where magnetic blow will interfere to this extent are very few, and form an extremely small percentage of the total fabrication completed by arc welding. The benefits to be had by eliminating magnetic blow are more than offset by the disadvantages of a.c. welding equipment.

There is no a.c. welding equipment at the present time that can compare with the average d.c. equipment for all types of welding. Magnetic blow, while in some cases a serious factor, is usually blamed for more than it is really responsible for.

Part 3

Generators

PRINCIPLES OF THE GENERATOR

While it is not a part of the welder's work to repair a welding machine, he should at least understand the general principles, and know how to care for the machine which he uses daily, as well as be acquainted with the various parts.

The generator may be defined as a machine that converts mechanical energy to electrical energy. This conversion is accomplished by two main parts, the **rotor,** or part that rotates, and the **stator,** or that which is stationary.

Alternating Current Units. These units are transformers with taps taken off the turns to regulate the amount of current needed. They work well in mild steel welding, and the arc is smoother as the number of cycles is increased. They also cause little arc blow. With alloy wire, however, and chromium bearing in particular, a.c. is not very suitable. Much heavy welding is done with a.c. units, for they can be made in any range; but d.c. sets are most common in shipyard work.

Direct-Current Units. In the type of generator generally used for d.c. welding, the rotor is composed of the armature assembly, which includes brushes, commutator and armature. The stator is generally the field; the armature is rotated by an outside source such as a gas, or Diesel engine, or an electric motor coupled to its shaft. Figure 37 shows a motor generator set. Here the rotating source is an electric motor coupled to the generator, and both are enclosed in the same housing, forming a single unit.

Welding generators, unlike those used for other purposes, are designed to operate under short-circuit conditions. Weld metal crossing the arc gap causes the welding generator to short-circuit a number of times a second. When this happens, the resistance to the flow of electricity is so small that a large surge of current tends to flow. If this surging effect were not prevented, it would cause excessive heat, spatter of the weld

Figure 37: Motor-driven welding generator. (Lincoln Electric Co.)

metal, and sticking of the electrode. A welding generator of the proper design will limit the surging effect and prevent sticking and spatter. Every time the generator is short-circuited, the voltage drops almost to zero because of the small amount of resistance. The instant each short circuit is cleared, it is necessary that full arc voltage be restored, in order to maintain the arc and prevent "pop-outs."

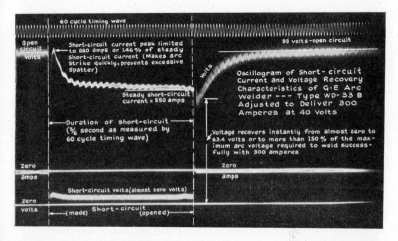

Figure 38: Typical oscillogram of d.c. single-operator arc welder, type WD, taken while output terminals were short-circuited for ⅝ second. Current trace shows that peak current is less than three times steady short-circuit current. Voltage trace shows that instant recovery voltage is more than needed to keep arc working. (General Electric Co.)

The high speed with which current and voltage variations take place makes it necessary to use other means than the ordinary ammeter and voltmeter for measuring arc voltage recovery after short circuit. The only instrument with sufficient speed to measure and record these changes is a high-speed oscillograph (Figure 38). This instrument will make photographic records of the actual amount of current and voltage produced by an arc welder throughout a fraction of a second. Since reaction to short circuit is the real test of d.c. arc welder performance, it is common practice to take oscillograms of short circuit over the entire range of adjustment for comparison or testing purposes. The faster a generator will recover from short-circuit effect and restore full arc voltage to the arc, the steadier will be the arc.

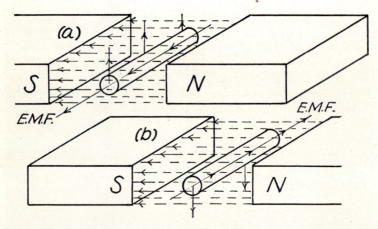

Figure 39: (a) When conductor moves upward, the direction of the induced e.m.f. is towards the reader. (b) When conductor moves downward, the direction of the e.m.f. is away from the reader.

Principle of Generator Operation. If a conductor is placed in a magnetic field, nothing apparent happens; but if it is moved up or down as in Figure 39a, an e.m.f. will be induced in the direction shown. That is, when the conductor moves upward, the e.m.f. flows in a direction towards the reader. When the conductor moves down, the direction of the e.m.f. is reversed, and the e.m.f. flows in a direction away from the reader. Reversing the direction of the conductor will reverse the direction of the e.m.f., provided the direction of the magnetic field is not changed (Figure 39b). It should be noted that the three sets of arrows showing the motion of the conductor, the direction of the e.m.f., and the direction of the magnetic field, are all at right angles to one another. It is on this principle that the following, which is known as Fleming's Right-Hand Rule, is based.

Fleming's Right-Hand Rule

The thumb, forefinger, and middle finger are placed at right angles to one another. Then, if the forefinger points in the direction of the magnetic field, and the thumb in the direction the conductor is moving, the middle finger will point in the direction of induced e.m.f.

Consider now a conductor in a magnetic field as in Figure 40. Here the conductor is in the form of a coil and is rotated in the field. Through part of the rotation the coil is perpendicular to the magnetic field (Position 1), and while in this position it is not cutting through the magnetic field. As it rotates toward Position 2 it starts to cut into the magnetic field. It was said previously that, until the conductor is in motion no effects are produced just by having the conductor in a magnetic field. In other words, until the magnetic lines are cut by the conductor, nothing happens. While the coil is in Position 1, the field is not being cut into and no effects are produced. As soon as the coil starts to rotate and cut into the field, an e.m.f. is generated.

This e.m.f. will increase as the rate of cutting the lines of the field increases. At first, the coil is cutting these lines at a wide angle, but as it approaches Position 2, it begins cutting them in a perpendicular fashion. It is obvious that when these lines are being cut perpendicularly, they are being cut at the greatest possible rate. Therefore, the e.m.f. generated when the coil is in Position 2, is the maximum e.m.f. produced. While the coil was moving from Position 1 to Position 2, the e.m.f. increased from a minimum value to a maximum value, these varying values being due to the varying angle at which the lines

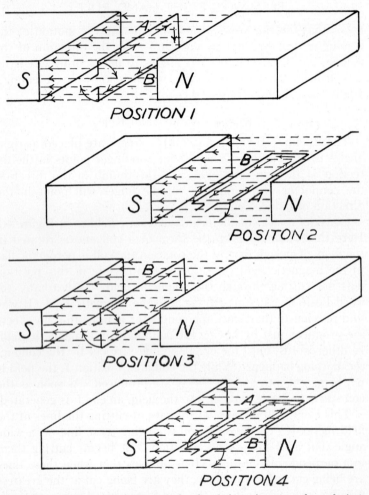

POSITION 1

POSITON 2

POSITION 3

POSITION 4

Figure 40: **Position 1**—Arrows inside of coil show direction of e.m.f. during first quarter-turn of coil. **Position 2**—Arrows show direction of e.m.f. during second quarter-turn of coil. **Position 3**—Direction of e.m.f. reverses direction after completing first half-turn. **Position 4**—Direction of e.m.f. at start of fourth quarter of revolution. After completing the fourth quarter of revolution, the e.m.f. will again reverse direction, and will be in the same direction as in Figure 39(b).

of the magnetic field were cut during the first quarter-turn of the coil.

Position 2 shows the coil position for the second quarter-turn, Position 2 to Position 3. Position 2 has already been established as the point at which the e.m.f. reaches a maximum value, because here the lines are cut perpendicularly. As the coil travels from Position 2, the coil steadily becomes less perpendicular to the lines of the magnetic field, until at Position 3 the situation is the same as it was in Position 1. No lines are being cut and the generated e.m.f. has again reached a minimum value. So far the coil has made a full one-half revolution, from 1 to 3, and during this time the e.m.f. has gone from a minimum value (Position 1) to a maximum (Position 2) and back to a minimum value (Position 3).

All during this time, coil side A has been moving in a downward direction while coil side B has been moving in an upward direction. It was shown in Figures 39a and 39b that the direction of the e.m.f. will reverse when the motion of the conductor reverses. The arrows in Positions 1 and 2 show the direction of the e.m.f. for the first half revolution of the coil. Check this direction with the Right-Hand Rule.

As the coil starts the second half of the revolution, the e.m.f. is at a minimum value and will increase to a maximum value at Position 4; but note that the direction of the e.m.f. has been reversed in the coil sides, because side A is now moving upward while side B is moving down. The e.m.f., after reaching this maximum value, will again decrease as the coil assumes its original position (1).

To sum up the action and effects of the coil through its entire revolution, consider Figure 41. The figure represents what is known as a sine wave, and is generally used to represent the action of alternating e.m.f. The numbers 1, 1a, 2, 2a, 3, 3a, 4, 4a and 1 represent the positions of the coil through an entire revolution or cycle from the start back to its original position.

In Position 1 the induced e.m.f. was at a minimum value because the coil was not cutting into the magnetic field; at Position 2 the induced e.m.f. reached a maximum value in one direction as represented by 2 in Figure 41; the value of this e.m.f.

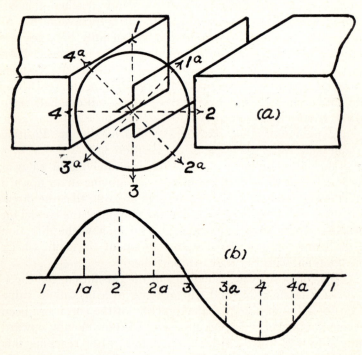

Figure 41: Positions of generator compared with magnitude and direction of e.m.f.

decreased until another minimum value was reached at Position 3; from here, the value of the e.m.f. increased to a maximum (4) in an opposite direction, and again decreased to a minimum as it approached its original position. In other words, an alternating e.m.f. is continually changing in both direction and magnitude.

Frequency. Frequency is the number of cycles per second.

If it took one second for the coil to make a complete revolution, the frequency would be one cycle. If the coil made 60 complete revolutions per second, the frequency would be 60 cycles. If 60 coils were placed evenly about a shaft and the whole assembly made one complete revolution per second, the frequency would be 60 cycles. From this it can be seen that for any desired frequency there must be a definite relation between the number of coils and the number of revolutions the coil makes. That is, if the armature on which the coils are wound is to rotate at high speed, then the number of coils wound on the armature may be less than if the armature is to rotate at a low speed.

GENERATOR PARTS AND CARE

Field Poles. In Figures 39 and 40 the magnetic field is maintained by magnets. The field poles of a commercial gen-

Figure 42: Field poles of commercial welding generator.
(Lincoln Electric Co.)

erator act the same as the magnets, and maintain a magnetic field in the same way. Figure 42 shows the field poles of a Lincoln welding generator. Actually, these poles have coils wound around them instead of being just a plain magnet.

There will always be an even number of field poles in a generator with one N pole directly opposite an S pole. In this way there will be more than one magnetic field for the armature coils to cut. Increasing the number of magnetic fields will result in increasing the frequency in the same way as increasing the number of coils. For instance, a two-pole machine will provide one magnetic field for the coils to cut. If four poles are built into the machine, there will be two magnetic fields. In the latter case, the induced e.m.f. will reach the minimum and maximum values and reverse its direction twice as fast as it would in the two-pole machine. The more poles in a machine, the slower the machine may run and at the same time maintain a given frequency.

The Armature. The d.c. welding generator has an armature such as shown in Figure 43. It is actually a cylindrical piece

Figure 43: Rotating element of a 300-amp., a.c. motor-driven, Type SCF, Flexarc welding set, showing the relative positions of the generator armature, motor rotor, fan, and bearings. 1) Commutator; 2) Armature; 3) Fan; 4) Motor Coupling. (Westinghouse Electric & Mfg. Co.)

of iron with a number of slots cut into its surface longitudinally. In these slots are placed copper conductors in the form of coils. The coils are put into the slots in layers. The greater the number of coils in the armature slots, the greater will be the output of the generator.

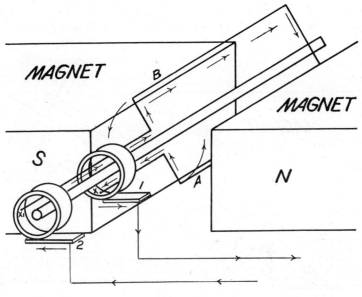

Figure 44.

The coils must be so placed that the e.m.f. of every coil travels in the same direction and reverses at the same time. In this way the full value of the generated e.m.f. is delivered to the external circuit. (The external circuit is that part of the circuit outside of the generator, while the internal circuit is that within the generator itself.)

Figure 44 shows how this e.m.f. is delivered to the external circuit by the use of slip rings. The path of travel is out from conductor A and then back through conductor B. The two curved arrows indicate the direction of rotation. A is moving upward, while B is moving down. The magnetic field has the same direction as in Figures 39 and 40. The e.m.f. flows through coil side A to the ring where A is connected (X in Figure 44); through the ring to brush 1; through the brush to the cable connected to the brush, and out to the external circuit. The rings are connected to the shaft, as is the coil, and the whole assembly rotates as a single unit. The brushes are

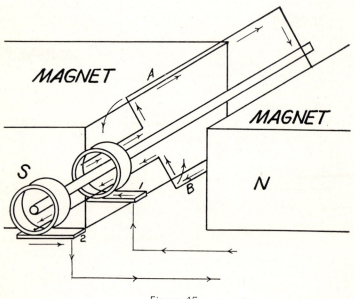

Figure 45.

stationary, but are always in contact with the rings. Figure 45 shows how the path of travel has reversed one-half revolution later. The e.m.f. now leaves by way of conductor B and returns by way of A. Check with Right-Hand Rule. The result is an alternating e.m.f., that is, an e.m.f. which is changing direction every half-revolution of the coil. If the e.m.f. is continually changing direction, the current must also change direction. The result, then, is that with this type of generator we get an alternating current.

Rectification. If direct current is to be obtained for welding, it is obvious that something must be done to the alternating current to prevent its continually reversing direction. This something must keep the current flowing smoothly in one direction all the time. In order to have direct current, the path of travel of the current must be such that it leaves the generator by one terminal all the time and returns by way of the other terminal all the time, rather than leaving by way of one terminal for a part of a revolution and returning by way of this same terminal, a half revolution later.

Figure 46 shows both ends of an armature coil attached to one ring instead of two, as in Figures 44 and 45. The ring in Figure 46 has two saw cuts, and is known as a split ring. These saw cuts prevent the coil from short-circuiting, because the generated current cannot flow beyond the saw cuts. In the position shown in Figure 46, the armature and ring are rotating counterclockwise, conductor A has just reached the topmost point of its revolution, and the current is shown as flowing out of conductor A by way of brush (1). Conductor B, by way of ring B, is ready to make contact with brush (1) as it starts to move upward. The ideal time for the ring segments to change brush contact is when the armature is perpendicular to the field, because at this time the armature is not cutting into the magnetic field and the generated e.m.f. is at a minimum. If the change in brush contact were to take place when the e.m.f. was at any other value, there would be serious arcing at the brush contacts, with a resultant loss of power.

The ring revolves with the armature, and the points (1) and (2), representing brushes on a generator, are sliding contacts;

so that as the current is ready to leave the armature, conductor A will be in contact with brush (1) and remain in contact, while the current from A varies from a minimum to a maximum. When the e.m.f. of the armature is ready to reverse and

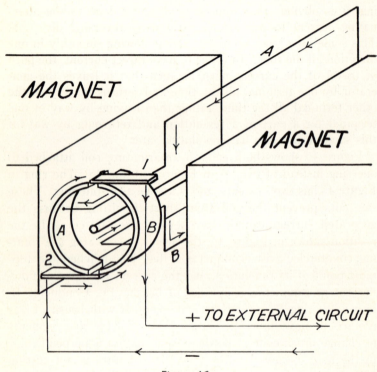

Figure 46.

leave by conductor B, this conductor will be in contact with brush (1) and remain so until the e.m.f. is ready to reverse again, at which time A will come in contact with brush (1). In this way the e.m.f. is being impressed on the external circuit in the same direction at all times; that is, it is going out by way of brush (1) at all times and returning by way of brush (2) at all times, even though it is reversing within the armature conductor. The action of this rectified current may be represented by Figure 47.

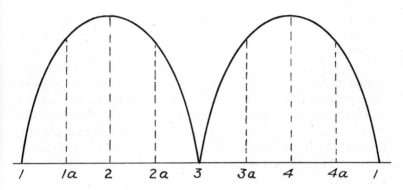

Figure 47: Representation of unidirectional current.

Direct current has been defined as current traveling in one direction only. While the current from the type of circuit just discussed will travel in one direction only, and is considered as direct current, it does not satisfy the requirements for welding. The reason is that the current in the above circuit will be continually pulsating or changing in magnitude, from a maximum to a minimum. Therefore, after solving one part of the problem, that of keeping the current from reversing and getting it to flow in one direction, it now becomes necessary to solve the rest of the problem, which is to find a way to eliminate the pulsations; and to have a current that will travel in one direction only, at as steady a magnitude as possible.

The Commutator. The split ring of Figure 46 represents what in an actual generator is known as a commutator. The commutator is made up of a large number of copper segments.

Each segment is insulated from the one next to it by mica. The insulation of mica between the segments is comparable to the saw cuts of the split ring. If the ring had a large number of saw cuts made in it and there were a large number of coils with one coil end attached to each split section of the ring, the effect would be the same as that produced by a real commutator. That is, the current would become less pulsating as the number of coils and ring sections increased. In a welding generator there is a large number of segments on the commutator and a large number of coils in the armature. The segments are slitted at one end, and into these slits are soldered the ends of the armature coils. The current then travels from the armature windings to the commutator segment, and as the commutator rotates, the current flows through the brushes, which are stationary. From the brushes the current flows out to the external circuit. The commutator is mounted on the same shaft as the armature, as shown in Figure 43.

The Brushes. It can be seen that to conduct the current from the commutator to the brushes efficiently, there must be a minimum of resistance. In order to keep this commutator resistance at a minimum, it is essential that good contact is maintained. The brushes are made of carbon, or copper and carbon, and in order that they may maintain proper contact with the commutator, they are shaped at one end to fit the circumference of the commutator and then placed in the brush-holders, which contain a small spring. The pressure exerted by the spring is sufficient to insure contact. Due to the fact that the copper commutator is constantly rubbing against the carbon brushes, the brushes will in time wear out. If this is allowed to continue too long, the purpose of the brush is not fulfilled, resulting in injury to the commutator. For this reason brushes have to be replaced at various intervals of time. This is easily accomplished by removing the worn brush from the holder and replacing it with a new one.

If dirt or dust gathers on the commutator surface, it is likely to score the segments when they are rubbing against the brushes. For this reason the commutator should be kept as clean as possible. If the commutator becomes slightly scored, it may be smoothed out with some fine sandpaper. Do not use emery.

Figure 48: Brushes and commutator of welding generator.

After the generator has been in service for some length of time, it may happen that the mica insulation between the commutator segments will be higher than the segments themselves. This is known as "high mica." When this occurs, the commutator will continually arc, resulting in a loss of power to the external circuit and damage to the generator. To offset the condition for as long a time as possible, a new machine usually has the mica undercut. That is, the mica will not be as high as the copper segments. When "high mica" occurs, the commutator should be removed and turned down on a lathe. When carbon collects on the surface of the commutator, it will act as a resistance, and it should be removed with an oily cloth. Do not use waste for this purpose.

Figure 48 shows the commutator and brushes of a welding generator.

Cause of Commutator Wear. It might be thought that "high mica" is due to the carbon brushes causing more wear on

Figure 49: A view through the commutator inspection opening of a 300-amp., d.c. Flexarc, Type SCF, welding generator, showing how the brush holders are mounted on the rocker ring, how the rocker ring is supported on the generator bracket, and how the brushes are arranged in the brush holders. It also shows the stainless steel brush-holder springs. The brush holders are brass, thus making the assembly free from corrosion trouble. (Westinghouse Electric & Mfg. Co.)

the copper than on the mica. This, however, is not true. What actually happens is that minute particles of the copper are removed from the segments by extremely small arcs that exist between the brushes and the commutator. The resistance of the small gaps where these arcs are produced is known as the contact resistance. This contact resistance is higher when carbon brushes are used; but copper brushes have another and a worse fault. They create too much wear on the commutator. The disadvantages of both types may be overcome by using a composition of graphite and copper, which will reduce contact resistance without cutting the commutator (Figure 49).

Figure 50: Air passages in frame of machine to allow proper ventilation. Windings, poles and commutator are cooled by a built-in fan.

Overheating. If a generator is short-circuited, it will start to heat up. This heating up will have a deteriorating effect on the insulation of the windings of the machine. If the insulation becomes ineffective, due to this heating, the machine will become what is known as "burnt out." Usually the machines are equipped with an automatic device that stops the machine when the temperature of the atmosphere around the windings reaches a certain temperature. However, continued overheating will have a progressive harmful effect on the insulation, and will eventually destroy it. Therefore, the welder should make certain that the machine is not "grounded" when not in use.

At the ends and center of the machine frame are ventilating ducts (Figure 50) through which a fan draws in cool air and expels the warm air, thereby keeping the temperature inside the machine from rising to the point of overheating. It should be seen to that these vents are not blocked by material outside of the machine in such a way as to prevent free circulation of the air.

Care of the Generator Summarized

1) Keep the machine in as clean a place as possible to prevent dust and dirt from interfering with the operation of the machine.

2) Replace brushes when needed; do not wait for them to wear down to the holder frame.

3) Turn down commutator when necessary. Do not allow the machine to run when excessive sparking occurs at the brushes.

4) If the commutator has an undercut mica, it is possible for the grooves to fill up with dirt, resulting in short circuiting of the commutator segments. Keep the grooves clean.

5) Do not attempt to use cotton waste to clean commutator.

6) Do not use emery on the commutator.

7) Do not place any article so close to the ventilating ducts that it might interfere with the proper circulation of air inside the machine.

8) Do not leave electrode holder where it will ground, when the machine is started.

GENERAL NOTES

Choice of Generators. Because there are many companies manufacturing electric welding machines, there is keen competition in this field, and the resultant product is, in general, one that can be relied upon to produce good results. It would be impossible to pick out any one make of machine and consider it superior to any others. There are some that undoubtedly are inferior, but the general run, and particularly the more popular makes, are such that, when choosing a machine, it is more a case of which type a person is best acquainted with.

There are some things applying to all machines that should be observed.

Locating the Machine. All machines should be located in a cool, clean, dry, and well-ventilated place, free of steam, acid fumes, dust, and excessively high temperatures. Dust particles and dirt from the air will in time cause scoring between the commutator and brushes and cause poor contact at these points. Excessively high temperatures tend to cause quicker overheating. Steam on condensing may cause short circuits in the machine, and will in time cause corrosion.

For stationary machines, the foundation should be sufficiently solid to prevent vibration.

Lubrication. Check directions with each machine regarding lubrication, as different makes will have different means of lubrication.

Rotation. On every machine there will be an indicator of some sort to show the proper rotation. If the generator is being driven by an a.c. motor and, upon starting, the direction of rotation is not correct, the motor should be reversed. This may be done by simply interchanging one phase of the a.c. power supply. If a d.c. motor is used, it will run in the correct direction of rotation regardless of how the leads are connected. However, proper connections are shown on the diagrams supplied with the set. To insure the correct polarity in all cases, the motor connections should be checked against these diagrams.

Exciter. There are some types of generators that supply

their own field current, while in others the field current is supplied from another source. The source used to excite the field of the latter type is a very small generator. This generator is called the exciter. The current from the exciter is known as the

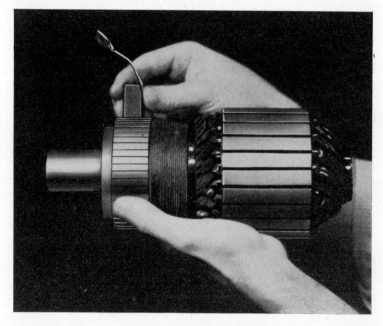

Figure 51: Exciter for providing field current.

exciting current, and is maintained at a certain strength. The strength of this exciting current determines the strength of the generator field (Figure 51).

LINCOLN WELDING GENERATORS

Location (Figures 52 and 53). The welding machine should, if possible, be located in a clean, dry and well-ventilated place. Use the same discretion that you would in locating any piece of electrical apparatus. It should be set on a foundation as free from vibration as practical.

Figure 52: Heavy-duty "Shield Arc" welder. (Lincoln Electric Co.)

It is good practice to blow out the machine occasionally with compressed air.

Wiring and Connection of Set (Figure 54). First check the nameplate of the set to be sure that the voltage, phase and cycles of the equipment are correct for the power available.

Figure 53: Vertical type welder. (Lincoln Electric Co.)

All connections between the control box and the set are already made, so that all that is necessary is to connect the power lines to the proper terminals in the control box. The motor is capable of heavy overload, so the size of the power lines should

Figure 54: Electrode, ground and motor terminals are readily accessible.
(Lincoln Electric Co.)

be a little larger than for a motor of the same rating, to insure full voltage being applied to the motor.

After the machine has been in operation for some time, all external connections should be checked to make sure they are tight.

Starting. After the machine is connected to the source of power, the machine should be started by the pushbotton and the direction of rotation checked. All machines are equipped with an arrow showing the proper direction. When the power supply is direct current, the set will rotate in the correct direction, irrespective of the polarity of the power lines, but if the voltmeter reads in the wrong direction, the two power leads should be reversed.

Electric power-driven machines are equipped with push-

Figure 55: Accidental starting impossible. Safety pushbutton can be locked in "off" position as shown, so that if bumped or pressed unintentionally, it will not start the welder. Recessed button must be pressed deliberately. Welder can be stopped by pressing outer button. (Lincoln Electric Co.)

button starters. (See Figure 55.) Full instructions in regard to the starter will be found on the inside of its case.

Motor Protection (Figure 56). The a.c. motor is protected by a thermostat which definitely limits the maximum temperature of the machine. When the windings reach the maximum safe operating temperature from any cause—too frequent overloads, high room temperature plus overload, abnormally high or low voltage, phase unbalance, poor ventilation

Figure 56: No-voltage motor protection. Should power fail for any reason, the welder will disconnect itself from the line. When power returns, the operator must start it again intentionally. (Lincoln Electric Co.)

—the thermostat which is imbedded in the motor field windings automatically disconnects the motor (through a control relay) from the source of power. The control relay is shown in the diagram of the control panels. This relay will not permit the starter switch to remain closed if the power supply is single-

Figure 57: Protective device against overheating. (Lincoln Electric Co.)

phase, and, in case of a blown fuse resulting in single-phase current while the machine is in operation, it will automatically shut off if the machine is running at normal or heavy load. It is a completely self-protecting motor, for any overheating directly in the windings will cut the machine off the power line. After cooling, the machine can again be started.

The protective device comprising snap-action thermostats and current transformers (Figure 57) functions as follows:

1) If welder is operated in a very hot room or oven and exceeds safe operating temperature, thermostats trip open.

2) If motor is cold and excessive harmful currents occur for a short period of time, thermostat operates before the motor reaches an unsafe temperature.

3) If welder is started on single-phase lines, excessive heating of thermostat due to single-phase locked current stops the machine immediately.

4) If welder is running and one fuse blows, causing motor to operate single-phase, or if welding load is sufficient to overheat the motor, thermostat trips out.

5) If rotor is locked with normal 3-phase power applied, thermostats open the circuit due to high current.

6) If welder is operated for long periods and sustained overloads, both high input current and high motor temperature cause thermostats to open.

7) If power line disturbances send the voltage below a safe value, the motor is automatically disconnected from the line. Overheating and burn-out hazards are thereby prevented.

The thermostats reset automatically when the motor temperature becomes safe; no manual operation is required to start the machine except pushing the start button.

A special circuit allows the starter button to be held "in" after the thermostats have tripped and trouble has been rectified, in order to speed up cooling of the welder.

The **Welder Control Cabinet** (illustrated in Figure 58) has mounted thereon the following controls:

A) Starter Button—by means of which a.c. motor-driven welders are started and stopped. The green button starts the machine and the red button stops it. It may be locked in the "off" position so that the welder cannot be started by an accidental pressing of the green button. This button in the case of d.c. motor-driven welders is mounted in the starter case. Obviously, this button is not required nor furnished with engine-driven or belted (coupled) machines.

B) Job Selector—this permits varying the machine voltage and selecting the slope of the volt-ampere curve to suit the work.

C) Current Control—varies the welding current without changing the machine voltage.

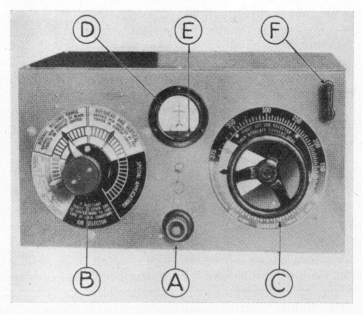

Figure 58: Welder control cabinet. (Lincoln Electric Co.)

D) Voltammeter—this is a combination voltammeter which normally indicates the voltage of the machine; but by pressing the meter button the current is indicated. The meter, being of the zero-center type, also indicates the polarity of the welding current.

E) Meter Button—pressing the meter button permits reading the current of the welder.

F) Polarity Switch—this reversible voltage control permits the operator to select either normal or reversed polarity of the welding current. To change the polarity turn this handle to the other vertical position—at any time, whether or not current is being drawn from the welder. By placing the handle in the horizontal position no voltage or current is generated in the

Figure 59: Polarity-reversing switch—exterior. (Lincoln Electric Co.)

welder. In the case of d.c. motor-driven welders (115 or 230 volts only) this polarity switch is located at the back of and within the control cabinet. It is not furnished for d.c. motor-driven welders over 230 volts. (See Figs. 59 & 60.)

In addition to the above, some welders, when especially

ordered in that manner, are equipped with a dual-voltage motor
and control which permit the a.c. motor to operate from either
220- or 440-volt power lines. In such cases the dual-voltage
control switch is mounted on the left-hand end of the control

Figure 60: Polarity-reversing switch—interior. (Lincoln Electric Co.)

cabinet, and is clearly marked to show the proper switch position for either voltage.

7) Dual-Continuous Control, with self-indicating dials. The
varied requirements of present-day welding make it highly desirable to be able to vary both the voltage and the current
separately, each in small increments, throughout the machine
range.

The **job selector** dial is divided into 4 sections, each of a different color. The yellow section, which gives a high open-circuit voltage, is used chiefly for large electrodes and high welding currents, or when a "rubbery" arc is desired. The black section, marked "Normal Welding Range," gives a medium high, open-circuit voltage, and is generally used on positioned work, for some of the larger sizes of electrodes, or where poor fitup exists on overhead or vertical welding. The red section, marked "Overhead and Vertical," provides a medium low, open-circuit voltage to give the proper snap to the arc to force the metal across the arc gap and make it penetrate for these overhead and vertical jobs. This section may also be used for some of the smaller sizes of electrodes. The section marked "Special Applications" provides a still lower open-circuit voltage and is used for those special jobs requiring the smallest sizes of electrodes and very low currents.

The **continuous current control** dial is calibrated directly in amperes. The arrow plate on the current control hand-wheel has 3 colored arrows—yellow, black, red—corresponding to the similarly colored sections of the job selector. When the job selector is set on the yellow section of its dial, the approximate welding current will be indicated by the yellow arrow or pointer on the current control. The same is true of the black and red arrows of the current control when the job selector is set on those sections of its dial. The operator can easily see the practical workings and the great advantages of these self-indicating controls by a few simple experiments.

Operation of Machine. Start the machine and set the Job Selector on "Normal Welding Range" and the current-control black arrow at approximately half the rated current of the machine (150 amps. on a 300-amp. welder). Using an electrode requiring this amount of current (about $\frac{5}{32}''$), weld a short bead. Now turn the job selector to the yellow section, noting that the open-circuit voltage has been reduced to less than that indicated on the first setting for normal range. Again make a short bead and notice that the welding current has been reduced to about 100 amps., as indicated by the red arrow on the current control. This shows how the job selector primarily varies the open circuit voltage of the welder but also varies the welding current output.

Now, with the job selector set at "Normal Welding Range," place the black arrow of the current control at 100 amps. and weld a short bead. Next, set the black arrow at 150 amps. and weld another short bead. Now, set the black arrow at 200 amps. and weld again.

This demonstrates how the voltage and current may be varied independently of each other. Finer adjustments of welding currents can be obtained by following these instructions.

Turn both the job selector and current control to the right as far as possible (the minimum settings) and, by clamping the electrode holder to the ground plate or cable, short-circuit the machine. Note that the voltage drops very low. Then press the meter button and read the current. Keeping the button pressed so that the meter will continue to read amperes, gradually turn the job selector to the left. Watch carefully, how the current gradually increases as the job selector is turned farther and farther to the left. Then turn it back again to the right or minimum position, noting the gradual decrease of current. Repeat this with the meter reading voltage. This will show how the voltage as well as the current may be varied in small increments by the job selector. If the machine has become warm during this test, remove the ground or put the polarity reversing switch in the horizontal or neutral position, and allow the machine to cool.

Now, again set the machine with the job selector and current control at their minimum settings and short-circuit the machine as before. This time leave the job selector alone, press the meter button to read current, and turn the current control very slowly to the left. Note the gradual increase in amperage that can be obtained without touching the job selector. Turn the handle back to the original position, noting the gradual decrease in current. Again disconnect the shorted leads and allow the machine to cool.

From these tests it is easy to see how the operator can select a given current for the particular job he has to do. In one case he may be welding outside in a strong wind, where a "rubbery" arc is needed, so he sets his job selector on the yellow scale; another may be an overhead or vertical job where he wants a short, forceful, digging arc, so he sets his job selector on the red scale; then, his next job may be an ordinary one where he requires a normal setting—on the black scale.

A welder with any degree of experience fully realizes the necessity for dual control of the arc in order to secure satisfactory welding results. He knows that for certain types of work he requires a volt-ampere curve of gradual slope, as indicated by a low open-circuit voltage—for others he needs a steeper curve, as indicated by a higher open-circuit voltage. Two welding applications can require the same welding current but, because of the difference in metals or welding conditions, will require different open-circuit voltages.

Hence, for proper results, the welder finds it necessary to have control of both welding current and open-circuit voltage.

What effect does dual continuous control have on the performance of the welding arc?

Consider what happens to the welding current when this control is operated. By varying the left-hand control—the "job selector"—the open-circuit voltage is changed, producing any desired volt-ampere curve such as those shown in Figure 61a.

By varying the right-hand control—the "current control"— the welding current is changed with any given open-circuit voltage, producing any desired volt-ampere curve such as those shown in Figure 61b. An indeterminate number of volt-ampere curves can be produced for each open-circuit voltage adjustment.

In other words, the combination of the two controls allows the operator to blanket the entire range of the welder as shown

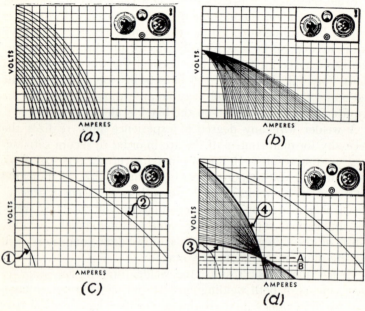

Figure 61.

in Figure 61c. He can choose a volt-ampere setting which can be **anywhere** or of **any slope** between the curve of lowest open-circuit voltage (Curve 1) and minimum current, and that of the highest open-circuit voltage and maximum current (Curve 2).

Now, to see why the operator can get varying penetration at any welding current with dual continuous control, glance at

Figure 61d. Select any welding current and its corresponding arc voltage, such as the point A. Through that point, any number of volt-ampere curves can be produced, varying in slope as shown, from the gradually sloping Curve 3 to the steep Curve 4. (In actual operation this effect is produced by varying the open-circuit voltage with the job selector, while maintaining the same welding current with the current control.)

Now, suppose the arc was shortened, decreasing the arc voltage to B:

It is clearly evident from the two curves that this shortening of the arc gives a material increase in the welding current for Curve 3, whereas, it causes little effect in the current of Curve 4. The greater the pick-up in current, the greater the penetration of the arc. It is, therefore, obvious that by varying the slope of the volt-ampere curve, we vary the penetration; and by means of dual continuous control this can be done to any desired degree at each and every desired value of welding current.

In welding at considerable distance from the machine, care should be taken that ample-size welding cables are used. Too small cables for long-distance welding simply help to reduce the output of the machine.

Bearings. Each welder is equipped with ball bearings having sufficient grease to last one year under the most severe service. The following instructions should be followed to get the maximum number of years of service from the bearings:

1) Lubrication: An ounce of grease each year is sufficient for each bearing. A pad of grease 1″ long, 1″ high and 1″ wide weighs approximately 1 oz. Also, the grease cup when used holds approximately ½ oz.

2) Cleanliness: Dirt is responsible for more ball-bearing failures than any other cause. This dirt may get into the grease cup when it is removed to refill, or it may get into the grease in its original

container. Before removing the grease cup or pipe plug, it is important that it be wiped absolutely clean. A piece of dirt no larger than the period at the end of this sentence may cause a bearing to fail in a short time. Even small particles of grit that float around in factory atmospheres are dangerous if present in sufficient quantity.

3) Lubricant: Ordinary cup grease is not satisfactory for proper lubrication of ball bearings. The following precautions should be taken in the selection of grease:

a) Do not buy bulk grease unless proper dispensing container is available.

b) Buy only those greases which come in factory-sealed containers if small quantities are desired.

c) Keep grease clean, use only clean instruments to transfer grease from can to bearing. Do not wipe any parts with a dirty rag. The best grease, if dirty, is worse than a poor grease which is clean.

d) Avoid a grease which is so thin that it may run through the grease seal. Grease should be no thinner than apple butter.

e) Avoid channeling greases.

f) Do not use any grease which contains mica or graphite. (Such greases usually so specify on label.)

g) Smell the grease. If it has a rancid odor, do not use.

h) Dig into the grease with a clean stick or clean screwdriver. If color is not the same throughout or if any oil has separated, do not use.

i) Turn the can upside down. If any oil runs out, do not use.

j) Place a spoonful of grease in a can lid. Heat slowly (avoid sizzling or crackling of grease) until it is melted, then cool.

Do not use if:

a) Grease is definitely either harder or softer than before heating.

b) Layer of oil remains on surface.

c) A layer hardens so that it may be broken like thin ice.

4) Inspection: The bearings in this welder are thoroughly sealed from dirt. Provided that no dirt is allowed to enter with the grease when the bearing is lubricated, no grit or dirt can get into the bearing. Therefore, it is unnecessary and inadvisable to inspect the bearings at any time.

Commutator and Brushes. The brushes on the generator and exciter are properly adjusted when the outfit arrives. No particular attention is required to keep the brushes in good condition. As the brushes wear out, they must be replaced with

(continued on page 105)

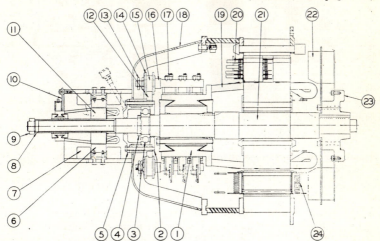

Figure 62: Welder for operation by gasoline engine—close-coupled type. (Lincoln Electric Co.)

Parts List

1. Commutator
2. Inner Dust Cap
3. Bearing
4. Bearing Locknut & Washer
5. Outer Dust Cap
6. Exciter Field Poles
7. Exciter Field Coils
8. Exciter Sleeve Collar
9. Exciter Sleeve Locknut
10. Exciter Rocker & Brush Holder Assembly
11. Exciter Armature, with Commutator, Wound
12. Rocker
13. Brush Holder Stud Nuts
14. Insulating Washer
15. Insulating Tube
16. Brush Holder Stud
17. Brush Holder
18. End Bracket
19. Armature Coils
20. Main Field Coils (shunt or series)
21. Shaft
22. Fan Assembly
23. Coupling, Generator Half (does not show drive pins or rubber bushings used between generator coupling and engine flange)
24. Interpole Coil

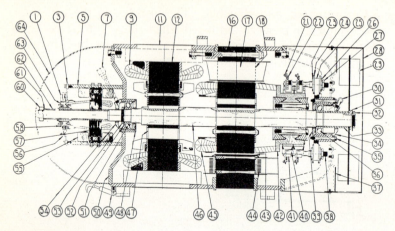

Figure 63: Welder for operation on a.c. power supply. (Lincoln Electric Co.)

Parts List

1, 4. Exciter Brush Holder and Rocker Assembly
5, 50. Exciter Frame and End Bracket Assembly
7. Grease Cup
9. Stator Coils
11. External Cover, Motor Frame
12. Stator Lamination
16. Generator Laminated Frame
17. Field Coils (shunt or series)
18. Field Poles (shunt or series)
21. Brush Holder Spring
22. Brush Holder Finger
23, 26. Clamping Washer
24. Insulating Washer
25. Rocker
27. Brush Holder Stud Nut
28. External Fan Guard-Cover
29. Ventilating Fan
30. Grease Pipe Assembly

31, 32. Locknut and Washer
33. Bearing Clamping Sleeve
34. Outer Dust Cap
35. Dust Cap Bolts
36. Ball Bearing, Generator End
37. Fan Baffle and Bracket
38. Brush Holder Stud
39. Inner Dust Cap
40. Brush, Generator
41. Brush Holder
42. Commutator, Generator
43. Field Poles, Interpole
44. Field Coils, Interpole
45. Armature Coils
46. Shaft
47. Rotor
48. Inner Dust Cap, Motor End
49. End Shell Attaching Latch
50, 5. End Bracket and Exciter Frame Assembly

(continued next page)

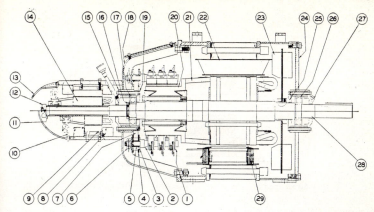

Figure 64: Welder for operation by belt or coupling. (Lincoln Electric Co.)

Parts List

1. Brush Holder
2. Brush Holder Stud
3. Clamping Washer
4. Insulating Washer
5. Insulating Tube
6. Brush Holder Stud Nuts
7. Rocker
8. Exciter Field Coils
9. Exciter Field Poles
10. Exciter Rocker & Brush Holder Assembly
11. Exciter Sleeve Collar
12. Exciter Sleeve Locknut
13. Exciter End Shield
14. Exciter Armature, with Commutator, Wound

15. Outer Dust Cap
16. Bearing Locknut and Washer
17. Bearing
18. End Bracket, Commutator End
19. Inner Dust Cap
20. Commutator
21. Armature Coils
22. Main Field Coils (shunt or series)
23. Fan Assembly
24. End Bracket, Drive End
25. Inner Dust Cap
26. Bearing
27. Outer Dust Cap
28. Shaft
29. Interpole Field Coil

Figure 63—Parts List (continued)

51. Ball Bearing, Motor End
52, 53. Locknut and Washer
54. Outer Dust Cap, Motor End
55. Exciter Field Coils
56. Spring, Exciter Brush Holder
57. Exciter Field Poles
58. Brush, Exciter

60. Exciter Sleeve Locknut
61. Exciter Sleeve Collar
62. Exciter Armature Sleeve (Complete Assembly of wound armature)
63. Exciter Commutator
64. End Shell

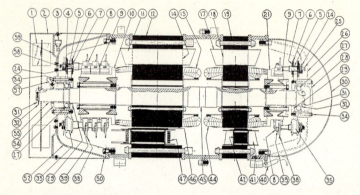

Figure 65: Welder for operation on d.c. power supply. (Lincoln Electric Co.)

Parts List

1. Ventilating Fan
2. External Fan Guard-Cover
3. Grease Cup
4, 7. Clamping Washers
5. Brush Holder Insulating Tube
6. Brush Holder Insulating Washer
7, 4. Clamping Washers
8. Brush Holder
9. Brush
10. Commutator, Generator End
11. Field Coils, Generator End (shunt or series)
12. Generator Laminated Frame
14. Field Poles, Generator End (shunt or series)
15. Armature Coils, Generator End
17. Field Coils, Motor End (shunt or series)
18. Field Poles, Motor End (shunt or series)

19. Motor Laminated Frame
21. Commutator, Motor End
24. Brush Holder Stud Nuts
25. Brush Holder Stud, Motor End
26. End Bracket, Motor End
27. Ball Bearing
28. Outer Dust Cap, Motor End
29. Inner Dust Cap
30. End Shell
31, 32. Locknut and Washer
34. Dust Cap Bolts
35. Rocker
38. Brush Holder Finger
39. Brush Holder Spring
40. End Shell Attaching Latch
41. Field Coils, Motor End, Interpole
42. Field Poles, Motor End, Interpole
44. Armature Coils, Motor End
45. Shaft

(continued next page)

new ones. One complete set of brushes should always be kept on hand. New brushes must be sanded in before they can be used on the machine. This is accomplished by removing the old brush from the holder and putting the new brush in position with a piece of medium sandpaper placed under the brush. A second person should hold the brush in its normal position by a slight pressure of the fingers. The sandpaper then should be drawn back and forth under the brush with the back of the sandpaper held closely in contact with the commutator. This will wear the brush down to the curve of the commutator. When the end of the brush has the proper curve, the operation is complete. Care should be exercised to blow all of the carbon dust away from the commutator.

The commutators require practically no attention. They should be cleaned from time to time with a clean rag, or, while running, with a piece of fine sandpaper. Never use emery cloth or paper for this purpose. It is desirable to check the brush springs occasionally to make sure they are holding the brushes on the commutator with a firm, even pressure.

Details of Welder Control Panel (Type E). The various drawings shown in Figures 66 and 66A illustrate control panels used with a.c. motor-driven welding sets, Model SAE. The same general type of panel, with interchangeable parts, is used for other sets driven by d.c. motor, gasoline engine or by belt—but the motor-starter parts shown and listed are not used with the latter three types. On a.c. motor-driven sets with

(continued on page 109)

Figure 65—Parts List (continued)

46. Field Poles, Generator End, Interpole
47. Field Coils, Generator End, Interpole
50. External Cover, Generator End
52. End Bracket, Generator End
54. Outer Dust Cap, Generator End
55. Bearing Clamping Sleeve
57. Grease Pipe Assembly
58. Brush Holder Stud, Generator End
59. Fan Baffle and Bracket

Figure 66: Front of welder control panel, Type E. (Lincoln Electric Co.)

Figures 66 & 66A—Parts List

1. Control Cabinet Case
2. Rheostat Handle and Shaft
3. Voltammeter
4. Current Control Handle
5. Polarity Reversing Switch Handle
6. Push Button
7. Master Meter Jack
8. Current Control Shaft and Insulation
9. Current Control Assembly
10. Resistor, Polarity Switch
11. Brush Fingers and Coil Springs for Current Control
12. Assembly of Current Control Brush Holder, Brush Fingers and Springs
13. Rheostat
14. Motor Starter Leads
15. Relay to Resistor Lead
16. Resistor for Protective Relay
17. Electrode Stud
18. Meter (Harness) Leads

19. Ground Stud
20. Polarity Reversing Switch
22. Shaft for Polarity Reversing Switch
23. Stationary Contact
24. Barrier Assembly
25. Moving Contact
26. Contact Rivet
27. Contact Spring
28. Shaft
29. Shaft Insulation
30. Contact Arm
31. Contact Lead
32. Shaft Clamp
33. Contact Block
34. Contact Block Cap Screw
35. Terminal Lug
36. Contact Support
37. Protective Relay Assembly
38. Protective Relay Coil Assembly
39. Protective Relay Stationary Contact Assembly

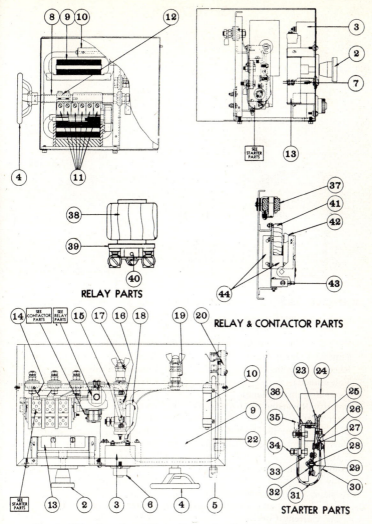

Figure 66A: Details of Type E panel. (Lincoln Electric Co.)

40. Protective Relay Plunger and Moving Contact Assembly
41. NVR Coil, Specify Voltage & Cycles or give Marking on Coil
42. NVR Moving Lamination Assembly
43. Interlock Assembly
44. Stationary Lamination Assembly

107

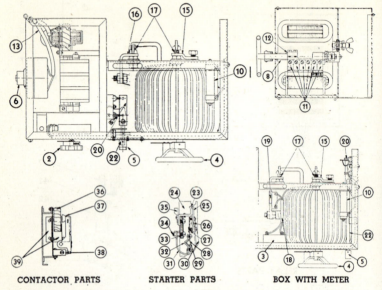

CONTACTOR PARTS   STARTER PARTS   BOX WITH METER

Figure 67: Welder control panel, Type G. (Lincoln Electric Co.)

Figures 67 & 67A—Parts List

1. Control Cabinet Case
2. Rheostat Handle and Shaft
3. Voltammeter
4. Current Control Handle
5. Polarity Reversing Switch Handle
6. Push Button
7. Polarity Reversing Switch Plate
8. Current Control Shaft and Insulation
9. Complete Current Control Assembly
10. Resistor, Polarity Switch
11. Brush Fingers and Coil Springs for Current Control
12. Assembly of Current Control Brush Holder, Brush Fingers and Springs
13. Control Harness-Push Button & Thermostat

14. Wing Nuts
15. Connection Strap—Ground
16. Connection Strap—Electrode
17. Electrode Stud or Ground Stud
18. Meter Harness
19. Meter Shunt
20. Polarity Reversing Switch
22. Shaft for Polarity Reversing Switch
23. Stationary Contact
24. Barrier Assembly
25. Moving Contact
26. Contact Rivet
27. Contact Spring
28. Shaft
29. Shaft Insulation
30. Contact Arm
31. Contact Lead

(continued next page)

dual-voltage motor and control an additional voltage-selector switch is mounted at the left-hand side, facing front of panel. On d.c. motor-driven welders the reversing switch is located where the starter parts are shown.

Details of Welder Control Panel (Type G). The main diagrams in Figures 67 and 67A show control box without meter and meter accessories. For standard boxes with meters, polarity-reversing switch is located in upper right corner of control box.

WESTINGHOUSE SINGLE-OPERATOR WELDING SETS

Location (Figure 68). If at all possible, it is desirable to locate the equipment in clean, dry, well-ventilated places, free from acid fumes, steam, and excessively high temperatures. It

REAR SUB-PANEL

Figure 67A: Details of Type G panel. (Lincoln Electric Co.)

Figures 67 & 67A—Parts List (continued)

32. Shaft Clamp
33. Contact Block
34. Contact Block Cap Screw
35. Terminal Lug
36. NVR Coil, Specify Voltage & Cycles or give Marking on coil
37. NVR Moving Lamination Assembly
38. Interlock Assembly
39. Stationary Lamination Assembly

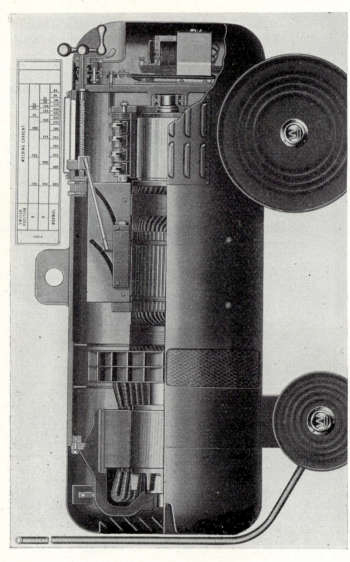

SWITCH POSITION				WELDING CURRENT			
							85
							90
							106
		25		105		110	
		50		155		160	
	75			200	205		
				250	230		
			300		272		
					300		
		375			355		
					350		
		500			575		
	125	313	453		480		
NORMAL	B	A					

Figure 68: A cross-section view of the 300-amp., a.c., motor-driven, portable Type SCF, Flexarc welding set. This shows the location of the bearings, the rectox, the motor, the fan, the armature, the current-

should be recognized that the cooler the air surrounding the equipment, the greater will be the amount of power which can be obtained from the equipment. The foundation for all stationary equipment should be sufficiently solid so that harmful vibration will be avoided. If the set vibrates and seems to be out of balance, check to see if this may not be due to the foundation.

Bearing Lubrication. This set is equipped with sealed cartridge-type ball bearings. The seal for retaining the grease is built into the bearing itself. The grease provided in the bearing will furnish adequate lubrication for at least three years. No grease need be added within this time. At the end of three years the shield on the outer end of the bearing should be removed and the grease examined. If the grease is discolored and has a bad odor, the bearings should be cleaned and repacked with the special grease obtainable at the manufacturer's district offices. This grease is especially refined and treated to provide adequate lubrication for long periods. Ordinary commercial greases are not satisfactory for this type of bearing construction. If upon examination the grease in the bearing shows no discoloration and has no offensive odor, the shield may be replaced and the bearing put back in service for several years.

There are two bearings, one at each end of the shaft. The front and rear covers and the front and rear brackets may be removed to get at the bearings.

1) A ball bearing should never be removed from its shaft unless it is necessary to replace with a new bearing.

2) If it is necessary to lubricate the bearing, use only the grease specified.

3) Dirt and grit, even in very small quantities, will rapidly destroy any anti-friction bearing. Every care should be observed to keep the bearing clean.

4) An anti-friction bearing should never be cleaned with a grease-cutting fluid such as gasoline, kerosene, alcohol, etc.

Only light oil such as light machine oil should be used for this purpose.

On portable sets the roller bearings in the wheel hubs should be greased occasionally. The wheels can be removed to accomplish this. (See Figure 69.)

Connection. The motor starter for the a.c., motor-driven sets is the "de-ion" linestarter mounted under the front-end

Figure 69: 200-amp. d.c.-drive, portable welder, pushbutton-operated, magnetic-reduced voltage starter. This set is furnished with 115-volt, 230-volt or 400-600 volt, d.c. motor drive. (Westinghouse Electric & Mfg. Co.)

cover. (See Figure 71.) The leads come out through an opening in the bottom of the cover. To connect a set to the line, remove the small plate holding the condulet fitting. Insert the supply cable (either in BX-conduit or rubber-covered cable) and connect the supply cable to the leads from the starter

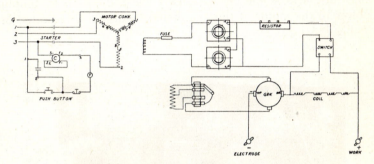

Figure 70: a.c.–d.c. schematic diagram.

above the detachable plate. Then attach the plate with the connections pushed up inside the end cover of the set. Some care should be taken that these connections are not so bulky as to foul the starter. The starters are pushbutton operated, magnetic starters with overload and low-voltage protection. The overload protection is provided by a thermoguard on the motor windings. This thermoguard automatically resets itself when the motor cools off. If the starter opens because of low voltage, the motor will not start until the start button is depressed. However, the starter will not hold in until the voltage comes up to proper value.

The d.c. starter is located in the same position as the a.c. starter and is also a pushbutton magnetic starter with overload and no voltage protection. The overload relay is automatically reset.

The accelerating period may be adjusted by setting the time-delay relay properly. The time-delay is changed by adjusting the resistor marked Res. #1 in Figure 73. The accelerating relay should be set for a time-delay of 3 to 5 seconds.

On the a.c. sets, a fourth lead marked "G" is brought out for grounding the machine as a safety measure. This connection is not necessary for the operation of the sets. On d.c. machines, the third lead is the ground lead. The cable used to supply power to the motor of this set should be of a size indicated in Table 2.

Figure 71: The Class 15-825 magnetic linestarter, used on a.c. motor-driven Flexarc welding sets. The coils on 220- or 440-volt starters are reconnectable for use on either voltage.

TABLE 2. MOTOR LEAD SIZE

Set Size	3-Phase a.c.			d.c.		
	220	440	550	115	230	550
200	#6	#10	#12	#00	#4	#8
300	#3	#6	#8	#000	#1	#6
400	#1	#6	#6	#0000	#00	#4
600	#00	#4	#6		#000	#3

Under no circumstances should smaller motor leads than those recommended be used. If the leads are abnormally long, a size larger should be used. If the motor leads are too small or are exceptionally long, the voltage at the set will be so reduced that trouble may be encountered from the magnetic starter not closing tightly. Low motor voltage will also lower the efficiency of the set and make the motor run unnecessarily hot.

Starting. Before starting, examine the set for any obvious defects. Try each of the generator and d.c. motor brushes to see that they slide freely in the brushholders.

After starting, the direction of rotation should be checked against the direction arrow name plate on the generator. If rotation is wrong, it should be reversed. To reverse an a.c. motor, it is necessary only to interchange the leads to one phase of the a.c. power supply. In the case of a d.c. motor, it will run in the correct direction of rotation regardless of how the leads are connected to the d.c. power supply; but if the set is not connected as shown in Figure 73, the polarity of the welding leads will be wrong.

A.C. Motor Voltage. Alternating-current motors, 3-phase, 60 or 50 cycles, connected for 220 or 440 volts, may be changed for use on a 440- or 220-volt circuit of identical phase and frequency by removing the rear cover, reconnecting the motor leads, and removing the front cover and reconnecting the starter, as shown on the set name plate.

Parallel Operation. When two or more duplicate generators are to be operated in parallel, first make certain that the ground leads of the welding circuits are not connected to each

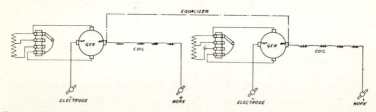

Figure 72: Parallel operation diagram. (Westinghouse Electric & Mfg. Co.)

other either directly or through conduction metal such as the work. Then determine the total welding current required and divide this value by the number of machines to be used. This will give the current setting for each machine. Each current pre-set control should be set so that each generator will deliver this current. The polarity-reversing switches and current-range switches of all generators should be thrown to the same position. Then connect an equalizer cable of about 25,000 circular mils cross-section to the bottom brush-holder arm of each machine and connect them all together. (See Figure 72.) Then start the sets and connect the ground leads to the work and all of the electrode-holder leads to a single electrode holder. When machines are thus connected together no one should be permitted to operate the reverse polarity switch on any one of the machines. Do not attempt parallel operation without the equalizer connections between brush-holder arms, as one of the machines will be sure to reverse the other and circulate a damaging current.

Polarity Reversal. As shown in Figure 70, the general idea of the rectox polarity control is to produce in the welding generator's series field at no load a small direct current (5 to 10 amps.). The direction of this current controls the residual polarity of the generator, and, by inserting a reversing switch as shown between the generator's field and the rectox, we can use it to reverse the polarity of the generator's terminals. To

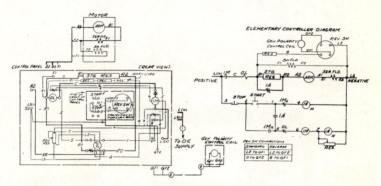

Figure 73: d.c.–d.c. diagram.

limit the current discharge by the series field through the rectox when the welding circuit is broken, we insert a resistor in this circuit, as shown.

Since the generator's series field has a very low resistance (.004 to .009), the supply voltage for the rectox can be very low (5.5 to 12 volts). This voltage is obtained from a coil of a few turns wound in the motor stator slots. Since the voltage across this coil remains the same for either voltage of a dual-voltage motor, no changes in this circuit need be made as long as the motor is reconnected properly for the voltage used.

In cases of abnormally low motor voltage or of rectox aging, the rectox current through the series field may be insufficient. This current can be increased by changing to a lower tap on the resistor in the rectox circuit. The need for this change will be

Figure 74: View of the generator end of d.c. Flexarc welding set with d.c. motor drive. The cover over the control has been removed and the push-button-operated, magnetic-reduced voltage starter, the polarity switch, and arc control switch are shown. (Westinghouse Electric & Mfg. Co.)

indicated by difficulty in starting the arc immediately after reversing the polarity.

Care of Commutator and Brushes. The brushes are set in the proper position at the works and the brush-holder rigging is doweled into position. This setting should not be changed. The commutator must be kept clean and the brushes properly

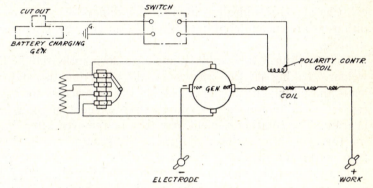

Figure 75: Engine-driven operation diagram.

adjusted and fitted to the commutator. Use no lubricant on the commutator. A dirty commutator may be cleaned while running with fine sandpaper or a commutator stone. Do not use emery cloth to clean a commutator.

General Care. It is good practice to blow out the entire machine occasionally with clean, dry compressed air. It is advisable when blowing out the machine to set the current control at the maximum current and blow out any dirt which may collect under the leakage plate.

Current Adjustment. The welding current may be adjusted to the desired value, before welding, by manipulating only one device, the "current pre-set handcrank." Turning this crank to the right increases the current, and to the left decreases it. The current-range switch below the crank changes the welding characteristics of the generator to suit all requirements. The calibrated scale on top of the generator indicates the current for which the machine is adjusted. The scale corresponding to the position of the current-range switch should be used in setting the current. In the large majority of cases the normal scale will be used. Where the characteristics of the normal scale are not satisfactory, the A and B scales are provided to give characteristics ideally suited to such difficult welding conditions as are encountered in overhead, deep-groove and corner welding.

Dismantling. It is quite simple to dismantle the SCF welder. Taking off the rear cover, disconnecting the stator leads and taking out the motor bracket will give access for any repair on the motor stator or for the replacement of the rear bearing. The rotating element may then be removed after lifting the generator brushes. To get at the generator coils, the front cover and bracket can be removed.

The extreme simplicity of this welder and the absence of a great multiplicity of parts makes repairs infrequent and easy.

Gasoline-Engine Equipment (Figure 76). See that the radiator is full of clean water and that oil is in the crankcase before starting the gasoline engine.

If the set is stored without being used for a time, evaporation of the gasoline in the carburetor may leave a gummy residue which will clog up the jets and result in the engine shirking the load when the arc is struck. This gum can be dissolved with alcohol or acetone. When starting after storage, the first 5 gallons should have 1 quart of alcohol or ½ pint of acetone added to it.

When engine-driven sets are being transported, the gasoline line should be shut off at the tank to prevent leakage caused by bouncing of the carburetor float.

The engine oil should be changed after every 50 hours of service. The general care and maintenance of the gasoline engine used with welding generators is specified in the instruction book supplied with the equipment by the engine manufacturer.

Repair parts can be obtained at the parts depots maintained by the engine manufacturing companies. A list of these depots will be found in the engine instruction book attached to the set.

Governor. If trouble with the governor cannot be corrected by reference to the following instructions, refer the matter to

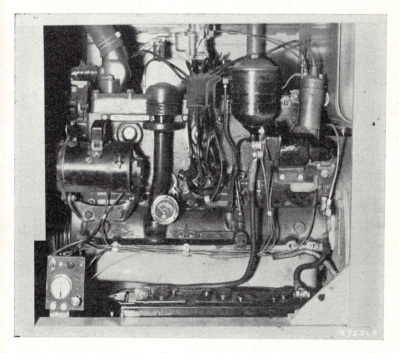

Figure 76: View of the accessory side of the Chrysler engine on a 200-amp., Type SCF, Flexarc welding set. The battery, battery-charging generator, starting pushbutton, ignition switch, choke control, battery-charging ammeters, oil pressure gauge, oil filler pipe, water pump, thermostat, carburetor, fuel filter, oil filter, distributor, ignition coil, and starter are shown.
(Westinghouse Electric & Mfg. Co.)

the nearest district office of the manufacturer, who will send a new governor to replace the old one. The old governor should be returned.

The centrifugal-type governor for regulating the speed of gasoline-engine equipments is built by the Pierce Governor Company of Anderson, Indiana. It is of the flyball type, automatically lubricated from the oil-pressure system of the engine.

If trouble is experienced with the governor, it may be due to one or more of the following causes:

1) Manifold vacuum acting on control valve
2) Water in gasoline
3) Improper carburetion
4) Improper engine timing
5) Bad spark timing
6) Improper setting of governor and throttle levers
7) Bind in connecting rods
8) Lost motion in connecting rods
9) Internal friction within the governor
10) Worn internal parts within the governor
11) Lost motion in the governor drive
12) Lack of proper lubrication
13) Leak in manifold gaskets
14) Bind in control-valve shaft

The above causes will result in various symptoms, among which are the following combinations:

a) Surging at no load only. Items 1 to 14, inclusive.
b) Surging at full load only. Items 2, 3, 5, to 14, inclusive.
c) Surging at part load only. Items, 1, 2, 3, 5, 6, 7, 8, 11, 12, 13, 14.
d) Too much over-run. Items 1, 6, 7, 8, 10, 11, 14.
e) Too much drop-in r.p.m. between no load and full load (excess 75 r.p.m.) Items 1, 3, 4, 5, 6, 7, 8, 9, 10, 14.
f) Too much under-run as load is applied. Items 1, 2, 3, 4, 5, 6, 7, 11, 13, 14.
g) Speed changes after governor has been in use. Items 2, 3, 4, 5, 7, to 14, inclusive.
h) Governor is sluggish. Items 1, 6, 7, 9, 10, 11, 12, 14.

Velocity-type governors are made by the Hoof Products Company of Chicago. These governors are made of the best non-corrosive materials, and sealed after adjustment. The speed of the engine can be altered by breaking the seal and

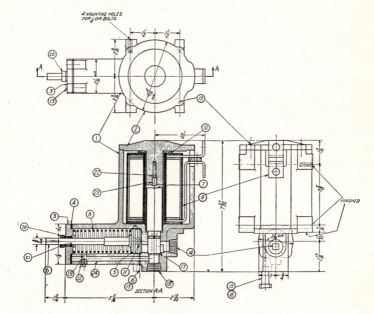

Figure 77: Idler cross section.

turning the screw in the end of the governor housing. These governors require no periodic lubrication or readjustment.

Idling Control. The idling control is an electro-hydraulic mechanism which permits the gasoline engine to operate at about one-third of full-load speed when the welding generator is not delivering current. It consists of a piston (5) (Figure 77) and piston rod (6), which is connected by suitable linkage to the throttle. A spring (8) encircling rod (6) presses against the rear face of the piston in a direction to open the throttle suddenly when oil pressure is released from the front face of piston (5).

Coil (9) is connected in the welding circuit and encircles plunger (7), at the lower end of which is a poppet-type release valve (17), which releases oil pressure against the front face of piston (5) when sufficient current in the welding circuit flows through coil (9). Oil pressure from the engine oil pump is admitted through an adjustable, globe needle valve (15), thence through port (16) to the front face of piston (5). If no current flows through coil (9), valve (17) is closed and oil pressure through (15) and (16) will build up against piston (5), gradually forcing it against spring (8) to close the throttle. The rate of closing is adjusted to suit the requirements by adjusting the globe needle valve (15).

When the electrode is touched to the work to start welding, current through coil (9) opens valve (17) and oil pressure is immediately discharged by piston (5), through valve (17) and port (18) into the engine crankcase. Oil is, of course, constantly pumped through valve (15), but under these conditions it discharges into the crankcase. The rate of oil flow is so low, however, that it has no effect on the pressure in the oil system. The immediate movement of piston (5) instantly opens the engine throttle, so that the welding arc can be readily established.

Any oil leakage past piston (5) drains directly to the crankcase through port (19), passage (24) and port (18).

Buffer pin (23) and spring (22) are to prevent magnetic-sealing plunger (7) after coil (9) is de-energized.

Coil (9) requires approximately 20 amperes to raise plunger (7) and open discharge valve (17) to start welding. The minimum idling speed for which the engine should be adjusted is therefore limited to that which will permit the generator to pass 20 amperes through the welding circuit when the electrode is touched to the work. The idling speed is adjusted at the carburetor throttle valve. It will be about 600 r.p.m.

It is usually desirable to adjust the globe needle valve so that a period of about 30 seconds will elapse after the welding

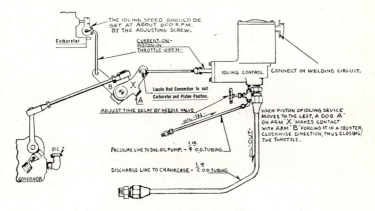

Figure 78: Idler connections.

current is interrupted, before the throttle is moved to the idling position. This will give the operator time to change electrodes without idling the engine.

To connect the idler into the welding circuit when building your own set, remove the wire leading from the terminal marked "Electrode" in the generator to the top brushholder. Connect a cable from the end of this wire to one of the idler-coil terminals and another cable from the other idler-coil terminal to the brushholder. The oil pressure piping and throttle levers should be connected as shown in Figure 78.

GENERAL ELECTRIC WELDING GENERATORS

Type WD Arc Welders. These are made in four different sizes, in NEMA ratings of 200, 300, 400 and 600 amperes. The

300-amp. welder is shown in Figure 79. They are furnished with either electric-motor drive or gasoline-engine or Diesel-engine drive. A separate welding generator can also be furnished for assembling with a gasoline engine or an existing line shaft.

Figure 79: Single-operator, portable, motor-generator, arc welder. 300 amps., Type WD, having a.c. motor. Oblique view of operative side and generator end. (General Electric Co.)

The welding generator and the current-control devices of all models are the same except for size and rated output.

The Split-Pole Type Generator Provides Limited Current Peaks, Instant Recovery Voltage. Oscillograph measurements of the reaction of this welder to short circuit demonstrate two qualities of split-pole construction:

First, current peaks never exceed three times the steady short-circuit current on any adjustment. As a result, excessive and wasteful weld spatter is prevented, and operators find it easier to keep the electrode from sticking to the work.

Second, full arc voltage is generated instantly after short circuit; therefore, unexpected pop-out of the arc is avoided, and the operation of the welder is not interrupted.

Figure 80: Control panel on single-operator, arc-welding set, 1937 model, with generator, 300 amps., Type WD-33. (General Electric Co.)

Reliable protection against overloading is provided by iso-thermic overload relays operated in conjunction with the motor starter. When a harmful temperature is approached, the relays automatically remove power but avoid needless shutdown.

Current Controls

Because WD welders provide instant recovery voltage after a short circuit, simple controls (Figure 80) are all that are required to maintain a steady welding current.

A tap switch is provided for making broad changes in the current setting. Finer adjustments are made with a special fine-step rheostat.

With these two controls, any desired welding current within the range of the machine can be maintained. Current will remain steady at the rating for which the controls are set until changed by the operator.

Figure 81: Two-unit, sleeve-bearing, dripproof, motor-generator, d.c. arc welder, 105 kw., 1200 r.p.m., consisting of synchronous motor, 160 h.p., 1200 r.p.m., 440 volts, 60 cycles, 0.8 p-f, Type TS-963-6; and compound-wound d.c. generator, 105 kw., 70/70 volts, Type CD-1254-4. Side view. (General Electric Co.)

A polarity switch, equipped with a large handle, is also provided to permit selection of either straight or reverse polarity.

Starting

With all WD welders the arc starts quickly, without sticking or "freezing" of the electrode, on any current setting within the range of the machine. Short-circuit current peaks are automatically controlled to provide the correct current for instant starting, yet heavy surges that cause "freezing" are prevented.

Current Range

The current range of all WD welders makes it possible for them to handle a wide variety of work. For example, the 300-amp. welder gives satisfactory results with electrodes as small as $\frac{1}{16}''$, or as large as $\frac{3}{8}''$ in diameter.

Maintenance

The low excitation voltage and the heavy-conductor shunt-field windings give low electrical stress and high mechanical strength to the shunt field. Insulating varnish, applied to multi-layer field windings by the vacuum-dip and bake method, protects the welders against grounding or short-circuiting, even when operating continuously under heavy load. It is of drip-proof construction, with ball bearings selected for a 10-to-1 safety factor, filler and relief pipes for bearing grease, and rigid cast-iron bearing-supports.

Electric-Motor Driven Welders. Electric-motor driven WD welders are available in four models: WD-32B, 33B, 34B, and 36B, with NEMA ratings of 200, 300, 400 and 600 amps., respectively. (See Figure 82.) Each is a complete, self-enclosed unit, with welding generator, current control, driving motor, and starter. Portable arc welders are also equipped with a running gear, having either steel wheels or solid-rubber tires.

All these welders are of the horizontal, two-bearing design, except those of the 600-amp. size, equipped with a d.c. or a 25-cycle a.c. motor drive. Because of their size and weight, these two 600-amp. models are equipped with four bearings. The driving motor of all a.c. two-bearing models is overhung, while d.c. motors are mounted conventionally.

Figure 82: Typical single-operator, d.c. portable, motor-generator arc-welder, Type WD, in cut-away section. (General Electric Co.)

Choice of A.C. or D.C. Motor

All motor-driven WD welders are furnished with either an a.c. or a d.c. driving motor, depending upon the preference of the user and the type of current supply available at the point of use. Both types of motors give equally satisfactory results. Rotors of the cast squirrel-cage construction are used in the

Figure 83: Wound armature and end shield, and overhung squirrel-cage induction-motor rotor (removed) for single-operator, arc-welding motor-generator set. Type WD-33-B. (General Electric Co.)

a.c. motors because of their efficiency and durability. The a.c. motors can be used with either a 220-volt or a 440-volt power supply and, if desired, a dual-voltage switch can be provided to facilitate switching from one voltage to the other.

All d.c. driving motors used in WD welders are of the dependable constant-speed, shunt-wound design.

Starter

A push-button starter that gives both undervoltage protection and isothermic overload protection is provided on all welders driven by an a.c. motor. Either 220-volt or 440-volt starters can be used, and both have ample capacity to handle either voltage. However, unless a dual-voltage switch is used, the overload-relay heaters and coils must be changed to match the line voltage when the change from one to the other is made.

D.C. motor-driven welders are equipped with a magnetic reduced-voltage starter which also provides both undervoltage protection and isothermic overload protection.

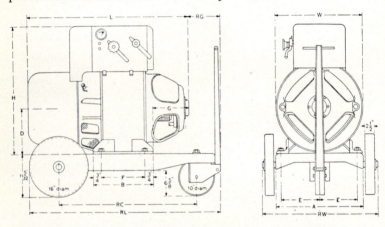

Figure 84: Electric-driven arc-welding generator. See Table 3. (General Electric Co.)

Running Gear and Other Optional Features

All-steel running gear with pressed steel wheel, as illustrated below, is available as an optional feature for all WD motor-driven welders.

Running gear can be furnished equipped with solid rubber or balloon tires when available.

Other optional features include special motors for operating welders on unlisted power supplies; sheet-steel and canvas canopy for protection against the weather; dual-voltage switch; resistors for extra-low currents; and other special equipment.

TABLE 3. APPROXIMATE DIMENSIONS OF ELECTRIC-DRIVEN MODELS (Figure 84)

Type of Welder	Dimensions in Inches												
	Stationary Welder with 60-, or 50-Cycle Drive												
	Overall				Base					Running Gear ***			
	L *	W	H	A	B **	D	E	F **	G	RL	RC	RW	RG
WD-32B	38 5/16	20 1/2	31 1/16	19 1/4	12 3/4	10 1/2	8 3/8	11 1/4	10 3/8	46 1/2	32	27 3/4	11
WD-33B	44	23 3/4	35	23 3/4	15	12	10 1/2	13 1/2	9 3/4	42	29 1/2	31 1/2	8
WD-34B	47	23 3/4	36 7/16	23 3/4	15	12	10 1/2	13 1/2	12 3/16	42	29 1/2	31 1/2	5 9/16
WD-36B	57	23 3/4	36 7/16	23 3/4	15	12	10 1/2	13 1/2	18 3/16	55 1/4	41 1/4	31 7/8	11 5/16

* Welders driven by d.c. motors or 25-cycle a.c. motors are 3 1/2" to 6" longer than the "L" dimension listed.
** Dimension "B" for welders driven by d.c. motors is approximately twice the length listed, the angles extending back to support the motor frame. There are three bolt holes on each side, "F" inches apart.
*** Running gear for the WD-36B model is of fabricated angle-iron construction and has 3 wheels of 14" diameter with 3" face.

(table continued next page)

TABLE 3 (Continued)

WIRING DATA

A. With A.C. Motor Drive on 3-Phase Power *

Type of Welder	220 Volts A.C.					440 Volts A.C.					550 Volts A.C.				
	Full-load Line Amp.	Power-lead Size B&S	Min. Fuse Size Amp.	Trumbull Fusible Switch Size Amp.	Cat. No.	Full-load Line Amp.	Power-lead Size B&S	Min. Fuse Size Amp.	Trumbull Fusible Switch Size Amp.	Cat. No.	Full-load Line Amp.	Power-lead Size B&S	Min. Fuse Size Amp.	Trumbull Fusible Switch Size Amp.	Cat. No.
WD-32B	40	6	100	100	72323	20	10	60	60	72362	16	12	50	60	72362
WD-33B	56	4	125	200	72324	28	8	75	100	72363	23	10	70	100	72363
WD-34B	70	3	175	200	72324	35	8	110	200	72364	28	8	90	200	72364
WD-36B	105	0	225	400	72325	53	4	110	200	72364	42	6	90	300	72364

* Listed data for a.c. motor drive apply to 3-phase power; with 2-phase power, full-load line amperes are approximately 15% less, for which allowance can be made.

134

B. With D.C. Motor Drive

TABLE 3 (Continued)

Type of Welder	115 Volts D.C.					230 Volts D.C.					550 Volts D.C.				
	Full-load Line Amp.	Power-lead Size B & S	Min. Fuse Size Amp.	Trumbull Fusible Switch Size Amp.	Cat. No.	Full-load Line Amp.	Power-lead Size B & S	Min. Fuse Size Amp.	Trumbull Fusible Switch Size Amp.	Cat. No.	Full-load Line Amp.	Power-lead Size B & S	Min. Fuse Size Amp.	Trumbull Fusible Switch Size Amp.	Cat. No.
WD-32B	135	000	150	200	72224	67	4	100	100	72223	26	10	40	60	72262
WD-33B	172	250†	200	200	72224	86	2	125	200	72224	36	8	50	60	72262
WD-34B	...	...	...	...	...	115	1	150	200	72224	48	5	75	100	72263
WD-36B	...	...	...	...	...	172	250†	250	400	72225	72	0	100	100	72263

† These power-lead sizes are expressed in thousands of circular mils.

135

TABLE 4. CHARACTERISTICS OF MOTOR-DRIVEN WD WELDERS

	Current Range			Speeds & Weights with A.C. Motor Drive					
		Range of Adjustment of Output		Full-load Speed, R.p.m.		Approx. Net Weight in Lb.			
						60 or 50 Cycles		25 Cycles	
Type of Welder	Rated Output Current Amp.	Min. Amp. at 20 Volts	Max. Amp. at 40 Volts	60 Cycles	50 and 25 Cycles	Stationary	With Running Gear	Stationary	With Running Gear
WD-32B	200	40	250	1750	1440	850	955	930	1035
WD-33B	300	60	375	1750	1440	1310	1420	1410	1520
WD-34B	400	80	500	1750	1440	1540	1650	1700	1810
WD-36B	600	120	750	1750	1440	2360	2525	3100	3625

TABLE 4 (Continued)

Type of Welder	Current Range			Speeds & Weights with D.C. Motor Drive					
	Rated Output Current Amp.	Range of Adjustment of Output		Full-load Speed R.p.m.	Approx. Net Weight in Lb.				
		Min. Amp. at 20 Volts	Max. Amp. at 40 Volts		115 or 230 Volts		550 Volts	
					Stationary	With Running Gear	Stationary	With Running Gear
WD-32B	200	40	250	1750	1060	1165	1150	1255
WD-33B	300	60	375	1750	1575	1685	1640	1750
WD-34B	400	80	500	1750	1840	1850	1950	2060
WD-36B	600	120	750	1760	....	....	....	....

These welders are rated in accordance with NEMA standards for 40-volt welders. With any listed welder, manual welding can be done all day long with any current up to rated output current.

"Build-Your-Own" Models. In general, it is more satisfactory and more economical for an operator to purchase a
complete unit, equipped with factory-built drive, than to build
one himself. But in some cases it is entirely practical for a

Figure 85: Single-operator, d.c., arc-welding generator, Type WD-32-B,
for belt drive or direct connection. Typical of 200- to 600-amp. sizes.
Back-end oblique control-side view. (General Electric Co.)

user who has the existing drive-power, the time, the ingenuity, and a few tools, to buy an arc-welding generator and provide his own drive by properly assembling the generator with a gasoline engine or by belting to an existing line shaft.

In providing his own gasoline-engine drive, the user will need, in addition to the proper engine, a suitable governor and a flexible coupling or pulleys to connect the engine to the generator. An automatic slow-down control is also frequently used to reduce engine-speed while the welder is idling. These additional items can be obtained from the manufacturer.

Any of the standard motor-driven WD welders listed above can be used for this purpose. When ordering, it should be specified "without motor." Speed of rotation (1750 or 1440, full-load r.p.m.) and counterclockwise or clockwise rotation should also be specified. Standard rotation is counterclockwise, facing the commutator end.

Engine-Driven. Engine-driven WD welders are furnished in 8 models, with NEMA ratings of 200, 300, 400 and 600

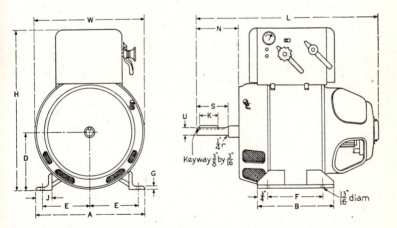

Figure 86: "Build-your-own" model arc-welding generator. (See Table 5.) (General Electric Co.)

TABLE 5. WEIGHTS AND DIMENSIONS OF "BUILD-YOUR-OWN" MODELS (Figure 86)

Type of Welder	Net Wt. in Lb. (Approx.)	Min. Recommended H.P. of Gasoline-engine Drive*	Dimensions in Inches									
			Overall					Base				
			L	W	H	A	B	D	E	F	G	J
WD-32B	670	30	33 1/16	20 1/2	31 1/16	19 1/4	12 3/4	10 1/2	8 3/8	11 1/4	3/8	3
WD-33B	1055	45	37 5/16	23 3/4	35	23 3/4	15	12	10 1/2	13 1/2	1/2	3 1/2
WD-34B	1310	55	40 5/8	23 3/4	36 7/16	23 3/4	15	12	10 1/2	13 1/2	1/2	3 1/2
WD-36B	....	85	48 5/16	23 3/4	36 7/16	23 3/4	15	12	10 1/2	13 1/2	1/2	3 1/2

TABLE 5 (Continued)

Type of Welder	Net Wt. in Lb. (Approx.)	Min. Recommended H.P. of Gasoline-engine Drive *	Dimensions in Inches			
			Shaft			
			U	S	N	K
WD-32B	670	30	1 13/16	4 11/16	6 3/16	3 1/4
WD-33B	1055	45	1 13/16	5 13/16	6 15/16	4 1/4
WD-34B	1310	55	1 13/16	5 13/16	6 15/16	4 1/4
WD-36B	. . . .	85	2 15/16	6 3/8	8 3/8	5

* This horsepower should be developed by the engine when it is operating at the speed required to drive the generator at full-load speed, and is sufficient to develop maximum output of which the generator is capable.

amps. and powered by Diesel-engine or gasoline-engine drive. Each model is a complete, ready-to-use unit, consisting of a standard G-E welding generator combined with an industrial engine of suitable power.

Operation

Quiet operation, with very little vibration, is provided by "floating-power" engine mounting. The engine and the gen-

Figure 87: Single-operator, d.c., arc-welding engine-generator set, Type WD-32-BH: Hercules gasoline engine, 1 XB, direct-connected to generator, Type WD-32-B. Oblique, operator's-side view. (General Electric Co.)

erator are kept in concentric alignment by a rabbet or dowel fit in the ring housing.

Assembly

Since the rear engine bearing has ample load capacity, it also serves as one of the generator bearings. This permits compact assembly and avoids excessive radial bearing stresses. The other generator bearing is designed to float in its housing, thus assuring that any end thrust will be absorbed by the engine-thrust bearing, which is specially designed for this purpose.

Figure 88: 10,000-Bbl. arc-welded, fabricated gasoline storage tank built by the Chicago Bridge and Iron Co., using G-E single-operator arc-welder, 300 amps. to 40 volts, driven by caterpillar D3400 Diesel engine at 1525 r.p.m. Welder operated 8 hours per day with fuel consumption of 1.3 gallons per hour. Fuel cost, 6.7¢ per hour. Tank owned by the Standard Oil Co., at Columbus, Ohio. (Courtesy General Electric Co.)

TABLE 6. CHARACTERISTICS OF ENGINE-DRIVEN WD WELDERS

Type of Welder	Rated Output Current, Amp.*	Min. Amp. at 20 Volts	Max. Amp. at 40 Volts	Model and Make of Engine	Governed Operating Speed, (R.p.m.)	Fuel-tank Capacity (U.S. Gal.)	Net Wt. in Pounds (Approx.)	Overall Dimensions in Inches (Approx.)			No. of Spec. Sheet
								Length	Width	Height	
WD-32BH WD-32BG	200	40	250	Hercules, Model IBX Continental, Model F-162	1750 1750	10 11	1220 1800	68 73	24 28	40 50	GEA-3584 GEA-3586
WD-33BG WD-33BD	300	60	375	Chrysler, Model T-118 Caterpillar Diesel, D-3400	1750 1525	24 25	2200 3700	76 88	28 30	50 54	GEA-3587 GEA-3588
WD-34BG WD-34BD	400	80	500	Chrysler, Model T-120 Caterpillar Diesel, D-4400	1750 1450	24 25	2550 4445	82 94	28 30	50 55	GEA-3589 GEA-3590
	600	120	750	Details furnished on request to General Electric Company, Schenectady, N. Y.							

* These welders are rated in accordance with NEMA standards or 40-volt welders. Manual welding can be done all day long with any current up to rated output current.

Figure 89: Pneumatic-tired 4-wheel trailer, "Type 3" (John Deere make), typical of those used with G-E engine-driven arc welders weighing 2000 lbs. or more. Side view from front. Welder mounted and hitch pole raised. (Courtesy General Electric Co.)

Part 4

Electrodes and Metals

Description: An electrode is a metal rod used as a source from which metal is added to the work being welded. Electrodes come in sizes varying from $\frac{1}{32}''$ diameter for very light work to $\frac{5}{8}''$ diameter for heavy construction work. The length is usually $14''$ or $18''$. Electrodes for direct-current welding may be divided into two general classes—the bare type and the covered type. A bare electrode is simply a piece of metal without any coating at all—or one which has a very light coating.

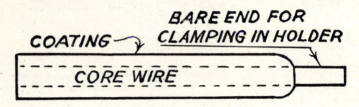

Figure 90: Covered type electrode.

Figure 90 shows the covered or coated electrode, which has a heavy coating around its circumference for the entire length, with the exception of one inch at one end.

The heat of the arc (*see* page 39) causes the electrode to melt, and this molten metal is transferred across the arc gap and deposited on the work to be welded. Figure 91a shows what happens within the arc caused by the bare electrode. The metal is transferred across the gap and is completely open to the elements of the surrounding atmosphere. There is no protection of the molten metal from the harmful effects of the oxygen and nitrogen that are present in the atmosphere. There is also no means of retarding the speed with which this

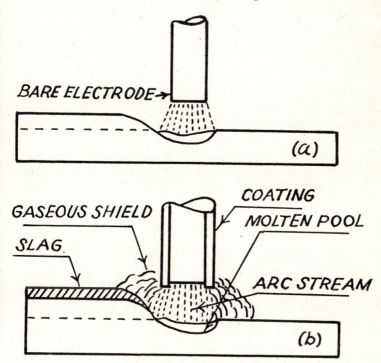

Figure 91: (a) Arc produced by bare electrodes. The molten metal has no protection from the atmosphere. (b) Arc produced with covered electrodes. Here the molten metal is shielded from the atmosphere by vaporization of the electrode covering.

metal cools from a molten to a solid state. The result is a brittle weld of comparatively poor quality and generally undesirable characteristics, as compared with the welds produced by coated electrodes.

The arc produced by the covered electrode is known as a shielded arc. This term comes from the fact that the arc is shielded by an envelope of inert gas caused by the vaporization of the coating or covering of the electrode. Inasmuch as a covered electrode has proven its superiority over the bare type, and since the covered electrode is by far the most extensively used, only this type of electrode will be considered from here on.

Figure 91b gives an illustration of the shielded arc as produced by these heavily coated electrodes.

The benefits obtained by using heavily coated electrodes may be listed as follows:

1) Atmospheric protection
2) Arc stability
3) Cleansing agent
4) Penetration control
5) Chemical composition control

6) Cooling control
7) Contour control
8) Speed
9) Strength

1) Atmospheric protection: The envelope of inert gas produced by the vaporization of the coating on the electrode prevents the harmful gases of the atmosphere from coming in contact with the weld metal until such time as it has solidified to the point where it is not susceptible to the harmful effects of the nitrogen and oxygen in the atmosphere. This gaseous envelope forms itself around the arc and molten metal.

2) Arc stability: The coating is a fairly good electrical insulator, and because of this it is possible to weld in deep grooves and corners without having the electrode arc along the side. In addition, the coating allows a greater variation of arc length and maintains a steadier arc than a bare electrode would.

3) Cleansing agent: After the coating has vaporized and formed a shield about the arc, it also mixes with the molten metal and then floats to the top of the weld. During this time

it actually cleans the metal of impurities and floats them out of the weld.

4) Penetration control: Different types of coatings may be put on the same type of metal, so that one of the finished electrodes will produce a greater or less amount of penetration in the base metal than another. This, then, allows a choice between deep and light penetration. Usually the electrode giving deep penetration gives less metal deposit in a given time, while the electrode giving light penetration will give a high rate of metal deposit.

5) Chemical composition control: During the welding process, some of the elements of the base metal may be burned out and, unless replaced, the result will be a weld of undesirable characteristics. These elements, however, may be added to the electrode coating so that during the welding process they may be replaced, thereby counterbalancing any loss. This method of introducing elements to the welded joint, by way of the electrode coating, in addition to replacing original elements of the base metal, may also be used to add to the base metal elements that will increase the quality of the weld.

6) Cooling control: After the coating has mixed with the metal and acted as a cleansing agent, it floats to the surface of the weld and completely covers the weld. This action prolongs the time it would otherwise take for the weld metal to cool. This gives an annealing effect to the metal and results in a more ductile weld.

7) Contour control: In some cases it is desirable to produce a bead that will be concave across the face; while in other cases a convex face is desired. The type of coating on the electrode will be responsible to a large degree as to which type of face contour is produced.

8) Speed: Because the arc is more stable and because it is possible to use higher current values with coated electrodes, the speed of welding is much higher than with bare electrodes.

9) The coated electrode produces welds with tensile values of 60,000 to 80,000 lbs. per square inch, yield points of 45,000 to 55,000 lbs. per square inch, elongation of 15% to 30% in 2 inches. In contrast to this, the bare wire electrode gives tensile values of 50,000 to 55,000 lbs. per square inch, yield

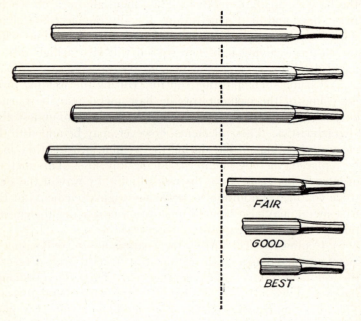

FAIR

GOOD

BEST

Figure 92: The top four electrodes show wastefully long stubs. No more than two inches should be left as a stub end on an electrode.

points of about 40,000 lbs. per square inch, elongation of 5% to 8% in 2 inches. The reason for these lower values is the introduction of oxygen and nitrogen into the molten metal, unprotected by any vapor envelope.

Economy of Electrodes: One of the many things overlooked by many welders is economy in the use of electrodes. Electrodes are expensive, and should be used with this thought in mind. Following are nine rules that will help to prevent unnecessary waste:

1) Always burn the electrode to at least 1" from the bare end.
2) Never bend an electrode unless absolutely necessary.
3) Do not make beads larger than necessary.
4) Have work properly fitted up before starting to weld.
5) Do not make unnecessarily large tack welds.
6) Hold a close arc at all times to prevent spatter, which results in a large percentage of electrode waste.
7) Weld without undercutting, which results in the necessity of running filler beads over the finished job.
8) Use the largest electrode possible for the particular job.
9) Protect the electrodes from moisture.

Following is an explanation of the above rules:

1) Remember that the last 2" of an electrode are as good as the first 2", and the waste of electrodes, due to throwing away long ends, can be chalked up to laziness or lack of co-operation on the part of the welder. He shows his lack of experience and ability when he does this. It is an inexcusable fault and waste. (Figure 92.)

2) Bending an electrode causes an unnecessary waste of from 1" to 2" on each electrode, and figuring this on a percentage basis for a 14" electrode, it can be seen that from 7–14% of each electrode is wasted. Multiplying this by every 100 electrodes used, there are from 7 to 14 electrodes out of every 100 that are actually thrown away. Unnecessary bending of the electrode is of absolutely no help to the welder, but is a habit with many. The only time an electrode should be bent is when the job demands it. (Figure 93.)

3) A certain job will call for a certain size weld. A good welder can lay a bead of exactly the size called for, and anything larger than that is simply another form of waste. Inasmuch as the size of the weld is calculated by the welding engi-

neering department, or by some person well qualified to do so, it is not necessary for the welder to feel he must lay a larger bead for any reason whatsoever; and when he does make a larger weld, he shows his inability to follow directions as well as his inability to weld correctly. (Figure 94.)

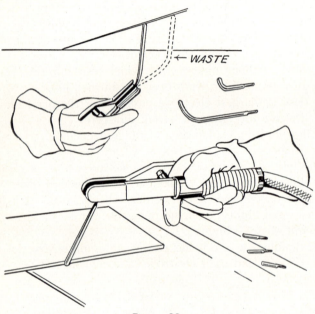

Figure 93.

4) Having the work properly fitted up is a necessary part of the welder's job. In some cases, the welder himself will have to do the fitting up; in which case the entire responsibility rests with the welder. If a shipfitter or ironworker is to do the fitting up, the welder should check the work for proper fit-up before starting to weld, and unless he receives the proper permission from his welding foreman, he should not start work

on a poorly fitted job. Figure 95 shows an example where there is twice as much electrode wasted as used because the two plates were not properly set together.

5) The purpose of tack welds is to keep the work in place until such time as it can be checked for accuracy and then

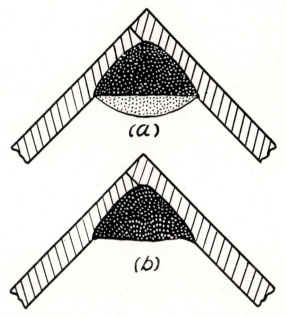

Figure 94: (a) A fillet too concave or convex is wasteful. Too much convexity is more common. (b) Good practice is to make the face of fillet welds as flat as possible.

completely welded. There is no advantage in making excessively large tacks, and there is the disadvantage of a large tack interfering with the appearance of the finished weld. Excessively large tacks are, therefore, another electrode waste.

6) One of the surest signs of an inexperienced or a careless welder is a badly spattered job. The appearance of the job is

spoiled, and the spatter represents a loss of electrode which might be as high as 10%, which would be approximately the same waste as throwing away long ends. By holding a close arc, the waste from spatter can be eliminated almost entirely. Holding a close arc will also add to the quality of the job in penetration and neat appearance.

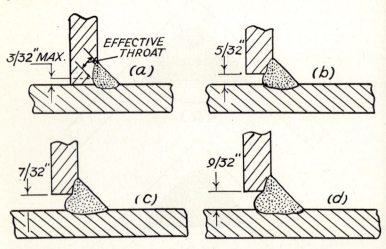

Figure 95: (a) Good practice. (b) A ⁵⁄₃₂″ gap means a ³⁄₈″ fillet must be made to produce the strength of a ⁵⁄₁₆″ fillet—50% more time, power and electrodes required. (c) Here the waste is 100%. (d) Here the waste reaches 200% over (a) for the same result.

7) Every welder should realize the necessity of eliminating undercut in the weld from the viewpoint of the strength of the joint. Often a welder is careless enough not to take the time to eliminate undercutting as he welds because he feels it is all right to add filler beads to take care of the undercutting. This results in waste of electrode, time and power, as well as producing an oversized and poor-appearing weld. Eliminate undercut at all times in all jobs.

8) Using the proper size electrodes is an essential factor in

considering economy. If just as good a job can be done with ¼″ electrodes, it is wasteful to do it with ⁵⁄₃₂″ electrodes, as there will be more electrode ends left with the smaller size and each end represents some waste. However, this point should be carefully considered, as it would not be wise economy to save the electrode at the expense of the job. The quality of the job should always be the first consideration.

9) When conditions are such that the coating of the electrode may be affected by moisture, special precautions must be taken. The moisture will affect the coating to the extent of causing it to chip off during the welding process, producing a weld of poor appearance and poor quality. Always store electrodes in a clean, dry place.

Choice of Electrodes: The choice of proper electrode is one of the most important parts of the job. The first consideration is the type of metal to be welded. The composition of the electrode used must be suitable for the particular metal being welded. It is generally considered that best results are obtained using an electrode of exactly the same analysis as that of the metal to be welded. The second factor to be considered is whether an all-position electrode is necessary, or whether a fast-flowing electrode of the type used for flat welding may be used. If the job is composed of flat grooves and fillets, an electrode specifically designed for this purpose may be used. The advantages of this type are speed and economy. On the other hand, if the job consists of all-position welding and of various types of joints, the all-position type of electrode may be used.

Another fact to be considered is the size of electrode. The proper size will depend upon the thickness of the metal to be welded and the size of welds to be made. The ideal electrode is one that will give a metal deposit of the same composition and characteristics as the base metal, that will replace any of the elements lost by the welding process and, at the same time, give a high rate of metal deposit.

Types: There are many manufacturers of welding electrodes, and each manufacturer usually puts a complete line of electrodes on the market with the result that there is a large field from which to choose electrodes for any particular job. There are electrodes containing various amounts of carbon for welding steels of different carbon contents, there are electrodes for welding various types of metal, and there are electrodes for welding in various positions. For instance, most manufacturers put out a mild steel electrode that is designed specifically for flat welding of mild steel, and other electrodes for welding mild steel in the vertical and overhead position. There are spe-

TABLE 7. MILD STEEL ELECTRODES

Mfrs. Name	A.W.S. No. 6010 Mfrs. No.	A.W.S. No. 6012	A.W.S. No. 6020	A.W.S. No. 6030
Air Reduction Sales Company	Airco #78 " 79 " 78E " 79E	Airco #87 " 187	Airco #81	Airco #83
Lincoln Electric Company	Fleetweld 5	Fleetweld 7	Fleetweld 11 " 9	Fleetweld 9 " 10
General Electric	W-22 W-22H	W-20 W-30	W-24	W-23
Westinghouse Electric & Mfg. Co.	AP	FP SW	DH	DH
Hollup Corp.	Sureweld B	Sureweld N	Sureweld F	Sureweld A

By glancing at the chart it can be seen that the Air Reduction electrode No. 78 falls under A.W.S. No. 6010, as does the Lincoln Electric electrode designated as Fleetweld 5. Therefore, both these electrodes may be used for the same type of work.

cial electrodes for the welding of thin sheet steel, and others for heavy welding where good penetration is an essential factor. Each electrode is usually identified by a number and a different colored coating.

All of these electrodes, however, may be divided into two general classes—straight and reverse polarity electrodes; some give better results on one polarity than on the other. As a general rule, each carton containing electrodes has printed on it the manufacturer's recommendations as to polarity, and these recommendations should be followed.

The types of electrodes are not generally standardized, and for that reason manufacturer A may put out an electrode which he will call #1, which will be in all respects the same as one put out by manufacturer B, which he will call #5. For this reason a comparison chart is given in Table 7.

USE AND APPLICATION OF ELECTRODES

A. W. S.–E-6010. This type of electrode is more generally used than any other. It can be used for all positions and on all types of joints. The main uses of E-6010 are for fabrication of steel plate, bridges, structural frames, and fabrication, pipe lines, boilers, ship construction and repair.

Procedure:

For use with d.c.—reverse polarity-weave or multiple beads.

Flat Welding:

Hold a close arc but do not allow coating to touch the molten pool. Clean slag from each pass before depositing the next one. Keep electrode tipped slightly into pool.

Vertical and Overhead:

Hold a close arc on both positions. On vertical welding keep

Figure 96: View of 304-mile pipe line, welded throughout with type E-6010 electrodes. (Courtesy Lincoln Electric Co.)

Figure 97: Lap-weld specimen made in mild steel with "Fleetweld 5," and E-6010 type electrode, showing relative effects of accelerated corrosion on the base metal and weld metal. (Courtesy Lincoln Electric Co.)

the electrode tipped slightly downward. For overhead fillets the electrode should be tipped at a small angle, 20° or less, to the vertical member. Vertical welding may proceed either from the top or bottom.

Properties	As Welded	Stress Relieved
Tensile Strength, p.s.i.	65,000–80,000	58,000–72,000
Yield Point, p.s.i.	50,000–60,000	44,000–58,000
Elongation in 2″	20–28%	27–37%

A. W. S.–E-6012. E-6012 is a fast flowing electrode and ideally suited for poor fit-up welding. It may be used in flat, vertical and overhead welding on tanks, structural work, shipwork, and general fabrication of mild steel. The finished weld is smoother than that obtained with E-6010.

Procedure:

For use with a.c. or d.c. With d.c. use straight polarity—weave or multiple beads.

Flat Welding:

Hold as short an arc as possible, with electrode tipped slightly into the pool. Clean each pass before making another.

Vertical and Overhead:

Vertical welding may be done from the bottom up, or from the top down, with satisfactory results. Keep the electrode tipped into the pool at an angle of 5°–10° when running a vertical bead. Hold the electrode straight up for overhead welding.

Properties	As Welded	Stress Relieved
Tensile Strength, p.s.i.	70,000–83,000	64,000–81,000
Yield Point, p.s.i.	57,000–70,000	47,000–64,000
Elongation in 2″	17–25%	23–28%

A. W. S.–E-6020. E-6020 is designed primarily for down-hand or flat fillet work. The finished weld is smooth with a heavy coating of slag. The slag is easily removed. It is used for fabrication of bridges, tanks, boilers, pipes, pressure vessels, structural stiffeners and beams. This electrode is not for vertical and overhead welding. Weaving is not recommended.

Procedure:

For use with d.c. or a.c. With d.c. use straight polarity. The electrode should be tipped into the pool and a very slight back-and-forth motion used. Excessive manipulation of the electrode will cause slag inclusions and holes. When using ¼″ or larger size electrodes, it is advisable to position the work, if possible.

Figure 98: Tank fabrication makes extensive use of E-6012 electrodes.
(Courtesy Lincoln Electric Co.)

Properties	As Welded	Stress Relieved
Tensile Strength, p.s.i.	63,000–74,000	61,000–71,000
Yield Point, p.s.i.	49,000–60,000	46,000–57,000
Elongation in 2″	21–32%	28–37%

A. W. S.–E-6030. This electrode is designed especially for deep-groove joints and finish, or dress beads in the flat position only. The slag is heavy but easily removed. It is used for fabricating gas holders, pipes, tanks, ships, and pressure vessels.

Vertical and overhead welding should not be attempted with this type of electrode.

Procedure:

May be used with d.c., either polarity, or with a.c. The electrode should be manipulated from side to side, but not excessively so. Too much sidewise motion will cause deep undercut.

Properties	As Welded	Stress Relieved
Tensile Strength, p.s.i.	62,000–73,000	60,000–70,000
Yield Point, p.s.i.	51,000–59,000	47,000–56,000
Elongation in 2″	21–32%	33–37%

When welding metal other than mild steel, it becomes necessary to use an electrode having the proper composition and characteristics for the metal being welded. If, for instance, the metal to be welded has a high carbon content (.50% carbon or better), it would be impossible to obtain a welded joint having high carbon characteristics if a mild steel (.20% carbon) electrode was used. Another example is with the corrosion-resistant metals. Here it becomes necessary to use electrodes that will give a weld deposit having corrosion-resisting qualities similar to those of the base metal to which the weld metal is being applied. In some cases the base metal is subjected in its regular use to acids, abrasion, or other particular circumstances, and when it is welded it becomes necessary that the weld deposit

Figure 99: An all-welded, 8900-ton cargo vessel built by Ingalls Ship-building Corp. E-6020 electrodes were used for high-speed fillet welding. (Courtesy Lincoln Electric Co.)

shall stand up as well as the base metal. For these reasons, it is necessary to have electrodes with the proper qualities for the particular job at hand.

Figure 100: Fractionating tower fabricated at a West Coast refinery, with E-6030 electrodes being used for deep-groove joints. (Courtesy Lincoln Electric Co.)

The A. W. S. E-7000 group of electrodes is similar to the A. W. S. E-6000 group previously described, with the exception that they are designed for the welding of low-alloy steels. That is, they contain alloying elements, and are used where higher strength values are required than can be obtained with the E-6000 type of electrodes. If compared with the E-6000 electrodes, it will be seen that the four electrodes of the E-7000 type listed below are similar in operation. That is, all, with the exception of E-7010, may be used with either direct or alternating current. It can be further seen that of the four, two are for use in the flat position only.

E-7010: For use with direct current, reverse polarity only—all-position welding.

This type of electrode is used for the welding of high tensile steels, such as Yoloy, Cromansil, Corten, Man-Ten, Silten, Jolten, Mayari, and Carbon-Moly, low-carbon nickel steels, structural silicon steels, and, in general, all low-alloy, high-tensile strength steels under .30% carbon.

Applications:

Shafts, carbon-moly piping, underframe railroad cars, oil well casing, gear teeth, and machinery fabrication.

Physical Properties

	As Welded	Stress Relieved
Tensile Strength, p.s.i.	77,000–82,000	75,000–80,000
Yield Point, p.s.i.	61,000–66,000	59,000–65,000
Elongation in 2″	20%–24%	25%–30%

The above properties will vary somewhat on the various steels, depending upon the admixture of the steel being welded. The properties given are average values of all weld metal specimens.

E-7011: For use with either direct or alternating current.

May be used with either reverse or straight polarity on direct current. Electrodes of this classification have the same physical property requirements as the E-7010, and may be used in all-position welding.

E-7020: May be used on direct current, either polarity, or with alternating current. Electrodes of this classification are for use in welding high tensile steels of the type mentioned previously. They can be used in the flat position and for horizontal fillets only, and are not for use in vertical or overhead welding.

Applications of this electrode include alloy steel tanks, high

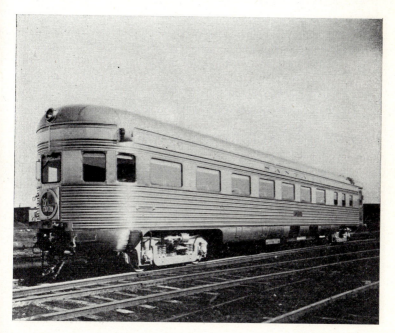

Figure 101: Modern streamliner locomotive welded with "Shield-Arc 85," and E-7010 type electrode. (Courtesy Lincoln Electric Co.)

tensile pressure vessels and piping, truck frames, and road-building equipment.

Physical Properties

	As Welded	Stress Relieved
Tensile Strength, p.s.i.	77,000–79,000	74,000–76,000
Yield Point, p.s.i.	60,000–63,000	58,000–66,000
Elongation in 2″	19%–23%	28%–29%

E-7030: For use with direct current, either polarity, or with

Figure 102: Welded underframe of locomotive shown in Figure 101.

alternating current. Designed for welding of deep U and V type grooves in flat position only. The physical properties are the same as for E-7020.

The only difference between the E-6000 and E-7000 types of electrodes is that the latter is for use where higher tensile strength welds are required. The welding coverage will average about the same for both groups when electrodes of a given size are used in the same positions. Where possible, high tensile steel should be given a preheat of 300° and kept at this temperature during the welding operation.

Figure 103: Electrodes of the E-7020 and -7030 classifications are used extensively for the fabrication of high-pressure, high tensile strength vessels and piping.

TABLE 8. TENSILE REQUIREMENTS OF DEPOSITED METAL

Electrode Classification Number	Capable of Producing Satisfactory Welds in Positions Shown [c]	General Description	Treatment of Welded Specimen [a]	Tensile Requirements of Material Deposited from $5/32$, $3/16$, and $7/32"$ Electrodes [b]	
				Tensile Strength min., p.s.i.	Elongation in 2", min., %
E-7010	V, F, OH, H	Heavy covering, useful with d.c., electrode positive only.	SR NSR	70,000 75,000	22 17
E-7011	F, V, OH, H	Heavy covering, useful with d.c., either polarity, or with a.c.	SR NSR	70,000 75,000	22 17
E-7020	H-Fillets, F	Heavy covering, usually used with electrode negative or a.c. for fillets, or electrode positive or a.c. for flat welding.	SR NSR	70,000 75,000	25 20
E-7030	F	Heavy covering, usually used with electrode positive d.c. or with a.c.	SR NSR	70,000 75,000	25 20
E-6010	F, V, OH, H	Heavy covering, useful with d.c., electrode positive only.	SR NSR	60,000 65,000	27 22
E-6012	F, V, OH, H	Heavy covering, usually used with electrode negative, d.c. or on a.c.	SR NSR	60,000 65,000	22 17
E-6020	H-Fillets, F	Heavy covering, usually used with electrode negative or a.c. for fillets, and electrode positive or a.c. for flat welding.	SR NSR	60,000 65,000	30 25
E-6030	F	Heavy covering, usually used with electrode positive on d.c., or with a.c.	SR NSR	60,000 65,000	30 25

Specifications for Arc-Welding Electrodes (Table 8).
Note (a): The abbreviations SR and NSR signify stress-relieved and non-stress-relieved, respectively. Stress-relieving
when prescribed in these specifications is for the purpose of
developing the fundamental properties of the weld metal un-
altered by locked-up stress. Values obtained from stress-relieved welded specimens are about 5% lower in tensile strength
and 10–20% higher in elongation than those of non-stress-
relieved specimens. The fact that an electrode test requires
stress-relief signifies only that it must develop the strength
required regardless of stress-relief, and not that stress-relief
must always be used in actual work. Stress-relieving shall be
within the range of 1150 ± 25° F. for 1 hr. per inch of thickness. Specimens shall be heated at the rate of 300 to 350° F.
per hr. and cooled at the same rate to 300° F. No specimen
shall be heated for less than 1 hr.

Note (b): The tensile strength of the deposited metal from
⅛″ electrodes shall be 105% of that prescribed in Table 8,
and that from ¼″ and larger electrodes shall be 95% of the
tensile strength prescribed in Table 8.

The elongation of the deposited metal from ⅛″ electrodes
shall be 90% of that prescribed in Table 8, and that from ¼″
and larger electrodes shall be 110% of the elongation prescribed in Table 8.

Note (c): The abbreviations F, V, OH, H, and H-Fillets indicate welding positions, as follows:

F—Flat
V—Vertical
H—Horizontal
OH—Overhead
H–Fillets—Horizontal Fillets

Approval of Electrodes for Welding. Rules for construction of unfired pressure vessels are covered by the A.S.M.E.
Boiler Construction Code issued by the American Society of

Mechanical Engineers, 29 W. 39th Street, New York City. The quality of weld metal and methods of testing joints for various classes of arc-weld unfired pressure vessels are given in Paragraphs U-68, U-69, and U-70. As an indication of the quality of weld metal required, these extracts are quoted:

"U-68—The tension-test specimen of the weld metal shall be taken entirely from the deposited weld metal and shall meet the following requirements:

"Tensile strength. The tensile strength shall be at least that of the minimum of the range of the plate which is welded.

"Elongation. The minimum elongation shall be 20% in 2″.

"Free-bend ductility. The ductility as determined by the free-bend test method shall not be less than 30%.

"All longitudinal and circumferential welded joints of the structure shall be examined throughout their entire length by the X-ray method of radiography."

"U-69—Tensile strength. For the reduced section tension-test specimens, the tensile strength shall not be less than 95% of the minimum of the specified tensile range of the plate used for double-welded butt joints or 85% for single welded butt joints.

"Free-bend ductility. The ductility as determined by the free-bend test method shall not be less than 20%.

"Soundness. The root-break, side-break, and nick-break tests of the weld shall show in the fractured surface complete penetration through the entire thickness of the weld, absence of oxide or slag inclusions, and a degree of porosity not to exceed six gas pockets per sq. in. of the total area of the weld surface exposed in the fracture, the maximum dimensions of any such pocket not to be in excess of $\frac{1}{16}$″, or provided the total area of the gas pockets per square inch does not exceed the area of six gas pockets each $\frac{1}{16}$″ in diameter.

"X-ray tests of the test plates as provided for in Paragraph U-68 may be substituted for the nick-break test."

"U-70—Tensile strength. For the reduced-section tension test specimen the tensile strength shall not be less than 85% of the minimum of the specified tensile range of the plate used. In no case shall the tensile strength be less than 42,000 p.s.i.

"Free-bend ductility. The ductility as determined by the free-bend test method shall be not less than 10%.

"Soundness. (Same as Paragraph U-69.)"

Hartford Steam Boiler Inspection and Insurance Co. insures boilers, pressure vessels, turbines, engines, and electric equipment against damage resulting from accidental failure, and follows the practice of making periodic inspection of all objects which it insures. In addition, it makes shop inspections during construction of boilers and pressure vessels constructed under the requirements of the A.S.M.E. Boiler and Pressure Vessel Code. The purpose of these inspections is to satisfy itself, through its inspectors, that the welding procedure used will produce welds that meet the requirements of the Code, and that the welding operators are competent as demonstrated by tests which are specified by the Code and conducted by the manufacturer of the boiler or pressure vessel. However, the Hartford Steam Boiler Inspection and Insurance Co. does not itself certify or qualify the welding operators, nor does it approve or certify the electrodes, or other equipments used in the fabrication of the object. Any electrode may be used, provided it will produce results which meet the requirements of the A.S.M.E. Code.

New Simplified Procedure

Requirements for the construction of various classes of pressure vessels are definitely outlined in the A.S.M.E. Boiler Code. To satisfy the Hartford Steam Boiler Inspection and Insurance Co. that the completed vessel meets these requirements, the following simplified procedure can be used:

For vessels built to comply with requirements of Paragraph U-68, no special assurance need be provided, since the test specimens and radiograph examination of completed joints provide adequate information.

For vessels built to comply with requirements of Paragraph U-69, the pressure-vessel manufacturer should:

1) Use electrodes "certified" by the manufacturer to comply with A.W.S. specifications for filler metal Grades 10 to 15.

2) See that the weld metal is deposited in such a manner as to obtain the appearance given by a standard "appearance weld," a photograph of which should be attached to the welding specification.

Pressure-vessel manufacturers who have previously satisfied Hartford Co. that they have a process for welding which will meet the requirements of the A.S.M.E. Code are not required to make "appearance-weld" photographs themselves, but may use such photograph supplied by the electrode manufacturer.

Pressure-vessel manufacturers employing Hartford for their shop inspection work for the first time are required to make their own "appearance welds." Plate thickness must be equal to the maximum when welding is done from one side only, or on a thickness equivalent to the deeper groove when welding is done from two sides. Such "appearance welds" are prepared in the flat position.

For vessels built to comply with requirements of Paragraph U-70, the same procedure should be followed as outlined for Paragraph U-69.

American Bureau of Shipping

Electrodes used for construction of hulls, boilers, and other structures under the jurisdiction of this bureau must be approved by it. No further tests of deposited weld metal from approval electrodes will be required, except for the purpose of qualifying operators, provided certificates are supplied, certifying that the types and sizes used have been tested and approved by the American Bureau of Shipping.

Lloyd's Register of Shipping

Electrodes used for construction of hulls, boilers, and other structures insured by Lloyd's must be approved by Lloyd's. No further tests of deposited weld metal from approved electrodes will be required, except for the purpose of qualifying operators. Certification of this fact can be obtained from Lloyd's local district office.

CHECK CHART FOR ELECTRODES

Efficiency and Ease of Operation	1. Burnoff rate—ins. per min.
	2. Deposition rate—lbs. per hr.
	3. Slag and spatter loss.
	4. Ease of striking and maintaining arc under all conditions and positions.
Physical Properties of Deposit	5. Tensile strength and yield point.
	6. Ductility (% elongation in 2").
	7. Fatigue and impact strengths.
	8. Resistance to corrosion.
Appearance of Deposit	9. Smoothness of bead. Absence of surface holes.
	10. Absence of overlap and undercut.
	11. Shape of bead. Flat or built-up.
	12. Condition of crater. Smooth or porous.
Slag Effectiveness	13. Viscosity. Even flow. No interference with arc.
	14. Ease of remelting for floating out on second pass. Absence of inclusions.
	15. Extent of coverage over bead.
	16. Ease of removal when hot or cold.
Uniformity of Analysis and Construction	17. Uniformity of chemical constituents.
	18. Concentricity of rod and coating.
	19. Clean ends best for holding and striking.
	20. Constancy of moisture content of coating.
	21. Proportion of coating.
	22. Durability of coating.
Extent of Usage and	23. Percentage of all welding users who use the electrode.

Originality

24. Percentage of welders using the electrode in qualifying for tests.
25. Percentage of welding codes which electrode meets.
26. Application background. Comparative tests by users.
27. Originality of electrode design. How extensively have other manufacturers attempted to copy its performance and appearance?

Ability to be
Matched
to the Job

28. Completeness of line for general and specific purposes, avoiding need for compromises.
29. Experience and skill of sales representative in welding application.
30. Reputation of manufacturer. Interest in your success in welding.

STEEL AND OTHER METALS

The weldability of a steel will depend upon the proportion of the various elements it contains. The amount of carbon present in a piece of steel is one of the most important factors governing its weldability. Carbon causes hardness in steel, and the greater the carbon content the harder will be the steel and the poorer will be the welding characteristics of the steel. For this reason then, the higher the carbon content, the less will be the give or **ductility** of the steel. To prevent cracking or fracturing due to lack of ductility, steels in the higher carbon ranges are usually heat-treated. Heat treatment may be divided into two classes. **Preheating** is the heat treatment given before welding. **Annealing** is that given after welding.

Steel is, in general, divided into three classes, according to its carbon content:

1) Low Carbon Steel—carbon content up to .25%
2) Medium Carbon Steel—carbon content up to .50%

3) High Carbon Steel—carbon content up to .80%

The low carbon steels are easily and quickly welded without any great difficulty; but as the carbon content increases, so the difficulty increases. The higher carbon steels should be carefully preheated and also annealed for the most satisfactory results. Preheating will slow down the rate of cooling, which in turn will reduce the hardening effects. Good results will be obtained along this line with preheats of about 150° F. for the lower carbon ranges to about 600° F. for the higher carbon ranges. The heat treatment after welding, which should be from 1100° F. to 1400° F., will increase the ductility of the job.

Various elements may be added to steel for increasing corrosion resistance, tensile strength, ductility or other desired effects. There are a number of different effects the alloying elements may produce, and because of this the proper kind of each alloy will depend upon the results required. The first thing to consider, then, is what the metal is to be subjected to: corrosion, bending, or high tensile loads. The effects and reaction due to welding and the economy of the job must also be considered.

The addition of alloying elements may improve the qualities of the finished product in one respect and decrease them in another. For instance, an increase of carbon will increase tensile strength, but will decrease ductility. The addition of chromium will increase corrosion resistance, but will at the same time increase the hardening qualities of the metal. Therefore, all the possible effects of an element should be known and considered before it is used.

The elements generally used in alloy steels are nickel, chromium, vanadium, copper, manganese, silicon, phosphorus, titanium, columbium, aluminum, tungsten, and molybdenum. There are many combinations of these alloying elements resulting in a large number of different types of steel which are usually given a trade name by the company manufacturing them.

Some of the various types of alloy steels and their use follow.

Jalten Steel. Jalten steel containing carbon in the lower range, up to .25%, will give excellent welding results. The electrode manipulation and welding procedure is the same as for regular low carbon steels. The manganese content makes this type of steel suitable for flame-hardening and for use where abrasion-resisting qualities are desired. The copper content gives corrosion-resisting qualities. Where the carbon is over .25%, it is advisable to stress-relieve this metal after welding. If both preheating and stress-relieving are to be used, the preheating temperature should be in the vicinity of 400° F., and the heat treatment after welding should be about 1100° F.

Man-Ten Steel. Man-Ten, like Jalten, is another of the so-called manganese steels, containing from 1.25% to 1.75% manganese. The copper content is less than that of Jalten. The welding and heat treatment are in general the same as for Jalten. On both of these steels the E-7000 type of electrodes may be used with satisfactory results.

Physical Properties

	Jalten	*Man-Ten*
Yield Point, lbs./sq. in.	60,000	55,000
Tensile Strength, lbs./sq. in.	85,000	90,000
Elongation, % in 2″	25	23

Chemical Content

	Jalten	*Man-Ten*
Carbon	.35% Max.	.30%
Manganese	1.3–1.75%	1.3–1.75%
Copper	.50%	.25%
Sulphur	.04%	.04%
Silicon	.25%	.20%
Phosphorus	.03%	.04%

Yoloy Steel. Yoloy steel is a copper-nickel alloy with a variable carbon content. The nickel content gives this steel improved impact resistance at extremely low temperatures, but also causes weld-hardening, particularly if the carbon content is .20% or greater. If Yoloy is to be welded without heat treatment, the carbon content must be held very low, as both carbon and nickel produce hardness; therefore, less carbon should be contained in the steel if the nickel content is high, for best welding results. The copper and phosphorus content add to its corrosion-resistant qualities. This type of steel, among other uses, is employed in the manufacture of dry ice.

Yield Point, p.s.i., 55,000
Tensile Strength, p.s.i., 68,000
Elongation in 2″, 30%

Carbon—	.07%–30%	Manganese—	.55%
Copper—	1.00%	Sulphur—	.03%
Silicon—	.25%	Phosphorus—	.02%
Nickel—	2.00%		

R. D. S. Steel. This is a copper, nickel and molybdenum alloy. As in other steels, best weldability is realized when the carbon content is held low. High carbon content produces a tendency toward air-hardening. The nickel content of R. D. S. is somewhat less than in Yoloy steel and, therefore, the carbon content may run higher in R. D. S. without air-hardening effects to the same degree. Where the carbon content is in the upper range, heat-treating should be employed. Preheating to 400° F. or 500° F. and annealing will give satisfactory results where heat-treating is necessary. Low alloy, high tensile electrodes should be used in welding.

Yield Point, 68,000
Tensile Strength, p.s.i., 83,000
Elongation in 2″, 34%

Carbon—	.10%–.30%	Copper—	1.00%
Manganese—	1.00% max.	Molybdenum—	.20%
Nickel—	.5–1.00%		

Corten Steel. Corten is a copper, chromium, silicon steel that is easily welded. The electrodes may be either of the low carbon type or the alloy type. The best results, particularly in regards to corrosion resistance, will be obtained if the alloy type of electrodes is used. The carbon content of Corten is usually low, doing away, in most cases, with the necessity of heat-treating, and giving excellent welding results. Where heat treatment is necessary, the annealing temperature should be in the vicinity of 1100° F. The physical properties of this steel are approximately the same as for mild steel; it features high corrosion resistant qualities.

Carbon—	.10%	Chromium—	.50%–1.50%
Silicon—	.50%–1.00%	Phosphorus—	.10%– .20%
Manganese—	.10%– .30%	Sulphur—	.04%
Copper—	.30%– .55%		

Cromansil Steel. This steel is used quite extensively where a high-strength structural steel is required. The carbon content is variable, and where it is in the upper limits, stress relieving is necessary. In the lower carbon ranges stress relieving is not necessary, and excellent welding results may be obtained. The alloying elements are chromium, manganese, and silicon, with the carbon ranging from .10% to .30%. With sections containing a high percentage of carbon, preheating to 400° F. will prove beneficial. Annealing of these same sections and of heavy sections in the low carbon range is recommended. The annealing temperature should be about 1200° F. Electrodes containing nickel will give higher tensile strength to the weld, while mild steel electrodes will produce a more ductile weld. Carbon moly electrodes may also be used.

Cast Iron. There are various types of cast iron. The proportion of the elements making up the composition determine just what the type of iron is. One of the elements contained in cast iron, carbon, is usually present in two different forms, as free carbon or graphite, or it may be in the combined form known as carbide of iron. One thing that determines the type of cast iron is the proportionate amount of carbon in each of the two forms. When a large amount of the carbon content is present in the form of iron carbide, the metal is extremely hard and brittle. On the other hand, when the carbon is contained in the free form, the casting is usually softer and readily machine-

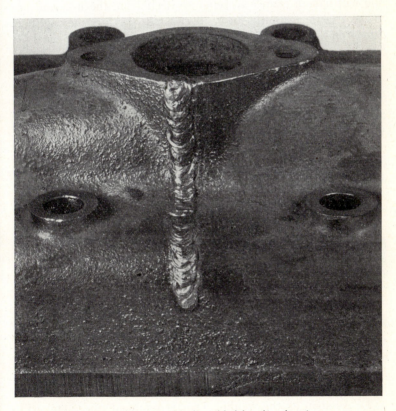

Figure 104: Cast iron block welded by the electric arc.

able. All cast irons contain from 2.5% to 4.00% carbon, but it is the form or state in which it is contained that causes two pieces to be of different characteristics.

When cast iron is in the molten state, practically all of the carbon content is in the form of iron carbide. If the casting is cooled very quickly, the carbon will remain to a large degree in this combined form. If the casting is cooled off slowly, the carbon will have a chance to separate itself from the iron and be in the free or graphitic form. Because of the fact that neither pure iron nor carbon in the graphitic form is extremely hard or brittle, the result is a softer piece of iron.

Irons containing a large proportion of free carbon are known as the **grey** cast irons, while those containing a large amount of combined carbon are known as the **white** cast irons. The color refers to the appearance of the metal when fractured. There is another general class of cast iron which is a mixture of both grey and white cast iron and is known as **chilled** cast iron. In some castings a section is purposely chilled to produce a white iron, while another section is cooled slowly, resulting in a grey iron. Between the two types is a section showing a mixture of both grey and white irons. This section is known as mottled iron. Malleable iron is another member of the cast iron family. This particular type is a white iron which has received an annealing treatment so that the carbon is separated from the iron and distributed through the iron grains in very fine particles.

Cast iron may be successfully welded (Figure 104) if the following is remembered and applied:

1) When the base metal is melted during the welding process, the carbon, regardless of the state or form it was originally in, will go into solution with molten metal, and its final state in the weld area will depend on its rate of cooling.

2) As soon as the welding heat is removed, the metal will solidify very quickly, which will cause the carbon to remain in

the combined form. Preheating, slow cooling, or annealing after welding will help control this condition.

3) Cast iron is comparatively hard and brittle and possesses very little ductility. For this reason it will crack or check if the expansion and contraction of the piece being welded is not properly considered.

Electric arc welding of cast iron should be carried out slowly, welding an inch or two at a time and peening immediately after the arc is broken. The electrodes used for cast-iron welding may be of ferrous or non-ferrous composition. The ferrous type may be of mild-steel core wire which has a coating of high carbon content, or a cast-iron electrode may be used. The non-ferrous types of electrodes may be nickel-copper alloys or bronze.

Wrought Iron. Wrought iron differs from other ferrous metals basically in its structure. It is composed of pure iron and iron silicate. The silicate is contained in this type of metal in the form of fibers, the content of silicate varying usually between 2% and 4%. Generally, the welding techniques used for mild steel welding may be employed in the welding of wrought iron. The rate of welding should be slightly less than for mild steel. This is due to the melting points of the iron and iron silicate. The melting point of the iron is slightly higher than that of mild steel, while the melting point of the silicate is several hundred degrees less. Therefore in order to be sure of good fusion of the base metal, it becomes necessary to reduce welding speed. The silicate, or as it is also known, the slag content, may cause some difficulty to the welder who is not acquainted with this type of metal. Undercutting can be easily eliminated by holding a close arc and keeping the rate of travel slow enough to insure a full metal deposit. The proper type of electrode with which to weld wrought iron is of the E-6000 classification, for use with direct current. The resultant weld will be one of higher tensile strength than the iron itself, while the ductility of weld will be less than that of the base metal.

Temperatures in the vicinity of 800° F. are usually sufficient for stress-relieving with this type of metal.

Physical Properties

Yield Point, p.s.i.—30,000
Tensile Strength, p.s.i.—47,000
Elongation in 2″—30%

Analysis

Carbon—	.04%	Manganese—	.05%
Sulphur—	.02%	Phosphorus—	.10%
Silicon—	.10%	Slag—	2%–4%

Stainless Steel. Stainless steel is used as a name for two general types of alloys, the chromium and the nickel-chromium types. The chromium types contain from 12% to 30% chromium, while the combination types contain from 18% chromium and 8% nickel to 25% chromium and 20% nickel. The most common of these alloys is perhaps the 18% chromium, 8% nickel type. The stainless steels are resistant to most acids, with the exception of hydrochloric and sulphuric. They also possess very high corrosion-resistant qualities. The combination chrome-nickel steels give the better welding results, although both types have good welding characteristics when properly treated.

The straight chromium types, however, have very marked air-hardening qualities, and a joint in the "as welded" condition is hard and brittle. Because of this, annealing must be used to restore ductility. The proper annealing temperature is about 1450° F. For best results the metal should be preheated and annealed. The preheating temperature should be in the vicinity of 350° F. The electrodes may be of a similar nature to the base metal, or chrome-nickel electrodes may be used. When annealing is to be carried out, the electrodes should be of a similar analysis to the base metal, but with a slightly higher chromium content. This additional chromium is to replace what might be lost from the base metal during the welding process.

If annealing is not to be carried out, then the chrome-nickel type of electrode should be used, as it will produce a more ductile weld than a straight chromium electrode. If a chrome-nickel electrode is used on a job that is to be annealed, the different expansion rates may prove injurious to the job. The expansion of the chrome-nickel combination is greater than for straight chrome alloys. Carbon, in this case as in others, produces hardening qualities and brittleness; for this reason the carbon content should be kept low.

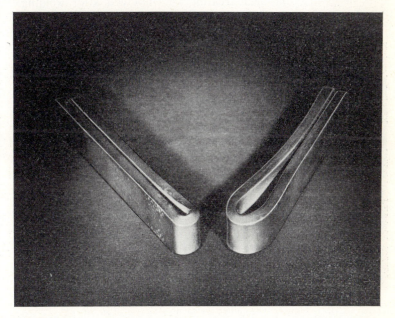

Figure 105: Bend test specimens of 18-8 stainless steel.

The chrome-nickel alloys are tough and ductile, and because of this, as well as their corrosion-resistant qualities, are used extensively. It should be remembered when welding any chrome alloy steel that the melting point is lower than that of mild steel. The expansion of chrome-nickel steel is greater, while that of a straight chromium alloy is lower, than that of mild steel. The chrome-nickel alloys when heated in the vicinity of 1000°–1500° F. have a serious precipitation of carbides if the carbon content is over .08%. This precipitation means that an area near the welding zone will be less resistant as far as corrosion is concerned, and what is known as weld decay may set in. If, then, it is desired that the corrosion-resistant qualities of this alloy be fully maintained as well as its physical properties, it is necessary that heat-treating be employed after welding. The heat-treating should be done at about 1900° F. This will

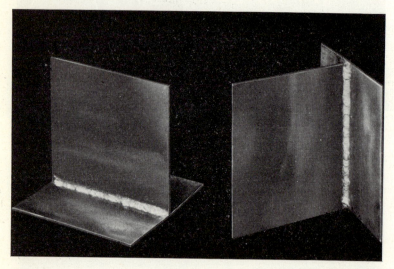

Figure 106: Fillet welds of stainless steel.

put the carbide back into solution. The cooling should be accomplished rapidly, before the carbide can again get out of solution. The usual method for heavy pieces is a water quench; air cooling will usually be sufficient for material of light gauge, $\frac{1}{8}''$ or less. Carbide precipitation may be reduced by reducing the carbon content and by increasing the alloying elements.

Stainless Clad Steel. A stainless clad steel is simply a piece of mild steel with a thin coating of stainless steel over its surface. The object of coating or cladding mild steel with stainless is to give the mild steel improved corrosion-resistant qualities. If only the corrosion-resistant qualities of stainless are required, it can be seen that a cladded mild steel would be more economical than using stainless steel. The electrode should contain a chromium content equal to or, preferably, greater than the chrome content of the cladding. The welding should be carried out on the steel side first, and the clad surface should be welded afterward. Excessive heating of the clad surface should be avoided in order to maintain the corrosion-resistant qualities of the cladding. The cladding may be of the straight chromium type or of the chrome-nickel type.

Aluminum. Aluminum has a comparatively low melting point, approximately 1200° F., and for this reason, the speed of welding is an important factor. The welder who attempts to weld aluminum for the first time will find he cannot puddle it as he can a piece of mild steel. This particular type of welding must be carried on quickly, about four times as fast as with mild steel. When welding aluminum, the best results will be obtained if the electrode is held nearly vertical to the work. There should be little or no agitation of the puddle, and no weaving should be attempted. The arc should be held as close as possible. Because of the high speed of welding and because this metal cannot be puddled, there is the possibility of poor fusion. In order to overcome this possibility, preheating should be carried out on heavy stock. It is not necessary on thin stock.

Before re-striking the arc, all slag should be thoroughly cleaned from the crater; and before a second layer is deposited, the first should be thoroughly cleaned. A 10% solution of nitric acid or sulphuric acid will remove whatever slag does not easily come off otherwise. When welding thin plate, the edges will not as a rule require any special preparation. For plates $\frac{3}{16}''$ and over the edges should be bevelled. The size and type of joint will depend upon the thickness of the metal. Aluminum electrodes are usually composed of 95% aluminum and 5% silicon. The physical properties of aluminum-welded joints will vary over a wide range, depending on the type of alloying elements used.

Nickel, Monel and Inconel. Monel and inconel are high nickel alloys; monel containing between 60% and 70% nickel and approximately 30% copper with small amounts of iron, silicon, manganese and carbon. Inconel is a nickel-chromium alloy containing about 80% nickel and 13% chromium, and small amounts of copper, iron, silicon, manganese and carbon. Nickel is manufactured under various designations, depending upon its composition and nickel content. For instance, "A" nickel contains about 99.5% nickel with 0.1% carbon, while low carbon "A" nickel contains the same amount of nickel but a still lower carbon content (0.01–0.02%), and is commonly known as carbon-free nickel. "D" nickel has about the same composition as "A" nickel, with the exception of a 4.5% content of manganese which replaces a like amount of nickel.

The welding of monel, inconel and nickel is the same as for steel welding as far as joint design and layout are concerned. The welding manipulation will be slightly different, particularly with nickel. The tendency of the nickel is to form a high narrow bead; therefore, a slight weaving motion will be required to make a presentable looking weld. The coefficients of expansion for the three metals are practically the same as for steel, which means that the same precautions regarding distortion must be taken as would be taken when welding steel. It is advisable when welding nickel or inconel to position the work for flat welding, although these metals can be welded by an experienced welder in any position. Monel can be welded in all positions as easily as steel. The welded joints of all three metals have the same properties as the base metal; heat treatment is not required to restore corrosion-resistant qualities. Only in special cases, such as stress-relieving to meet certain Code requirements, should heat-treating be used.

Reversed polarity should be used with the high-nickel electrodes which are used in the welding of nickel, inconel and monel. These electrodes are designed for use on direct-current generators, and will not produce satisfactory welds with an alternating-current, transformer type of welder. The following use for nickel electrodes is recommended by the International Nickel Company.

Electrode	*Application*
No. 130X Monel Arc Welding Rod	Metal arc welding of all forms of wrought and cast monel to monel; monel to steel, and nickel to steel; also for welding the monel side of monel-clad steel.
No. 131 Nickel Arc Welding Rod	Metal arc welding of all wrought or cast forms of pure nickel.
No. 132 Inconel Arc Welding Rod	Metal arc welding of all wrought or cast forms of inconel; also for welding the inconel side of inconel-clad steel.
No. 135 Nickel Arc Welding Rod	Metal arc welding of nickel side of nickel-clad steel.

These electrodes are of the shielded-arc type. There will be no spatter when welding these metals unless too much current is used or an excessively long arc is held. Arc blow will not interfere with the welding of high-nickel alloys. All three metals have high physical and corrosion-resistant properties.

	Nickel	Inconel	Monel
Tensile Strength, p.s.i.	65,000	85,000	75,000
Elongation, %	25	30	30

	Nickel	Copper	Iron	Chromium	Aluminum	Silicon	Manganese	Carbon
Nickel	99.4	0.1	0.15	...	...	0.05	0.2	0.1
Monel	67	30	1.4	...	...	0.1	1.0	0.15
"H" Monel	65	29.5	1.5	...	...	3.0	0.9	0.1
"S" Monel	63	30	2.0	...	...	4.0	0.9	0.1
"K" Monel	66	29	0.9	...	2.75	0.25	0.4	0.15
Inconel	79.5	0.2	6.5	13	...	0.25	0.25	0.08

The above figures represent the percentages of the various elements in the composition of the different metals. "H" and "S" Monel is produced in cast form only.

Nickel-Clad Steels. Mild steel plate may be coated with any of the nickel alloys or with nickel itself. The thickness of the cladding will vary to suit the specifications of the particular job. In welding clad steels it is usual to weld the steel side first and then the clad side. For welding the steel side, steel electrodes are used and for the clad side the electrode suitable for the particular type of cladding.

When welding the steel side first, the following procedure should be used.

1) Tack-weld the job from the steel side with steel electrodes.
2) Complete the steel welding.
3) Chip out the clad side to sound, clean steel.
4) Weld clad side.

The steel side should always be welded first in the case of a butt with an open root. If the metal is in close contact, either side may be welded first. When welding the clad side first, a small diameter electrode should be used when making the first steel pass. This is to prevent localized heating of the cladding. After the first pass is made, any size electrode may be used.

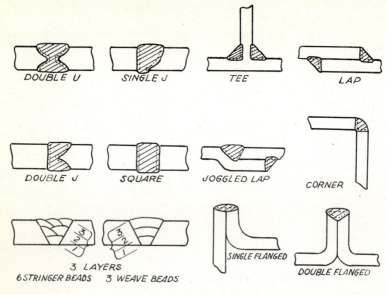

Figure 107: Types of welds.

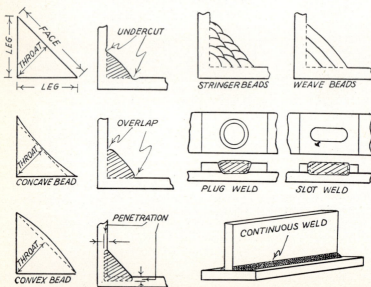

Figure 108: Continuous and other types of welds.

Part 5

Symbols and Joints

The following tables provide data on the approximate weights of the different types of electrodes required for welding the various joints in current use. These data will aid in estimating material requirements and costs.

The bases for the following tabulations are given below. Where variations from the given conditions or joint preparations are encountered, adjustments in the tabulated values must be made to compensate for such differences.

Electrode requirements have been calculated as follows:

$$W = \frac{S}{1 - L}$$

Where W = Weight of electrodes required
S = Weight of steel deposited
L = Total electrode losses

To arrive at the weight of steel deposited, it is necessary to calculate first the volume of deposited metal (area of the groove multiplied by the length). Then this volumetric value is converted to weight by the factor 0.283 pounds per cubic inch for steel. Where weld reinforcement is involved, it is added to the requirements for net, unreinforced welds.

Losses in arc welding are made up of the following elements:

      1) Scrap end losses
      2) Spatter and flux coating losses

1) Scrap end losses have been taken at 17% for the purpose of calculating the following tables. This is an average figure;

the actual losses are largely dependent upon welding technique and shop control and vary from 10% to 20%.

2) Spatter and flux coating losses vary with the types of electrodes being used. The average figure of heavily coated electrodes is taken as 27%.

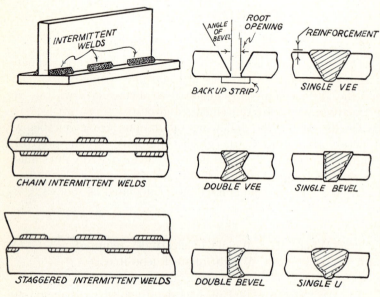

Figure 109: Intermittent and other types of welds.

The variation may be from 15% to 35%. The exact losses depend upon position of welding, operator experience and procedure, arc voltage, and welding current. In general, excessively high welding currents increase the losses due to spatter.

The following tables have been calculated for average conditions. Where the variables are more definitely known, then the formula above may be used to arrive at more accurate values for given cases than the tables of average figures.

TABLE 9

HORIZONTAL FILLET WELD

Size of Fillet l (In Inches)	Pounds of Electrodes Required per Linear Foot of Weld * (Approx.)	Steel Deposited Per Linear Foot of Weld	
	Heavily Coated	Cubic Inches	Pounds
1/8	0.048	0.094	0.027
3/16	0.113	0.222	0.063
1/4	0.189	0.375	0.106
5/16	0.296	0.585	0.166
3/8	0.427	0.844	0.239
1/2	0.760	1.500	0.425
5/8	1.185	2.340	0.663
3/4	1.705	3.375	0.955
1	3.030	6.000	1.698

* Includes scrapend and spatter loss as outlined on pages 191-192.

TABLE 10

POSITIONED FILLET WELD

Size of Fillet l (In Inches)	Pounds of Electrodes Required per Linear Foot of Weld * (Approx.)	Steel Deposited Per Linear Foot of Weld	
	Heavily Coated	Cubic Inches	Pounds
1/4	0.212	0.420	0.119
5/16	0.334	0.660	0.187
3/8	0.486	0.960	0.272
1/2	0.850	1.680	0.475
5/8	1.275	2.520	0.713
3/4	1.820	3.600	1.020
1	3.210	6.350	1.800

* Includes scrapend and spatter loss as outlined on pages 191-192.

TABLE 11

CORNER FILLET WELD

Size of Fillet (In Inches)	Pounds of Electrodes Required per Linear Foot of Weld * (Approx.) Heavily Coated	Steel Deposited Per Linear Foot of Weld	
		Cubic Inches	Pounds
1/8	0.07	0.144	0.041
3/16	0.16	0.336	0.095
1/4	0.30	0.588	0.167
5/16	0.46	0.923	0.261
3/8	0.67	1.335	0.378
1/2	1.19	2.350	0.665
5/8	1.86	3.680	1.043
3/4	2.68	5.300	1.502
1	4.77	9.41	2.670

* Includes scrapend and spatter loss as outlined on pages 191-192.

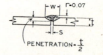

TABLE 12

WELDED ONE SIDE

Joint Dimensions (In Inches)			Pounds of Electrodes Required Per Linear Foot of Weld * (Approx.)		Steel Deposited Per Linear Foot of Weld			
			Without Reinforcement	With Reinforcement **	Without Reinforcement		With Reinforcement **	
t	w	s	Heavily Coated	Heavily Coated	Cubic Inches	Pounds	Cubic Inches	Pounds
3/16	3/8	0	. . .	0.16	. . . .	. . . .	0.312	0.088
		1/16	0.04	0.20	0.071	0.020	0.384	0.109
1/4	7/16	1/16	0.05	0.23	0.094	0.027	0.415	0.129
		3/32	0.07	0.26	0.140	0.039	0.504	0.143
5/16	1/2	1/16	0.06	0.27	0.118	0.033	0.540	0.153
		3/32	0.09	0.30	0.176	0.050	0.600	0.170

* Includes scrapend and spatter loss as outlined on pages 191-192.
** r = Height of reinforcement.

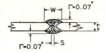

TABLE 13

WELDED TWO SIDES

Joint Dimensions (In Inches)			Pounds of Electrodes Required Per Linear Foot of Weld * (Approx.)		Steel Deposited Per Linear Foot of Weld			
			Without Reinforcement	With Reinforcement **	Without Reinforcement		With Reinforcement **	
t	w	s	Heavily Coated	Heavily Coated	Cubic Inches	Pounds	Cubic Inches	Pounds
1/8	1/4	0 1/32	. . . 0.03	0.21 0.24	. . . . 0.047	. . . . 0.013	0.42 0.467	0.119 0.132
3/16	3/8	1/32 1/16	0.04 0.07	0.36 0.39	0.071 0.141	0.020 0.040	0.70 0.77	0.199 0.218
1/4	7/16	1/16 3/32	0.10 0.14	0.47 0.53	0.188 0.282	0.053 0.080	0.92 1.02	0.261 0.288

* Includes scrapend and spatter loss as outlined on pages 191-192.
** r = Height of reinforcement.

STEEL BACKING STRIP

TABLE 14

WITH BACKING STRIP

Joint Dimensions (In Inches)			Pounds of Electrodes Required Per Linear Foot of Weld * (Approx.)		Steel Deposited Per Linear Foot of Weld			
			Without Reinforcement	With Reinforcement **	Without Reinforcement		With Reinforcement **	
t	w	s	Heavily Coated	Heavily Coated	Cubic Inches	Pounds	Cubic Inches	Pounds
1/8	1/4	0 1/16	. . . 0.05	0.11 0.15	. . . . 0.094	. . . . 0.027	0.210 0.304	0.060 0.086
3/16	3/8	1/16 3/32	0.07 0.11	0.23 0.27	0.140 0.211	0.040 0.060	0.456 0.526	0.129 0.149
1/4	7/16	3/32 1/8	0.14 0.19	0.33 0.38	0.282 0.376	0.080 0.107	0.649 0.742	0.184 0.210

* Includes scrapend and spatter loss as outlined on pages 191-192.
** r = Height of reinforcement.

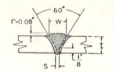

TABLE 15

"V" GROOVE BUTT JOINTS

Joint Dimensions (In Inches)			Pounds of Electrodes Required Per Linear Foot of Weld * (Approx.)		Steel Deposited Per Linear Foot of Weld			
			Without Reinforcement	With Reinforcement **	Without Reinforcement		With Reinforcement **	
t	w	s	Heavily Coated	Heavily Coated	Cubic Inches	Pounds	Cubic Inches	Pounds
1/4	0.207	1/16	0.15	0.25	0.300	0.085	0.504	0.143
5/16	0.311	3/32	0.31	0.46	0.611	0.173	0.911	0.258
3/8	0.414	1/8	0.50	0.70	0.995	0.282	1.390	0.394
1/2	0.588	1/8	0.87	1.15	1.730	0.489	2.263	0.641
5/8	0.702	1/8	1.35	1.68	2.660	0.753	3.330	0.942
3/4	0.847	1/8	1.94	2.35	3.840	1.088	4.650	1.320
1	1.138	1/8	3.45	4.00	6.810	1.930	7.90	2.240

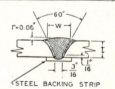

STEEL BACKING STRIP

TABLE 16

WITH BACKING STRIP

Joint Dimensions (In Inches)		Pounds of Electrodes Required Per Linear Foot of Weld * (Approx.)		Steel Deposited Per Linear Foot of Weld			
		Without Reinforcement	With Reinforcement **	Without Reinforcement		With Reinforcement **	
t	w	Heavily Coated	Heavily Coated	Cubic Inches	Pounds	Cubic Inches	Pounds
1/4	0.405	0.41	0.61	0.815	0.231	1.200	0.340
5/16	0.476	0.58	0.81	1.14	0.323	1.595	0.452
3/8	0.549	0.77	1.03	1.521	0.432	2.04	0.577
1/2	0.693	1.25	1.58	2.4600	0.696	3.12	0.882
5/8	0.838	1.82	2.23	3.600	1.020	4.40	1.248
3/4	0.982	2.50	3.00	4.960	1.405	5.91	1.675
1	1.273	4.23	4.83	8.350	2.370	9.57	2.710

* Includes scrapend and spatter loss as outlined on pages 191-192.
** r = Height of reinforcement.

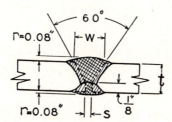

TABLE 17

WELDED BOTH SIDES

Joint Dimensions (In Inches)			Pounds of Electrodes Required per Linear Foot of Weld * (Approx.)	Steel Deposited Per Linear Foot of Weld	
			With Reinforcement **	With Reinforcement **	
t	*w*	*s*	Heavily Coated	Cubic Inches	Pounds
1/4	0.207	1/16	0.41	0.815	0.231
5/16	0.311	3/32	0.62	1.225	0.346
3/8	0.414	1/8	0.85	1.680	0.475
1/2	0.558	1/8	1.45	2.870	0.811
5/8	0.702	1/8	1.99	3.940	1.115
3/4	0.847	1/8	2.66	5.250	1.490
1	1.138	1/8	4.30	8.500	2.410

* Includes scrapend and spatter loss as outlined on pages 191-192.
** r = Height of reinforcement.

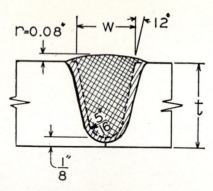

"U" GROOVE BUTT JOINTS

TABLE 18A

SINGLE "U" GROOVE

Joint Dimensions (In Inches)		Pounds of Electrodes Required per Linear Foot of Weld * (Approx.)		Steel Deposited Per Linear Foot of Weld			
		Without Reinforcement	With Reinforcement **	Without Reinforcement		With Reinforcement **	
t	*w*	Heavily Coated	Heavily Coated	Cubic Inches	Pounds	Cubic Inches	Pounds
½	0.652	1.18	1.49	2.325	0.659	2.95	0.835
⅝	0.705	1.70	2.04	3.345	0.947	4.02	1.140
¾	0.758	2.24	2.61	4.435	1.255	5.17	1.465
1	0.865	3.47	3.89	6.870	1.945	7.70	2.180
1¼	0.971	4.86	5.35	9.62	2.72	10.60	3.00
1½	1.077	6.41	6.95	12.66	3.59	13.72	3.89
1¾	1.173	8.08	8.65	16.00	4.53	17.10	4.84
2	1.292	10.00	10.65	19.75	5.60	21.04	5.96
2¼	1.396	12.05	12.75	23.80	6.75	25.20	7.12
2½	1.502	14.25	15.00	28.20	7.98	29.65	8.40
2¾	1.608	16.60	17.40	32.80	9.29	34.65	9.73
3	1.715	19.10	20.00	37.80	10.70	39.45	11.19
3½	1.927	24.70	25.50	48.60	13.80	50.50	14.30
4	2.140	30.90	31.90	61.00	17.30	63.10	17.90

* Includes scrapend and spatter loss as outlined on pages 191-192.
** r = Height of reinforcement.

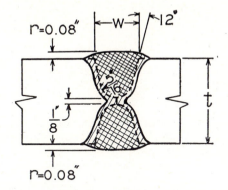

TABLE 18B

DOUBLE "U" GROOVE

Joint Dimensions (In Inches)		Pounds of Electrodes Required per Linear Foot of Weld * (Approx.)		Steel Deposited Per Linear Foot of Weld			
		Without Reinforcement	With Reinforcement **	Without Reinforcement		With Reinforcement **	
t	w	Heavily Coated	Heavily Coated	Cubic Inches	Pounds	Cubic Inches	Pounds
1	0.685	2.86	3.54	5.64	1.60	6.90	1.98
1¼	0.731	3.91	4.62	7.75	2.19	9.15	2.59
1½	0.784	5.05	5.83	10.00	2.83	11.55	3.27
1¾	0.838	6.30	7.12	12.47	3.53	14.10	3.99
2	0.891	7.60	8.46	15.08	4.26	16.74	4.74
2¼	0.944	9.00	9.90	17.80	5.04	19.60	5.55
2½	0.997	10.45	11.45	20.70	5.85	22.60	6.41
2¾	1.050	12.00	13.05	23.80	6.73	25.80	7.30
3	1.103	13.85	14.90	27.15	7.75	29.40	8.34
3½	1.211	17.20	18.40	33.98	9.61	36.30	10.30
4	1.316	21.00	22.30	41.55	11.75	44.00	12.50

* Includes scrapend and spatter loss as outlined on pages 191-192.
** r = Height of reinforcement.

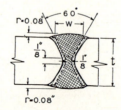

TABLE 19
DOUBLE "V" GROOVE

Joint Dimensions (In Inches)		Pounds of Electrodes Required per Linear Foot of Weld * (Approx.)		Steel Deposited Per Linear Foot of Weld			
		Without Reinforcement	With Reinforcement **	Without Reinforcement		With Reinforcement **	
t	w	Heavily Coated	Heavily Coated	Cubic Inches	Pounds	Cubic Inches	Pounds
⅝	0.405	0.90	1.29	1.775	0.502	2.56	0.724
¾	0.468	1.22	1.68	2.410	0.682	3.31	0.937
1	0.630	2.10	2.71	4.150	1.175	5.36	1.520
1¼	0.774	3.17	3.92	6.27	1.775	7.75	2.195
1½	0.919	4.45	5.35	8.85	2.495	10.59	3.00
1¾	1.063	5.95	6.98	11.80	3.335	13.82	3.91
2	1.207	7.68	8.88	15.20	4.30	17.58	4.97
2¼	1.352	9.60	10.95	19.00	5.38	21.65	6.12
2½	1.496	11.80	13.20	23.30	6.60	26.20	7.40
3	1.784	16.70	18.50	33.00	9.35	36.50	10.33
3½	2.073	22.60	24.60	44.70	12.65	48.70	13.80
4	2.368	29.40	31.70	58.15	16.45	62.80	17.80

* Includes scrapend and spatter loss as outlined on pages 191-192.
** r = Height of reinforcement.

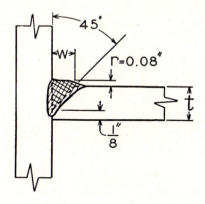

TABLE 20

SINGLE BEVEL GROOVE

Joint Dimensions (In Inches)		Pounds of Electrodes Required per Linear Foot of Weld * (Approx.)		Steel Deposited Per Linear Foot of Weld			
		Without Re-inforcement	With Rein-forcement **	Without Re-inforcement		With Rein-forcement **	
t	w	Heavily Coated	Heavily Coated	Cubic Inches	Pounds	Cubic Inches	Pounds
¼	0.125	0.05	0.10	0.096	0.027	0.216	0.061
5⁄16	0.188	0.11	0.20	0.216	0.061	0.396	0.112
⅜	0.250	0.19	0.31	0.372	0.106	0.611	0.173
½	0.375	0.43	0.61	0.840	0.238	1.211	0.343
⅝	0.500	0.76	1.00	1.500	0.425	1.980	0.560
¾	0.625	1.19	1.50	2.340	0.663	2.950	0.835
1	0.875	2.33	2.81	4.590	1.303	5.57	1.575

* Includes scrapend and spatter loss as outlined on pages 191-192.
** r = Height of reinforcement.

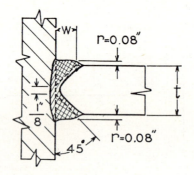

TABLE 21

DOUBLE BEVEL GROOVE

Joint Dimensions (In Inches)		Pounds of Electrodes Required per Linear Foot of Weld * (Approx.)		Steel Deposited Per Linear Foot of Weld			
		Without Reinforcement	With Reinforcement **	Without Reinforcement		With Reinforcement **	
t	w	Heavily Coated	Heavily Coated	Cubic Inches	Pounds	Cubic Inches	Pounds
½	0.188	0.22	0.39	0.42	0.120	0.78	0.221
⅝	0.250	0.38	0.62	0.756	0.213	1.238	0.350
¾	0.313	0.59	0.90	1.175	0.332	1.775	0.503
1	0.438	1.16	1.58	2.294	0.648	3.130	0.886
1¼	0.563	1.92	2.46	3.790	1.076	4.870	1.38
1½	0.688	2.87	3.54	5.607	1.607	7.00	1.98
1¾	0.813	4.01	4.78	7.92	2.245	9.47	2.68
2	0.938	5.33	6.25	10.53	2.985	12.33	3.50

* Includes scrapend and spatter loss as outlined on pages 191-192.
** r = Height of reinforcement.

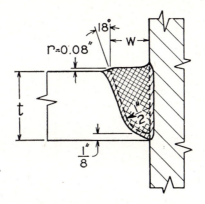

TABLE 22A

SINGLE "J" GROOVE

Joint Dimensions (In Inches)		Pounds of Electrodes Required per Linear Foot of Weld * (Approx.)		Steel Deposited Per Linear Foot of Weld			
		Without Reinforcement	With Reinforcement **	Without Reinforcement		With Reinforcement **	
t	w	Heavily Coated	Heavily Coated	Cubic Inches	Pounds	Cubic Inches	Pounds
1	0.625	2.55	2.85	5.03	1.43	5.64	1.60
1¼	0.719	3.64	4.00	7.20	2.04	7.91	2.24
1½	0.781	4.80	5.15	9.46	2.69	10.20	2.89
1¾	0.875	6.12	6.55	12.12	3.43	12.95	3.67
2	0.969	7.40	7.87	14.63	4.15	15.60	4.41
2¼	1.031	9.00	9.42	17.75	5.03	18.35	5.19
2½	1.094	10.60	11.10	20.90	5.92	21.95	6.21
2¾	1.188	12.30	12.92	24.35	6.90	25.55	7.23
3	1.281	14.20	14.80	28.10	7.95	29.30	8.29
3½	1.438	18.40	19.10	36.30	10.30	37.80	10.70
4	1.594	23.00	23.70	45.40	12.90	47.00	13.30

* Includes scrapend and spatter loss as outlined on pages 191-192.
** r = Height of reinforcement.

DOUBLE "J" GROOVE

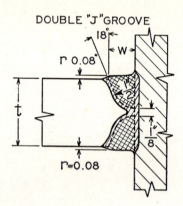

TABLE 22B

DOUBLE "J" GROOVE

Joint Dimensions (In Inches)		Pounds of Electrodes Required per Linear Foot of Weld * (Approx.)		Steel Deposited Per Linear Foot of Weld			
		Without Reinforcement	With Reinforcement **	Without Reinforcement		With Reinforcement **	
t	*w*	Heavily Coated	Heavily Coated	Cubic Inches	Pounds	Cubic Inches	Pounds
1	0.500	1.87	2.37	3.71	1.05	4.67	1.33
1¼	0.563	2.48	3.03	4.92	1.39	6.00	1.70
1½	0.594	3.52	4.08	6.95	1.97	8.10	2.29
1¾	0.625	4.37	5.00	8.635	2.45	9.83	2.79
2	0.656	5.47	6.11	10.80	3.06	12.06	3.42
2¼	0.688	6.55	7.21	12.97	3.67	14.29	4.04
2½	0.750	7.65	8.38	15.12	4.28	16.68	4.69
2¾	0.781	8.85	9.60	17.52	4.95	19.00	5.38
3	0.813	10.10	10.85	19.82	5.62	21.45	6.08
3½	0.906	2.70	13.55	25.05	7.12	26.80	7.58
4	0.969	15.70	16.60	31.05	8.78	32.80	9.28

* Includes scrapend and spatter loss as outlined on pages 191-192.
** *r* = Height of reinforcement.

MEANING OF WELDING SYMBOLS

The purpose of the following pages is to interpret, in detail, the meanings and use of the welding symbols.

Fillet Welds (Figure 110).

Sketch a

The arrow points to the right-hand side of the joint, but the symbol is on the far side of the reference line AB. Therefore, the weld will be deposited on the far side of the joint, as shown. The dimension on the left side of the symbol shows that the legs of this fillet weld are $\frac{1}{4}''$. The dimension indicating the size of a fillet weld is **always** on the left of the symbol.

Sketch b

The arrow points to the right-hand side of the joint and the symbol is on the near side of the reference line. Therefore, the weld is to be made on the arrow or right-hand side of the joint. In this case, the dimension indicates a $\frac{3}{8}''$ weld.

Sketch c

In this figure, there is a symbol on both sides of the reference line, indicating a weld on both sides of the joint. Both welds may be the same or different sizes. If both are to be the same size, the proper dimension will be placed as shown. If the welds are to be of different sizes, each symbol will carry its own dimension.

Sketch d

An intermittent weld is indicated in this figure. The dimensions 3-6 mean that each increment is $3''$ long, and the distance from the center of one increment to the center of an adjacent increment is $6''$. The increment dimension is always placed on

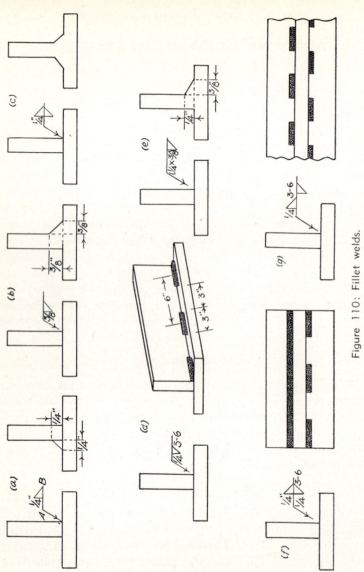

Figure 110: Fillet welds.

the right of the symbol. In this particular case the welding is to be done on the arrow side of the joint.

Sketch e

The weld shown is to have legs of different sizes. The vertical leg is to be ¼″; while the horizontal leg is to be ⅜″. This type of dimension is placed in parentheses. Unless this dimension is shown, it is assumed that both legs of the weld are to be equal.

Sketch f

When the joint is to have a continuous weld on one side, and an intermittent weld on the other side, it is as shown in Sketch f. Here the far side of the joint is to have a ¼″ continuous weld. The arrow side is to have a ¼″ intermittent weld.

Sketch g

In this figure the welding is to be intermittent on both sides. The increments are to be staggered. This is shown by staggering the symbols. Only one symbol is dimensioned, indicating that both sides are to have the same size increments. If the dimensions of one side are to differ in size, then both symbols must be dimensioned.

Groove Welds (Figure 111).

Sketch a

The vertical line shows that the joint is of the square-groove type. The bead symbol below this vertical line shows that the weld is to be made from the bottom side of the joint and only this side is to be welded. If the bead symbol was made at the top of the vertical line, it would show that the weld was to be made from that side.

Sketch b

When the joint is to be welded from both sides, the bead symbol will be shown at both top and bottom of the vertical

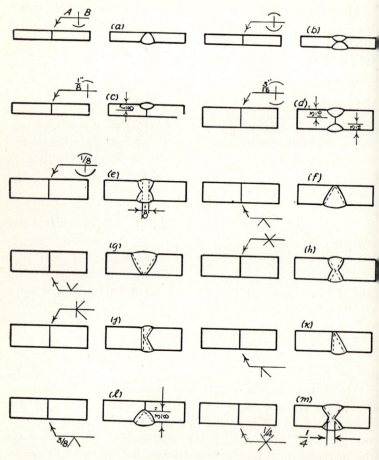

Figure 111: Groove welds.

line. Unless otherwise noted, it is assumed that complete penetration is to be obtained whether one or both sides are welded.

Sketch c

In this joint only ⅛″ penetration is required, and this is shown by placing the dimension to the left of the bead symbol. When this dimension is not placed on the symbol, complete penetration is required.

Sketch d

If the joint is to be welded from both sides and only partial penetration is required, the symbol is as shown. Here both beads are to have ³⁄₁₆″ penetration. It is necessary to dimension only one side.

Sketch e

The root opening of this type of butt is shown by placing the dimension between the bead symbol and the end of the vertical line. In this figure the joint has a root opening of ⅛″ and is welded from both sides.

Sketch f

The symbol shows that a single vee butt is to be made. The symbol is on the near side of the reference line. Therefore, the butt is to be made from this side.

Sketch g

The symbol in this case is on the far side of the reference line, so the butt will be made from the far side.

Sketch h

A double-vee joint—both pieces making up the joint are bevelled on both sides.

Sketch j

A double-bevel joint—one piece is bevelled on both sides.

Sketch k

A single-bevel joint—one piece is bevelled on one side.

It is assumed that all vee and bevel grooves are to extend the full depth of the stock. When a groove is not to extend the full depth of the stock, a dimension is placed to the left of the symbol, denoting the depth.

Sketch l

The dimension shows that the bevelling is to be ⅜″ deep. In this figure the symbol represents a single vee groove. The method of showing depth of bevelling would be the same with any other vee or bevel-type joint.

Sketch m

The dimension of the root opening is always placed inside the symbol, as shown. In this case, the symbol designates a double-V groove. For any other V or bevel groove, the root opening is shown in the same way.

More Groove Welds (Figure 112).

Sketch n

The included angle of a bevel or V groove is shown by placing the dimension inside the symbol, but outside the root opening dimension. In this case there is no root opening, so the dimension is zero.

Sketch o

This shows a compound symbol which takes in all three dimensions so far discussed on V or bevel butts.

Sketch p

A single-J groove.

Sketch q

A double-J groove.

Sketch r

A single-U groove.

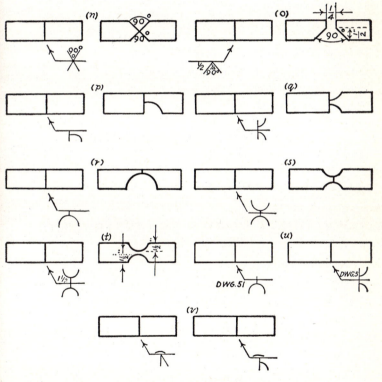

Figure 112: Groove welds.

Sketch s

A double-U groove.

Sketch t

Groove depth shown by placing dimension to left of symbol.

Sketch u

The proportions and size of U and J grooves may be detailed on another drawing. In this case, a note is made of this fact as shown in this figure. Here the reference is made to another drawing.

Sketch v

When a bead is to be made on the root side of the groove, the bead symbol is used on the opposite side of the reference line from the groove symbol.

In any case where a dimension is not used, it is to be assumed that the user's standard will be the proper dimension. For instance, if in a certain shop it was standard practice to make all V grooves with a 60° included angle, it would not be necessary to show this dimension on any V-groove symbols.

WELDING SYMBOLS AND INSTRUCTIONS FOR THEIR USE *

(The American Welding Society symbols given herein are a development of the welding symbols in use here and abroad, and supersede the Society's former symbols which were published in bulletin form in 1929 and revised in February 1935, September 1939 and October 1940. The symbols themselves given herein are the same as those which have been used heretofore but the method of using them has been improved and clarified.)

---

* Reprinted from the A.W.S. booklet. Prepared by Committee on Symbols. Approved by Board of Directors December 11, 1941.

Welding cannot take its proper place as an engineering tool unless means are provided for conveying the information from the designer to the workmen. Unimportant work may be directed by means of inadequate information on drawings, but when structures, the failure of which would endanger life and property, are to be welded, simple and specific means must be used to convey the ideas of the designer to the shop. Such practices as writing "To be welded throughout" or "To be completely welded" on the bottom of a drawing, in effect, transfer the design of all attachments and connections from the designer to the welding operator, who cannot be expected to know what strength is necessary. This practice in addition to being highly dangerous is also costly, for certain shops, in their desire to be safe, use much more welding than is necessary.

These symbols provide the means of placing complete welding information on drawings. Even though the legends, numerical data and the instructions involve a considerable mass of material, nevertheless the successful use of the scheme depends so little on the memory that hardly more than one reading of the instructions is necessary to obtain a working understanding of the system. In practice many companies will probably need only a few of the symbols, and if they desire, can make up their own legends to suit themselves, selecting such parts of the scheme as fit their needs and neglecting the others. If this is done universally, we shall all be speaking the same language even though some use but a few of the symbols contained herein.

In these symbols, the general principle of having the most usual form of any weld require a minimum of numerical data, has been followed. When a weld departs from the user's standard, supplementary data are necessary. This makes the user's standards a part of the symbols system, and means that the exact interpretation of the symbols will vary slightly among the different users.

It will be seen from Figure 113 that the arc and gas welding symbols are ideographic; that is, they are picture-writing symbols; they show graphically the type of weld required. The individual basic symbols become the building blocks with which compound symbols to indicate complicated welded joints composed of many welds, can be constructed. Every weld in the joint must be shown.

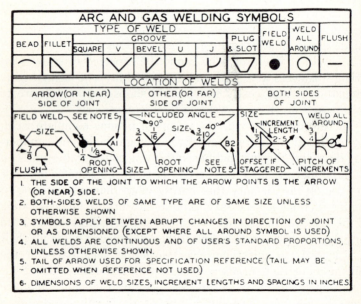

Figure 113: Legend for use on drawings specifying arc and gas welding.

The use of the words "far side" and "near side," etc., in the past has led to confusion because it was often not clear as to whether "side" referred to member, joint or weld. Also, when joints are shown in section, all welds are equally distant from the reader and the words near and far are factually improper. In the present symbol system the joint is the basis of reference. Any joint whose welding is indicated by a symbol will always have an "arrow side" and an "other side." Accordingly, the

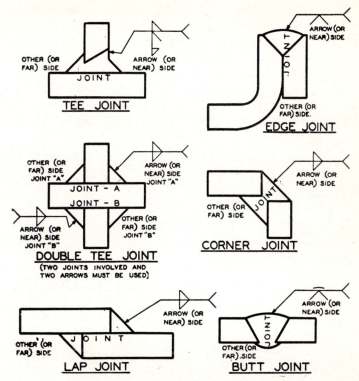

Figure 114: Location of line of joint in the various fundamental joints.

words "arrow side," "other side" and "both sides" are used herein to locate the weld with respect to the *joint*. Since the words near and far have been used in the past and in some cases do have significance, they have been retained in a subordinate position.

In Figure 114 are shown the various fundamental kinds of joints and the line of the joint is indicated thereon. The interpretation of the arrow side and other side is apparent.

The welding on hidden members can be covered as shown in Figure 115 when welding of the hidden member is the same as that of the visible member. The fact that there are two members must be covered by both the drawing and the bill of material. If the welding on the hidden member is different from that of the visible member, obviously specific information for the welding of both must be given.

The distinction between the symbols for the V- and bevel-groove welds and the U- and J-groove welds is not great. The draftsman should take sufficient care in the making of these

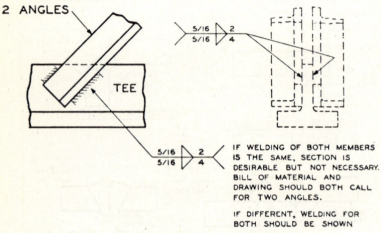

Figure 115: Method of calling for welding of hidden members.

particular symbols so that they do not become confused with each other.

The field weld symbol is the black dot used by the structural industry to indicate field riveting. In the case of work actually erected in the field, just what constitutes field welding is simple. In the case of work done in the shop, yet done in the actual erection of the final product, the case is not so simple. An illustration of this obtains when work is done in the shop on an assembly line, such as is used in the automobile or car building industries. In this case, the individual user must decide for himself whether such erection welding is shop welding or field welding.

Appropriate finish marks have been found to be necessary; however, recommendations as to what finish marks shall be used are not strictly within the province of the Committee. As soon as the American Standards Association has definitely decided upon a system of finish symbols, it will be desirable for all concerned to adopt this system. In the meantime, however,

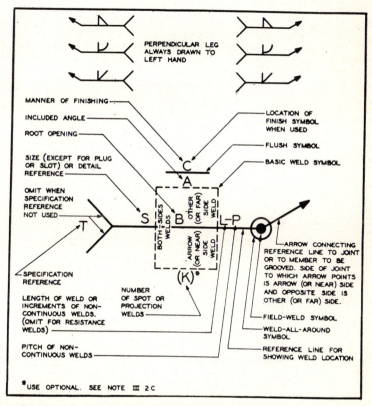

Figure 116: Standard location of information on welding symbols.

a suggestion with regard to finish marks is made. It will be noted in Section IV of the Instructions that these finish marks merely suggest the means of finishing; that is, whether chipping, grinding or machining be used, and not the degree; they do not say whether a weld is to be rough or finish machined, rough or smooth ground, etc. Any such fine distinction must

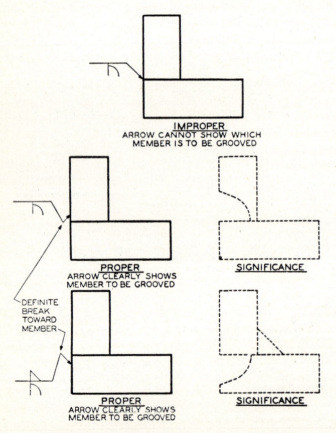

Figure 117: Use of arrows in section or end view to indicate which member is to be grooved, when welds are not shown.

be made in the user's standard manner until such time as a national standard is established.

The location of the Symbols, numerical and other data on the reference line always has definite significance. This is depicted in Figure 116 in which the standard manner of placing information on the symbols is shown diagrammatically. Particular attention should be paid to the fact that the perpendicular leg of the weld should always be to the left as shown at the top of Figure 116.

The proper and improper use of the arrows to designate the member to be grooved is shown in Figure 117.

A new feature incorporated in this revision is the use of the tail of the reference line for designating the welding specifications to be used in the making of the weld. If a welding operator knows the size and type of weld, he has only part of the information necessary for the making of that weld. The process, type and make of filler metal that is to be used, whether or not peening, or chipping are required and other pertinent data must be known before he can start the work. The specification to be placed in the tail of the reference line at present will have to be handled by each individual company which will set up its own requirement in any manner it sees fit, and it is hoped that in time a national set of standards will be prepared to coordinate the various specification processes in use. Steps in that direction are now under consideration. Such matters as stress-relief annealing, and final cleaning of the product cannot be referred to on the symbol because such treatment is applied to the product as a whole and not to a particular weld.

The symbols, together with the specification references, provide a shorthand system whereby a tremendous volume of information may be accurately indicated with a few lines and a minimum amount of numerical data. This is illustrated in Figure 118, where the words necessary to convey the information given by the symbol would make a very long paragraph.

The use of the symbols on a machinery drawing is shown

in Figure 119. In these views examples of the use of the specification references are given.

In Figure 120 are shown the resistance welding symbols. There are many similarities between the resistance and the arc welding symbols and three principal differences. The resistance symbols are only partially ideographic. The arc symbols designate the size of the weld, whereas the resistance welding symbols call for the strength of the required weld. This difference is necessary because in spot, projection and seam welding, the weld is inaccessible and therefore cannot be gaged as in fusion

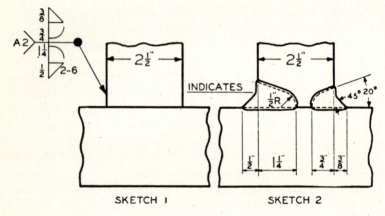

SKETCH 1   SKETCH 2

Figure 118: Double-fillet-welded, partially-grooved, double-J, tee-joint with incomplete penetration. (Type of joint shown by drawing.) Grooves of standard proportions (which are, ½″ R, 20° included angle, edges in contact before welding) ¾″ deep for other (or far) side weld and 1¼″ deep for arrow (or near) side weld. ⅜″ continuous other (or far) side fillet weld and ½″ intermittent arrow (or near) side fillet weld with increments 2″ long, 6″ center-to-center. All fillets standard 45° fillets. All welding done in field in accordance with welding specification number A2 (which requires that weld be made by manual, d.c., shielded, metal-arc process using high-grade, covered, mild-steel electrode; that root be unchipped and welds un-peened but that joint be preheated before welding).

This serves as a good comparison between symbolic and verbal methods of conveying welding information.

welding. Except for the case of projection welding where arrow (or near) and other (or far) refer to the member to be embossed, the resistance welding symbols have no arrow side and other side significance. Supplementary symbols such as those

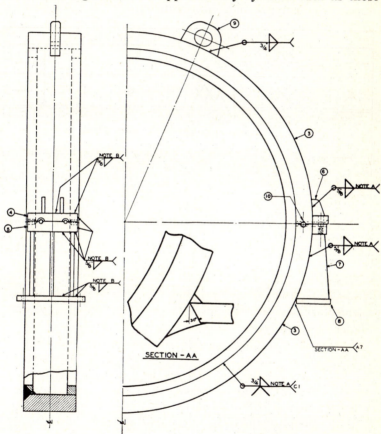

Figure 119: Typical machinery drawing, showing use of symbols. Note A: These welding symbols apply to the joints of all members of the same identification. Note B: Welding symbols shown here apply to both sides of center line.

for "finish" have their usual arrow side and other side significance when used on resistance welding symbols.

The system may be used in any of the ways listed below:

a) All symbol legends and explanatory matter may be issued as company standards on sheets separate from the drawing

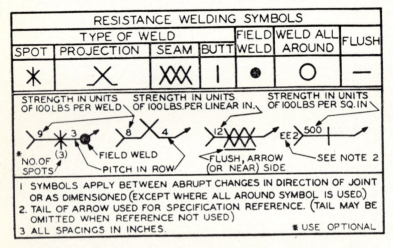

Figure 120: Legend for use on drawings specifying resistance welding.

in question; that is, the draftsman may have explanatory supplementary sheets as well as machinists, welding operators, inspectors, etc.

b) Legends and specification references may be placed on the drawing so that the latter is completely self-explanatory.

c) In either of the above cases, the welds may be drawn in sections and the symbol give only that information that is not obvious, such as size of weld, length of increment, etc.

d) In either of the cases (a) and (b) above, the welds may not be drawn in section and full information given by symbols.

e) The symbol legends, specification references and standard notes may be printed on the tracing or may be placed on tracings or prints by rubber stamps or any other means.

INSTRUCTIONS FOR USE
OF WELDING SYMBOLS

I   General

Do not use the word "weld" as a symbol on drawings.

(a) Symbols may or may not be made freehand as desired.

(b) Inch, degree and pound marks may or may not be used as desired.

(c)

(d) The symbol may be used without specification references or tails to designate the most commonly used specification when the following note appears on the drawing:
"Unless otherwise designated, all welds to be made in accordance with welding specification No. —."

(e) When specification references are used, place in tail, thus:

(f) Symbols apply between abrupt changes in direction of joint or to extent of hatching or dimension lines (except where all-around symbol is used).   See IV *d* and *e*.

(g) Faces of welds assumed to have user's standard contours unless otherwise indicated.

(h) Faces of welds assumed not to be finished other than cleaned unless otherwise indicated.

(i) All except plug, spot, and projection welds assumed continuous unless otherwise indicated.

II   Arc and Gas Welds

1.   General

(a) Do not put symbol directly on lines of drawing; place symbol on reference line and connect latter to joint with arrow, thus:

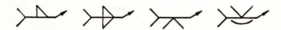

(b)　For welds on arrow (or near) side of joint show symbol on near side of reference lines, face toward reader, thus:

(c)　For welds on other (or far) side show symbol on far side of reference line, face away from reader, thus:

(d)　For welds on both sides of joint show symbols on both sides of reference line, faces toward and away from reader, thus:

(e)　Where the part shown is but one of a series of practically identical parts (see vertical ribs in Figure 119), the applicability of the symbols to the concealed parts shall be in accordance with the user's standard drawing practices with regard to dimensioning and part-numbering such parts.

(f)　Where one member only is to be grooved, show arrow pointing unmistakably to that member. (See Figure 117)

(g)　Read symbols from bottom and right-hand side of drawing in the usual manner and place numerical data on vertical reference lines so that reader will be properly oriented, thus:

(h)　Show symbol for each weld in joints composed of more than one weld, thus:

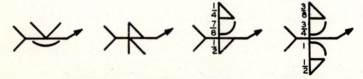

(*i*)   In complicated joints requiring large compound symbols two separate sets of symbols may be used if desired.

(*j*)   Show dimensions of weld on same side of reference line as symbol, thus:

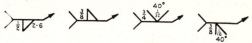

(*k*)   Show dimensions of one weld only when welds on both sides of the joint are of the same type and size, thus: (If size of undimensioned fillets is governed by a note on the drawing, all weld sizes different from that covered in the note must be given.)

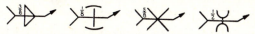

(*l*)   Show dimensions for welds on both sides of the joint, when the arrow-side and other-side welds are different, thus:

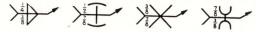

(*m*)   Indicate specific lengths of welds in conjunction with dimension lines, thus:

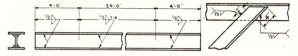

(*n*)   Show the welding between abrupt changes in the direction of the weld thus (except when all-around symbol is used; see IV *d* and *e*):

(o) When it is desired to show extent of welds by hatching, use one type of hatching with definite end lines, thus:

(p) If actual outlines of welds are drawn in section or end elevation, basic symbol is not necessary to show type and location; size or other numerical details only need to be given, thus:

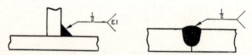

(q) Show fillet, bevel- and J-groove weld symbols with perpendicular leg always to the left hand, thus:

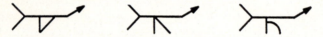

2. Bead Welds

(a) Show bead welds used in building up surfaces (size is minimum height of pad) thus:

(b) When a small but no specific minimum height of pad is desired, show thus:

3. Fillet Welds

(a) Show size of fillet weld to the left of the perpendicular leg, thus:

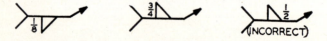

(b) Show specific length of fillet weld or increment after size so that data read from left to right, thus:

(c) Show center-to-center pitch of increments of intermittent fillet welds after increment length so that data read from left to right, thus:

(d) Use separate symbol for each weld when intermittent and continuous fillet welds are used in combination.

(e) Show two intermittent fillet welds with increments opposite each other (chain) thus:

(f) Show two intermittent fillet welds with increments not opposite each other (staggered) thus:

(g) Measure pitch of intermittent fillet welds between centers of increments on one side of member.

(h) Increments and not spaces assumed to be at ends of all intermittent welds and overall length dimensions govern to ends of those increments, thus:

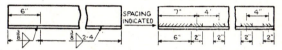

(i) Faces of fillet welds assumed to be at 45° from legs unless otherwise indicated.

(*j*)   When the face of a fillet weld is to be at any other angle than 45°, two dimensions are necessary to fully designate the size of the weld. Place these dimensions in parentheses so that the two dimensional size data will be a single entity and will not be confused with length of increment and spacing data. Show on drawings positions of legs relative to members.

4.   Groove Welds

(*a*) Show side from which square-groove weld is made by bead or flush symbols, thus (see III, 4*a;* IV, *h;* and IV, *j* and *k*):

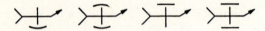

(*b*)   Total penetration of square-groove welds assumed to be complete unless otherwise indicated.

(*c*)   Show size of square-groove welds (depth of penetration) when penetration is less than complete, thus:

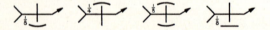

(*d*)   Show root opening of open, square-groove welds inside symbol, thus:

(*e*)   Total depth of V- and bevel-grooves before welding assumed to be equal to thickness of member unless otherwise indicated.

(*f*)   Show size of V- and bevel-groove welds (depth of single groove before welding) when grooving is less than complete, thus:

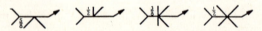

(g) Total depth of penetration of V- and bevel-groove welds assumed complete, unless with usual welding processes, depth of grooving is such that complete penetration is not possible, when depth of penetration is assumed to be depth of groove plus normal penetration. When using welding processes giving abnormal penetration, give information on latter by detail or note (see IV, *o*)

(h) Root opening of V- and bevel-groove welds assumed to be user's standard unless otherwise indicated.

(i) Show root openings of V- and bevel-groove welds when not user's standard, inside symbol, thus:

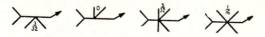

(j) Included angle of V- and bevel-groove welds assumed to be user's standard unless otherwise indicated.

(k) Show included angle of V- and bevel-groove welds when not user's standard inside symbol, thus:

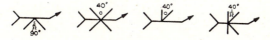

(l) Proportions of U- and J-groove welds assumed to be user's standard unless otherwise indicated.

(m) Show size of U- and J-groove welds (depth of single groove before welding) having user's standard proportions but incomplete penetration, thus:

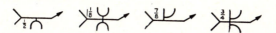

(n) When proportions of U- and J-groove welds are not user's standard, show weld by detail or reference drawing and use reference symbol, thus (see IV, *o*):

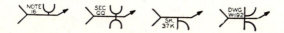

(o)   Show welding done from root side of single-groove welds with bead weld symbol, thus:

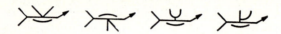

5.   Plug and Slot Welds

(a)   Show size of plug and slot welds (root opening and root length), thus:

(Root opening equals root length for plug welds.)

(b)   Included angle of bevel of plug and slot welds assumed to be user's standard unless otherwise indicated.

(c)   Show included angle of bevel of plug and slot welds when not user's standard, thus:

(d)   Show pitch of plug and slot welds in row, thus:

(e)   Show fillet welded holes and slots with proper fillet weld symbols and not with plug weld symbols.

III   Resistance Welds

1.   General.

(a)   Center resistance welding symbols for spot and seam welds on reference line because these symbols have no arrow side or other side (near and far side) significance; (see Figure 120 and also refer to IV *m*) but do not center projection welding symbols because the latter have such significance.

(b)   Designate resistance welds by strength rather than size (because of impracticability of determining latter).

(c)   Spot and seam weld symbols may be used directly on drawings, thus; but projection weld symbols should not:

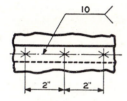 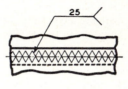

(d)   When not used on lines of drawing, connect reference line to center line of weld or rows of welds with arrow, thus:

(e)   Show welds of extent less than between abrupt changes in direction of joint, thus:

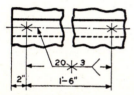 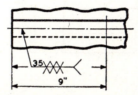

(f)   When tension, impact, fatigue or other properties are required, use reference symbol, thus (see IV, *o*):

2.   Spot and Projection Welds

(a)   Show strength of spot and projection welds in single shear
in units of 100 pounds per weld, thus:

(b)   Show strength and center-to-center spacing of spot and
projection welds in row, thus:

(c)   When a definite number of spot or projection welds is desired in a certain joint or connection, show that number by a
number in parentheses below the symbol, thus:

(NOTE: If specific number of spots of a certain strength is called
for and spacing omitted, strength of spots can be seriously affected
by decrease in spacing. Designers should be sure that when calling
for number of spots only, the strength of the connection will not be
jeopardized by decreased strength of spots due to variation in
spacing.)

(d)   Proportions of projections assumed given on drawing.

(e)   In a projection welded joint parallel, or nearly so, to the
plane of the paper, show whether the arrow (or near) side or
other (or far) side member is to be embossed by placing the
projection weld symbol on the arrow (or near) or the other
(or far) side of the reference line, thus:

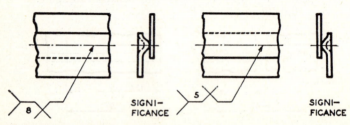

(*f*) In a projection welded joint shown in section or end view, show which member is to be embossed by pointing arrow to that member, thus:

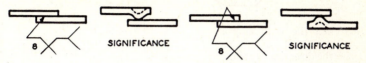

8   SIGNIFICANCE   8   SIGNIFICANCE

3. Seam Welds

(*a*) Seam welds assumed to be of overlapping or tangent spots. If any spacing exists between spots, welds considered a series of spot welds, and spot symbol should be used.

(*b*) Show shear strength of seam welds in units of 100 pounds per linear inch, thus:

4. Butt Welds

(*a*) Show resistance butt welds without bead weld symbol signifying that weld is not made from any side, but all at once, thus (see II, 4*a*):

(*b*) Resistance butt welds assuméd to be equal to strength of base metal in tension unless otherwise indicated.

(*c*) When a different strength is desired, show strength of butt welds in tension in units of 100 pounds per square inch, thus:

IV Supplementary Symbols

(*a*) Show "field" welds (any weld not made in shop), thus:

(*b*) Show "all around" welds, weld encircling joint (or joints) in so far as is possible, thus:

(*c*) When the weld encircles the joint but there is no abrupt change in the direction of the joint or parts of the joint (changes in the direction of rolled structural sections are considered abrupt even though there are fillets in the corners), the all-around symbol may or may not be used as desired, thus:

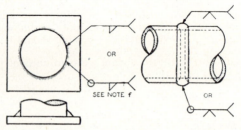

(*d*) The all-around symbol extends control of the welding symbol beyond abrupt changes in the direction of one joint, or parts of one joint, to encirclement of the complete joint in so far as is possible, thus:

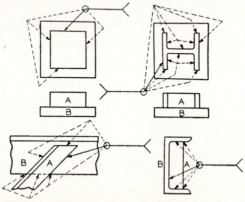

ONE JOINT BETWEEN TWO MEMBERS "A" AND "B"

(e) The all-around symbol extends the control of the welding symbol not only beyond abrupt changes in the direction of one joint, but to two or more joints to the encirclement of the joints in so far as is possible, thus:

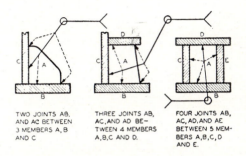

TWO JOINTS AB, AND AC BETWEEN 3 MEMBERS A, B AND C

THREE JOINTS AB, AC, AND AD BE- TWEEN 4 MEMBERS A,B,C AND D.

FOUR JOINTS AB, AC, AD, AND AE BETWEEN 5 MEM- BERS A,B,C,D AND E.

(f) When the use of an arrow-side or other-side symbol, together with an all-around symbol, results in a weld on both sides of the joint as a whole, it is advisable to use the both-sides symbol, thus, even though a one-side symbol may be strictly correct: See (g) below.

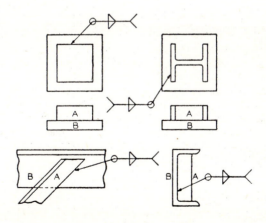

(*g*) When the member involved is hollow or annular and there is more than one encircling weld, and there is likelihood of confusion existing as to whether or not a both-sides symbol would refer to a part of the joint or to the joint as a whole, show each encircling weld with a separate arrow, thus:

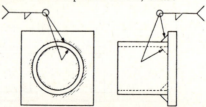

(*h*) The locations of the flush and finish symbols have the usual arrow and other (near and far) side significance and govern only the sides on which they are shown.

(*i*) Finish marks govern faces of welds only and not base metal either before or after welding.

(*j*) Show arc and gas welds made flush without recourse to any kind of finishing, thus:

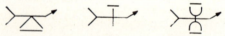

(*k*) Show arc and gas welds made flush by mechanical means with both flush and user's standard finish symbols, thus:

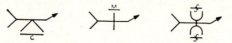

The following letters are suggested for indicating finishing processes:

    C—Chip   G—Grind   M—Machine

(*l*) Show finishing on face of arc and gas welds, which need not be flush, with user's standard finish symbols on bead symbol, thus:

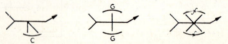

(*m*) Show spot, seam or projection welds made practically flush (with minimum indentation), thus:

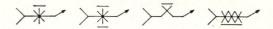

(*n*) Show resistance butt welds, finished by mechanical means, without flush symbol, thus:

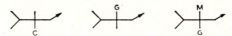

(*o*) Show special welds not covered by any of the above symbols by a detailed section or reference drawing, or give any supplementary information by means of a note and refer weld to section, drawing, or note by a reference symbol. Reference symbol has usual location significance, thus:

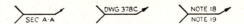

Part 6
Technique

There is no definite or particular technique that all welders must use when depositing metal. The final results determine which is the right and which the wrong way, and every welder has his own individual method of doing the job. The following discussion of technique is offered merely in the form of suggestion and as a guide for the man who is new to this type of work and as yet has not completely mastered the "tricks of the trade." The techniques described here are not to be regarded as the only way to weld; but they have been taught to hundreds of men who are now employed and advancing in this trade.

There are two general methods of welding under which all techniques may be listed:

1) Weave method
2) Multiple or stringer bead method

These will be described later.

Tabulation of Positions of Fillet Welds (See Fig. 121)

Position	Diagram Reference	Inclination of Axis	Rotation of Face
Flat	A	0° to 15°	150° to 210°
Horizontal	B	0° to 15°	125° to 150°
			210° to 235°
Overhead	C	0° to 80°	0° to 125°
			235° to 360°
Vertical	D	15° to 80°	125° to 235°
	E	80° to 90°	0° to 360°

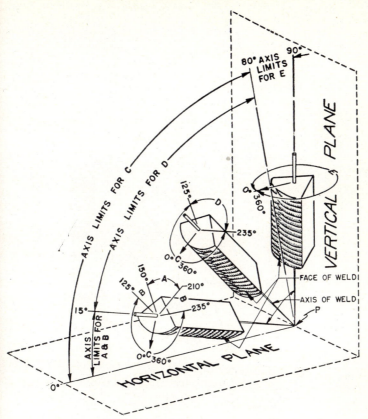

Figure 121: Positions of fillet welds.

The horizontal reference plane is taken to lie always below the weld under consideration.

Inclination of axis is measured from the horizontal reference plane toward the vertical.

Angle of rotation of face is measured from a line perpendicular to the axis of the weld and lying in a vertical plane containing this axis. The reference position (0°) of rotation of the face invariably points in the direction opposite to that in which the axis angle increases. The angle of rotation of the face of the weld is measured in a clockwise direction from this reference position (0°) when looking at point P.

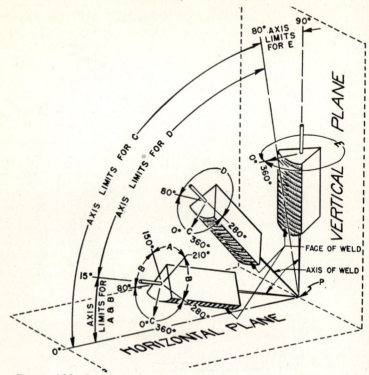

Figure 122: Positions of groove welds. (See Note on facing page.)

Tabulation of Positions of Groove Welds

Position	Diagram Reference	Inclination of Axis	Rotation of Face
Flat	A	0° to 15°	150° to 210°
Horizontal	B	0° to 15°	80° to 150°
			210° to 280°
Overhead	C	0° to 80°	0° to 80°
			280° to 360°
Vertical	D	15° to 80°	80° to 280°
	E	80° to 90°	0° to 360°

It is claimed by some that a more ductile weld is obtained by the weaving method, while greater tensile strength is obtained by the use of multiple beads. Although this may be true in some cases, in general, with other things equal, the characteristics of a welded job will depend more upon the ability of the welder and the materials used than upon the method of deposit.

Regardless of the technique used, there are certain fundamentals that must be applied in all cases. Every welder realizes that in order to have the metal from the electrode properly fused with the base metal, and so become a homogeneous mass, both electrode and base metal must reach the proper welding temperature at the same time. The particular spot where the metal from the electrode is to be deposited must be molten, and, therefore, a depression must be made in the plate to receive the metal from the electrode. In order to accomplish this, sufficient heat must be liberated in the arc to bring the base metal up to the proper temperature. The welding speed must be slow enough to give this heat time to act on the base metal. Many beginners impede their own progress because they use insufficient heat and also attempt to rush the work. This is particularly true of vertical welding, where the beginner is afraid of the metal piling up and rolling back.

Note to Fig. 122 (see facing page)

For groove welds in pipe, the following definitions shall apply.

Horizontal Fixed Position: When the axis of the pipe does not deviate by more than 30° from the horizontal plane and the pipe is not rotated during welding.

Horizontal Rolled Position: When the axis of the pipe does not deviate by more than 30° from the horizontal plane, the pipe is rotated during welding, and the weld metal is deposited within an arc not to exceed 15° on either side of a vertical plane passing through the axis of the pipe.

Vertical Position: When the axis of the pipe does not deviate by more than 10° from the vertical position (the pipe may or may not be rotated during welding).*

* Positions in which the axis of the pipe deviates by more than 10° and less than 60° from the vertical shall be considered intermediate, and shall require the procedure and operator to be qualified in both the horizontal fixed and the vertical positions.

It is not possible to give specific current and voltage settings for the following reasons:

1) The adjusting devices of welding machines are not standardized. One machine set to 100 amps. may liberate the same amount of heat in the arc as another machine set to 150 amps.

2) When a machine is new, a certain setting of the controls will give a certain amount of current. As the machine gets older, the setting will differ for the same amount of current.

The readings of these adjusting devices should not be considered as the correct amount of current flowing through the circuit.

3) An electrode made by one company may require a different heat from that produced by another manufacturer, even though both electrodes are the same type and used for the same purpose.

4) The mass of the stock being welded will also have to be considered. The greater this mass is, the more heat it will absorb from the weld area.

5) The skill of the operator is also a determining factor when considering the amount of heat to be used.

Another, and very important fundamental, is the arc length. In order to obtain proper penetration, the arc must be held close, about $\frac{1}{8}''$ from the plate. It is impossible to obtain this penetration and a neat finished appearance if the arc is long. Consider the metal as leaving the electrode in the form of an inverted "V." The further the electrode is held from the work, the greater will be the area the metal will cover. When this area is too great, the heat does not have a chance properly to act on the place being welded. On the other hand, when the arc is short, all the heat of the arc is concentrated on a smaller area, resulting in proper penetration of the plate.

The third general rule concerns the constant observation of the molten puddle. The width of the bead should be established before attempting to move ahead. In order that the finished bead may be uniform, it is necessary to keep the width of the puddle uniform. Any irregularities in the width of the bead can be detected if the puddle is closely watched, and remedied while the puddle is still hot and in a molten state. When the puddle seems to narrow suddenly, it is because the speed has increased too much. If the puddle seems to be increasing in width, the speed is too slow. Welding should be carried on in such a way that the puddle is kept the same size at all times.

MULTIPLE BEAD WELDING

The multiple or stringer bead method of welding is used more extensively than the weave method. In this stringer bead method, the completed weld will contain a larger number of individual beads than will a weave weld. In other words, each pass is smaller, with the result that less heat is put into the base metal at one time.

Wherever the stringer method is practiced, there seems to be one general technique used. The manipulation of the electrode is such that it is being constantly flipped in and out of the puddle. That is, the metal is deposited in the puddle and then the electrode is flipped completely out of and away from the puddle in the direction of travel. This manipulation is used in all positions of welding, and while it is the easiest and quickest way to learn welding, it is by no means the best. There are a number of undesirable possibilities when using this method; they include poor penetration, rough appearance, and slag inclusions.

When the arc is kept constantly in the puddle, the undesirable qualities just mentioned can be eliminated entirely.

It will, however, take a little longer to learn the techniques described below, particularly on the vertical. However, the benefits should more than make up for the extra time involved.

Flat Welding. The path or arc travel is shown in Figure 123. The puddle is first formed at the starting point of the weld. The width of the puddle, which is the desired width of the bead, is established. After this, the electrode is moved ahead to point (1). This point should be just about at the outer end, but not completely out of the puddle. The electrode is

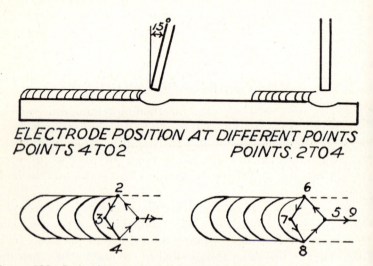

ELECTRODE POSITION AT DIFFERENT POINTS
POINTS 4 TO 2   POINTS 2 TO 4

Figure 123: Path of electrode travel and position of electrode at various points on the electrode path.

then moved back into the puddle at an angle, to the edge of the puddle at point (2), to point (3), in the center of the puddle. This last movement pushes the metal back a little and forms the shape of the bead. From here the electrode is moved to point (4) which is at the other edge, and from here the electrode travels to point (1) from where the procedure repeats.

Keeping the electrode within the confines of the puddle accomplishes two things: first, the puddle is kept molten, which will reduce the possibilities of slag inclusions; second, the base metal becomes molten at the desired spot and thoroughly pene-rated. If the electrode is moved completely out of the puddle, here will be a possibility of its not coming back far enough into he puddle. The result will be that a part of the base metal will not become molten. This means that a section of the weld will

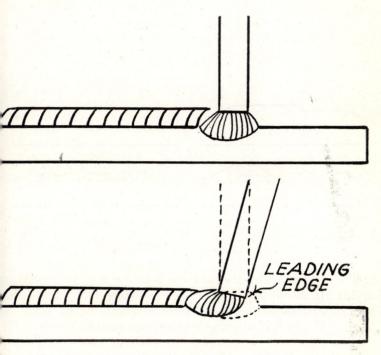

Figure 124: Cutting action of arc with electrode at different angles. Dotted lines in lower figure represent electrode in vertical position.

not be properly fused. As long as the arc is continually playing into the puddle, there can be no possibility of this happening. There is another undesirable possibility if the electrode travels too far out of the puddle. If the electrode is not brought back quickly enough, the slag will have hardened in the crater, and it may not be completely remelted. The result is an inclusion of slag.

The reason for moving the electrode out to the sides at points (2) and (4) is to keep the width of the bead under control, in order that it may be uniform. Another reason is to assure penetration at the edges of the weld. It is necessary that all the area of the base metal covered by the bead be thoroughly penetrated, and, by properly using the manipulation shown this can be accomplished.

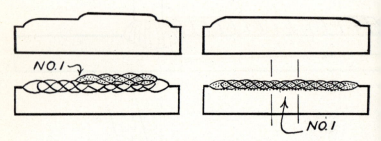

Figure 124A: Proper method of padding. Note that the first bead of each layer is made in the center of the plate.

The angle at which the electrode is held is also an important factor. It should be held as shown in Figure 123; that is, the melting end should be tipped into the puddle at an angle of about 15°. In this way the leading edge of the electrode will cut the plate as it moves along. An enlarged view of this position is shown in Figure 124. As the electrode is brought back to point (2) it should be raised to a position slightly nearer the perpendicular until point (4) is reached, after which it may again be tipped.

Flat Padding. Using the above-described manipulation of the electrode, lay a bead through the center of the plate. The second bead should be applied in such a way that it will overlap bead (1) about halfway. That is, one-half of bead (2) will be fused into (1) and one-half into the plate. In like manner, half of bead (3) will be fused into bead (2). The remainder of the job should be carried out in the same manner. Each bead must be thoroughly cleaned before the next one is applied. When the first layer is complete, a second one should be made. The beads of the second layer should not be laid di-

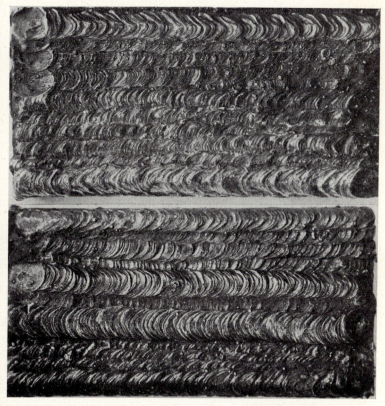

Figure 125: A satisfactory padding job. Note that the metal is built up evenly across the surface of the plate. The entire job is smooth, even and free from holes.

rectly over those of the first layer, but should be laid along the line where the beads of the first layer join, as shown in Figure 124A. This should be continued until results approximating those shown in Figure 125 can be easily obtained. It should be remembered that a good job of padding is smooth, free from

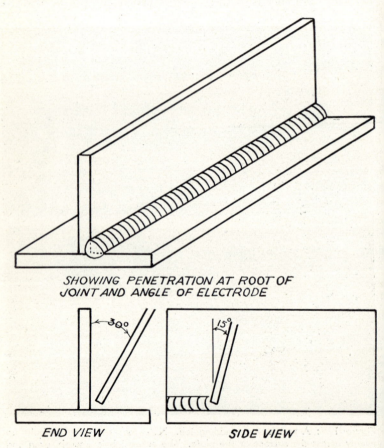

SHOWING PENETRATION AT ROOT OF
JOINT AND ANGLE OF ELECTRODE

END VIEW   SIDE VIEW

Figure 126: Proper penetration at root of joint, and electrode angle.

holes and ridges. All this can be accomplished if the overlapping is properly carried on. The practical use of padding is for building up worn parts.

Horizontal Fillets. The position of the electrode for horizontal fillet welding should be about 30° with the vertical, and about 15° in the direction of travel, as shown in Figure 126. The manipulation of the electrode should consist of the five steps already described. To insure proper penetration at the root of the joint, point (3) in Figure 123 should be carefully observed. The path of electrode travel or manipulation will be precisely the same, even though a vertical member is included in the joint. Point (2) will be on the vertical member; points (3), (5), and (1) all at the root of the joint, and point (4) on the horizontal member. In a joint of this type, care must be taken not to undercut the vertical member. Undercutting can be avoided if at point (2) of Figure 123, the electrode hesitates a short while and the arc is choked. At point (3) the arc must be brought well back into the puddle. This will cause a packing-up action of the metal to such an extent that the metal can be seen actually to flow back along both edges of the weld. This flowing-back action is bound to eliminate undercut.

When first attempting to weld a horizontal tee joint, only one bead should be made (Figure 127). After ability to run this first bead has been accomplished, multiple beads should be made. Figure 128 shows a ⅜" fillet weld made up in three passes. The first or root bead welds both the vertical and horizontal members together and penetrates well into the root. The second pass is half on the first pass and half on the horizontal plate. The third pass is put on in such a way that it is fused into both the vertical plate and the second pass, completely covering the first pass. The method of laying larger welds is exactly the same. A good fillet weld should be up to the specified size, smooth across the face, and free from holes and undercut. Figures 129-135 are examples of poorly welded fillets.

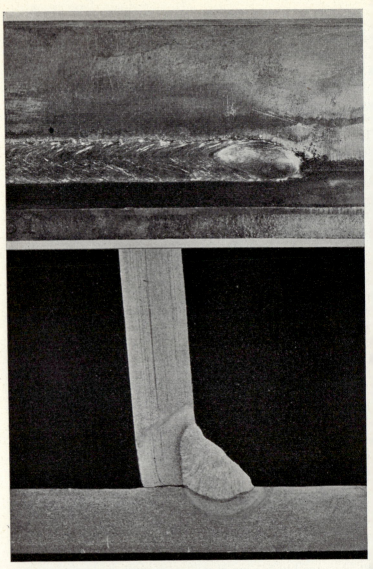

Figure 127: Satisfactory horizontal fillet weld. Appearance of bead i smooth, and ripples are evenly spaced. The cross section below shows eve penetration in both plates and into root of joint. The face is even, and bot legs of the bead are equal.

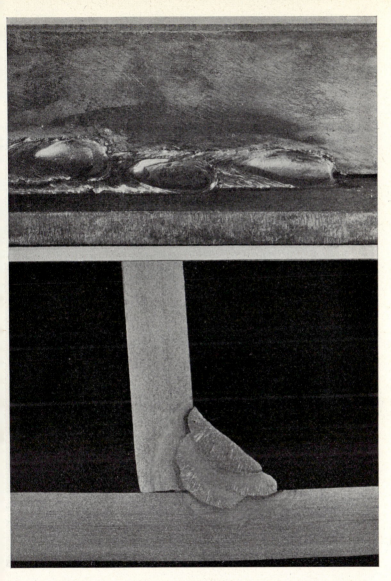

Figure 128: This is a two-layer fillet made with three beads. Note particularly how the beads overlap one another. The cross section below shows that the first bead penetrates into the root of the joint and deposits metal evenly on each plate. Each of the three beads is clearly shown to bring out the proper method of overlapping beads.

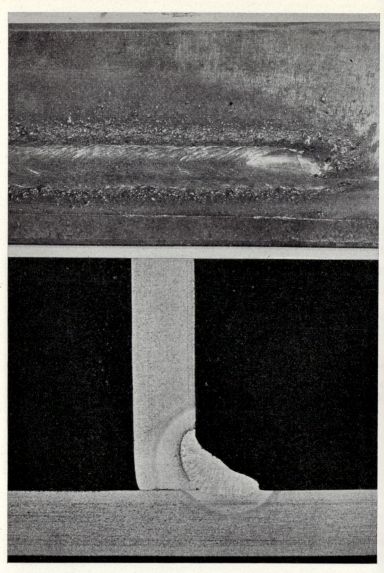

Figure 129: Unsatisfactory horizontal fillet weld.
Fault: Spatter, poor penetration. **Reason:** Weld was made with excessively long arc. Note in the cross section the uneven deposit of metal and lack of penetration at root of joint.

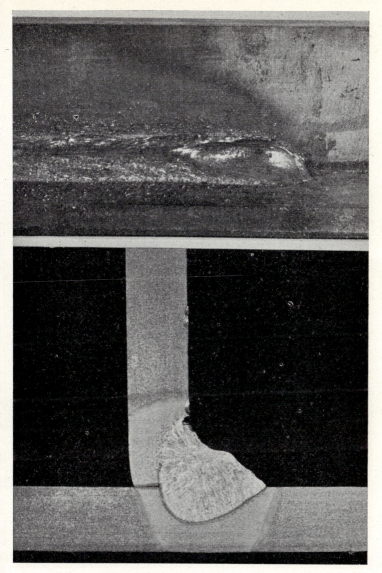

Figure 130: Unsatisfactory horizontal fillet weld.
Fault: Spatter, extremely long crater, too much penetration, bead is undercut on vertical plate, excessive metal is deposited on horizontal plate.
Reason: Too much heat.

Note in the cross section the undercut at top of bead and excessive penetration into horizontal plate.

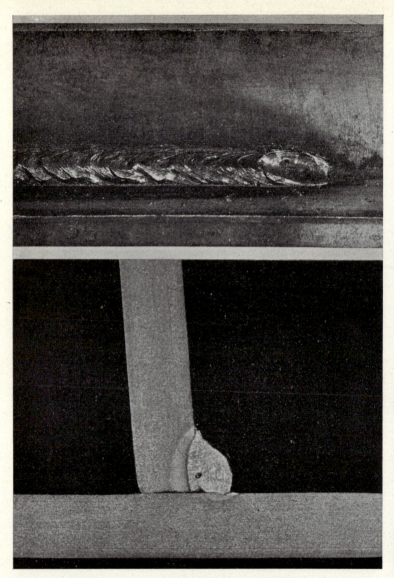

Figure 131: Unsatisfactory horizontal fillet weld.
Fault: Rough appearance, poor penetration. **Reason:** This weld was made with insufficient current, causing the electrode to stick a great deal.

Note in the cross section slag inclusion on vertical plate and lack of penetration at root of joint, also on horizontal plate.

Figure 132: Unsatisfactory horizontal fillet weld.
Fault: Undercut, uneven metal deposit, poor bead contour, excessively elongated ripples. **Reason:** Welding too fast.

Note in the cross section that most of the bead is on horizontal plate, and that there is deep undercut at both sides of bead.

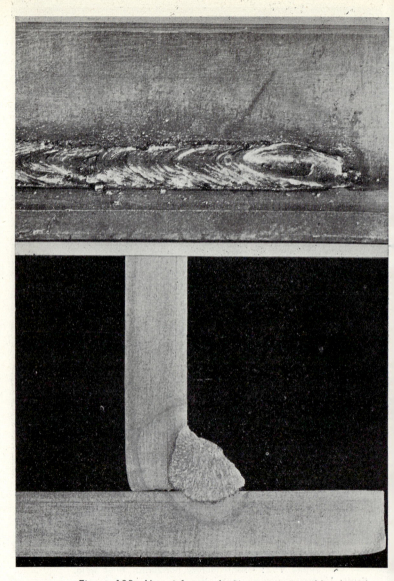

Figure 133: Unsatisfactory horizontal fillet weld.
Fault: Spatter, rough appearance and overlap. **Reason:** Welding proceeded too slowly.

Note in cross section the overlap at horizontal plate.

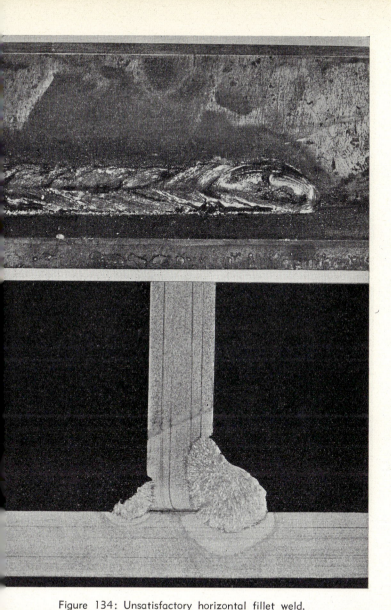

Figure 134: Unsatisfactory horizontal fillet weld.
Fault: Undercut, poor contour of bead, rough appearance. **Reason:** electrode was held at too great an angle with the work.
Note in cross section the undercut in top plate and piling up of metal in horizontal plate.

Figure 135: Unsatisfactory horizontal fillet weld.
Fault: Spatter, undercut, undesirable contour of weld. **Reason:** Angle between electrode and work was too small.

Note in cross section the difference in length between weld legs, undercut in vertical plate.

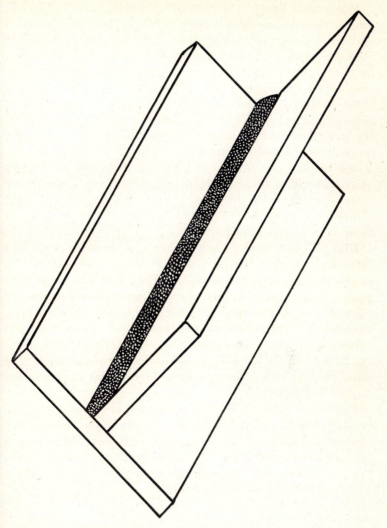

Figure 136: Flat or positioned fillet.

Horizontal Laps. The principle of welding a horizontal lap joint is the same as for a horizontal fillet. Care must be taken that the top edge of the top plate is not cut away. After the ability to make neat-appearing lap welds, the next step should be to test them. This can be done easily and quickly if only one side of the lap is welded. Place the work in a vise and break it with a hammer. Inspect the broken weld for holes, penetration, and slag inclusions. The complete area covered by the weld, both width and length, should show signs of being properly penetrated. If the weld breaks all on one plate, it is a sign of poor penetration of the plate from which it breaks away. The ideal break concerning penetration is through the center of the weld on this type of joint. When the size of weld called for exceeds $\frac{1}{4}''$, it should be made with a number of beads, as was shown for the fillets.

Flat or Positioned Fillets. When a weldment is positioned in such a way that the joint is as shown in Figure 136, it is known as a flat or positioned fillet. The purpose in positioning a joint of this type is to increase welding speed and reduce the possibility of poor welding. A positioned fillet weld will usually have better root penetration, and there is less chance of undercutting than with a horizontal fillet. Higher welding current can be used on the flat fillet than with the horizontal fillet. The same welding techniques can be used with flat fillets, as described in Figure 123.

Figure 137 shows a properly made weld in one pass and Figure 138 shows a properly made weld in two passes, using a $\frac{1}{4}''$ electrode. Figure 139 shows a single-pass weld made with a $\frac{5}{16}''$ electrode, and Figure 140 a two-pass weld made with a $\frac{5}{16}''$ electrode, both of which are examples of good welding. Figures 141-147 show faulty welding.

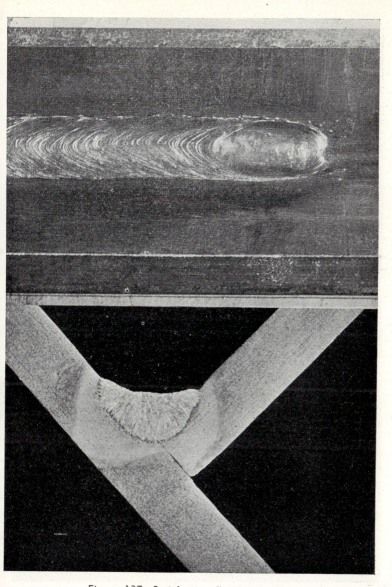

Figure 137: Satisfactory flat fillet weld.

It has smooth appearance, ripples are evenly and closely spaced, metal is deposited equally on both plates. Clear crater, showing sufficient penetration. Note in the cross section the good penetration at the joint.

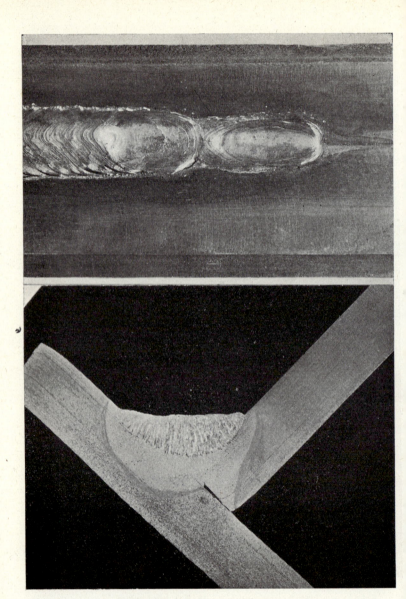

Figure 138: Satisfactory flat fillet weld.

This is a two-pass, two-layer fillet. Note how the second pass penetrates into the first, and, in the cross section, the good penetration and smooth appearance.

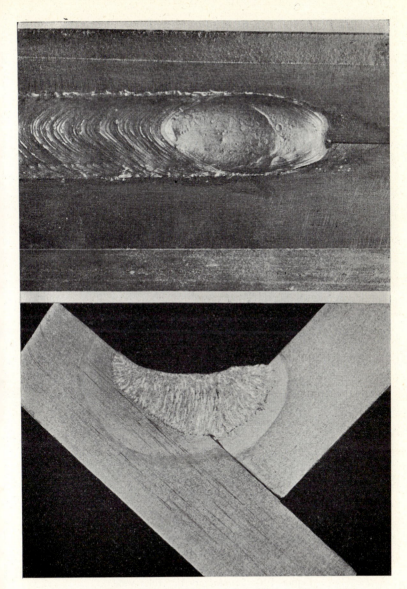

Figure 139: Satisfactory flat fillet weld.
This weld was made with a 5/16" electrode, giving a heavier deposit of metal. The cross section shows the larger metal deposit more clearly.

Figure 140: Satisfactory flat fillet weld.

This is a two-layer, two-pass flat fillet, made with a 5'16" electrode. Electrodes of this size afford a speedy method of weld deposit. The cross section gives an even better idea of the extra amount of metal that may be deposited with larger size electrodes.

264

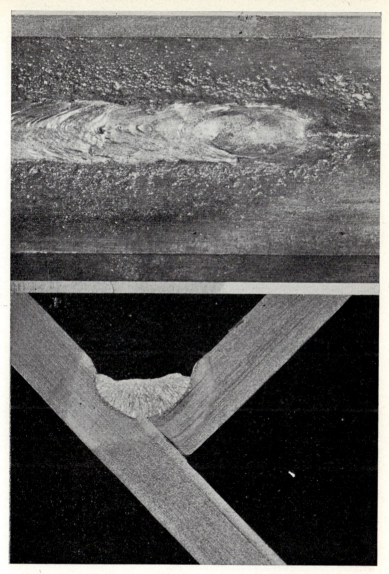

Figure 141: Unsatisfactory flat fillet weld.
Fault: Spatter, undercut, generally poor appearance. **Reason:** Arc was too long.

Note in the cross section the undercut on both sides.

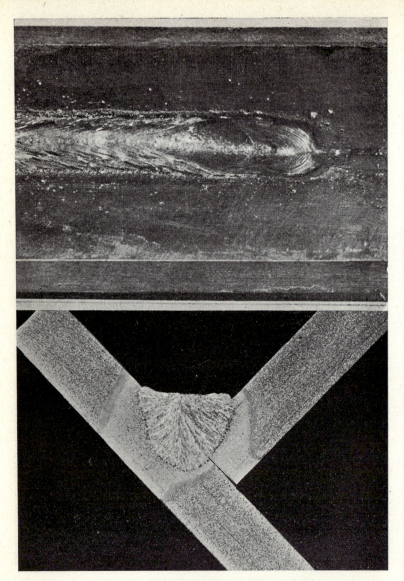

Figure 142: Unsatisfactory flat fillet weld.
Fault: Spatter, excessive penetration, extremely long crater. **Reason:** Too much heat.

Note in the cross section the excessive penetration in one plate.

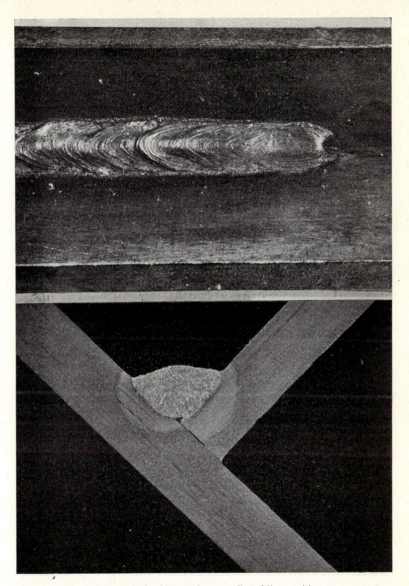

Figure 143: Unsatisfactory flat fillet weld.
Fault: Lumpy appearance, crater shows no penetration. **Reason:** Not enough heat.

Note in the cross section the lack of penetration, particularly at root of joint.

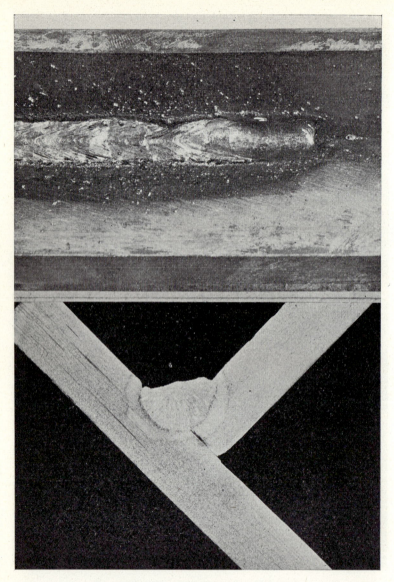

Fig. 144: Unsatisfactory flat fillet weld.
Fault: Width of bead varies. Note elongated ripples and spatter. **Reason:** Welding speed too fast.
Cross section shows undercut, poor contour.

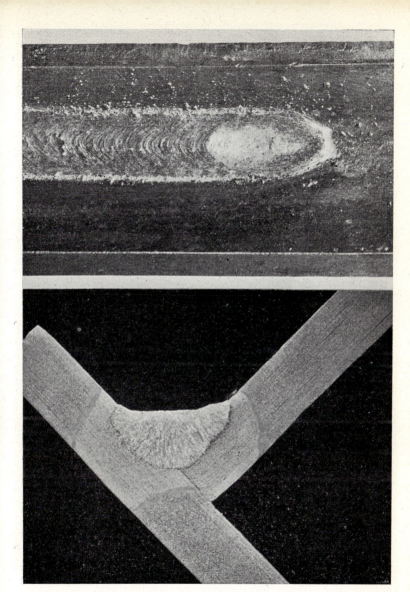

Figure 145: Unsatisfactory flat fillet weld.
Fault: Spatter. **Reason:** Welding speed too slow.
The cross section in this case does not show any fault. Usually there is piling up of metal when welding speed is too slow.

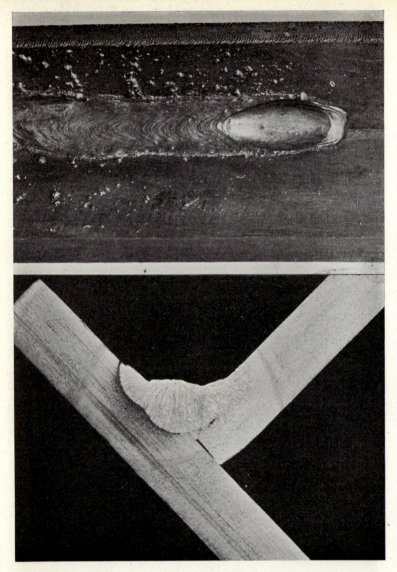

Figure 146: Unsatisfactory flat fillet weld.
Fault: Spatter, uneven bead contour. **Reason:** Electrode was held at too great an angle to work.

Note in cross section that contour of bead is not smooth, penetration in plates goes too far beyond face of weld.

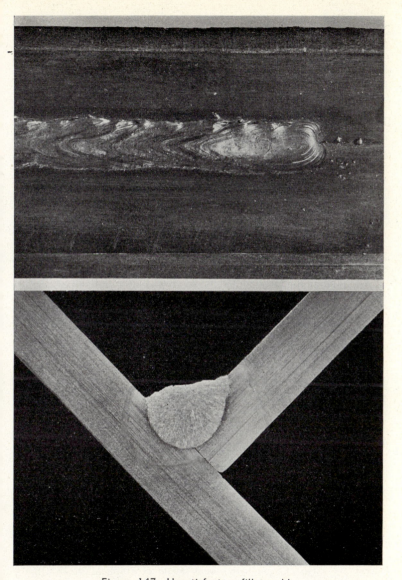

Figure 147: Unsatisfactory fillet weld.
Fault: Metal not deposited equally on plates. Appearance is rough, ripples are too long. The cross section shows unequal metal deposit and unequal penetration in plates.

Corner Welds. Where the stock is ¼″ or less in thickness, one pass will suffice to complete the joint shown in Figure 148a. Thorough penetration is a most important requirement. A visual inspection of the inside of the joint should show signs of penetration the complete length of the weld. The proper end

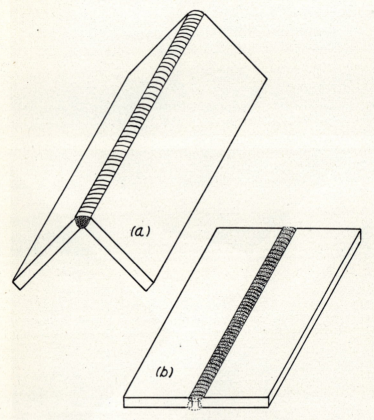

Figure 148: (top) Corner joint—weld should penetrate as shown. (bottom) Square butt joint—used on stock not over 3/16″ thick.

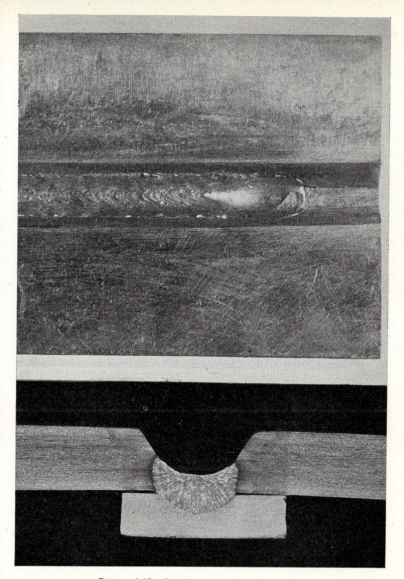

Figure 149: Satisfactory flat butt weld.

This shows the first pass of a single vee butt joint. Appearance is smooth and even, metal is evenly deposited on both plates, and penetrates the backing strip. Note in the cross section that the weld penetrates both bevelled plates and backing strip. The contour of the weld is such that it forms a smooth, unbroken line with the bevel of the plates.

appearance of the joint should be as shown in Figure 148a. This type of joint is easily broken for inspection purposes.

Flat Butts. For plates ³⁄₁₆″ thickness or less, the common type of butt used is the square butt. Here the edges are spaced about ¹⁄₁₆″ apart, as shown in Figure 148b. This butt should be completed in two passes, the first pass penetrating through the full thickness of the joint, and the second as a finish bead on the opposite side. For heavier stock there are a number of different kinds of joints in general use.

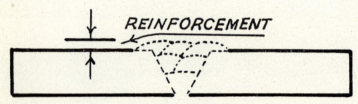

Figure 150: Reinforcement of a properly made single vee butt. Dimension between arrows is ⅛″.

Single Vee Butt. The V butt shown in Figure 149 may or may not have a backing strip. If no backing strip is used, the root bead should penetrate through the opening so as to form a bead on the underside. If a backing strip is used, the root bead should penetrate it thoroughly. In either case, the root bead should be well fused into the bevelled edges of both plates. The second bead cuts into half of the first one and also into the left-hand plate. When the third pass is made, the root bead should be completely covered as well as half of the second one. The entire surface should be flat. If there is a space between the second and third beads, or if there is undercut at the edges of any of the beads, it is likely to cause slag to be trapped in the weld. The surfaces of every layer should be kept flat.

Three passes are usually sufficient to fill a ⅜″ single vee butt nearly flush. If the weld inside the V is kept approximately ¹⁄₁₆″ below the level of the plates, the plate edges will form a guide for the finishing layer. This finishing layer should consist of four beads covering the joint and overlapping the edges by $\frac{3}{16}''$ on each side. The finish layer should be thick enough to reinforce the joint by $\frac{1}{8}''$, as shown in Figure 150.

Vertical Welding. Use E-6010 electrodes—welding to start at bottom and proceed upwards.

The technique of vertical welding to be described here is entirely different from the method generally used. The results have proven it to be superior in many ways. The first outstanding difference to be noted is the angle of the electrode. The electrode is tipped **downward** and into the puddle. There

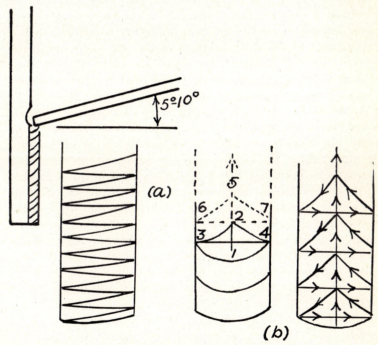

Figure 151: Path of electrode travel for vertical welding.

are two paths of travel that may be used as shown at (a) and (b) of Figure 151. In either case the angle of the electrode is the same.

If the proper heat is used, the leading edge of the electrode can be seen to cut continually into the base metal. As this cutting action takes place, the metal from the rest of the electrode end is filling the crater. Unless the base metal in the vicinity of the weld becomes overheated, the electrode never leaves the puddle. This is another difference to be noted. The action is that of continually cutting a trench into the base metal from one end of the weld to the other. This trench or pocket forms a receptacle for the molten metal to flow into. The fact that the electrode is pointing down into this receptacle assures perfect penetration because the full heat of the arc is concentrated at this point and the driving action of the arc forces the metal into the pocket formed. The electrode must be held close enough so that the leading edge is less than $\frac{1}{16}''$ away, almost touching the plate being welded.

If the metal starts to show signs of overheating, the electrode should be raised slightly to a position more perpendicular to the plate, but under no conditions is the electrode to point upwards. If after raising the electrode to this position, the metal still seems to be piling up, lift the electrode straight up to the top of the puddle but not completely out of it. Bring the electrode back into the puddle immediately. A lifting action will give the molten metal a chance to cool enough to set and prevent running. This lifting will not be necessary when the right amount of heat is used and the arc is held close enough. After the electrode is brought back to the puddle, continue as before. The electrode should hesitate at each side of the bead to prevent undercut. If the electrode hesitates the proper length of time, the metal can be seen to flow backwards along the edges of the bead.

Vertical Padding. Using the manipulation just described, pad a 4″ × 6″ plate with three layers of weld metal. The first bead should be welded up the center of the plate, the second deposited in such a way that it overlaps one-half of the first,

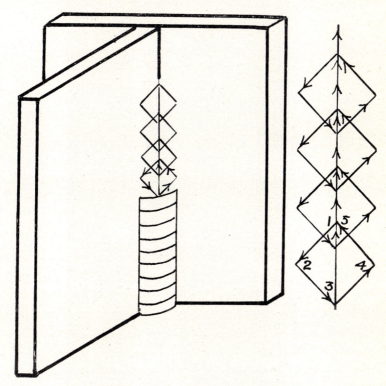

Figure 152: Path of electrode for vertical fillet welding.

the remainder of the second bead being fused with the plate. This method continues on both sides of the center bead until the entire surface of the plate is covered. Particular care must be taken properly to overlap each bead of the layer. This will keep the layer solid and level. It will also eliminate the possi-

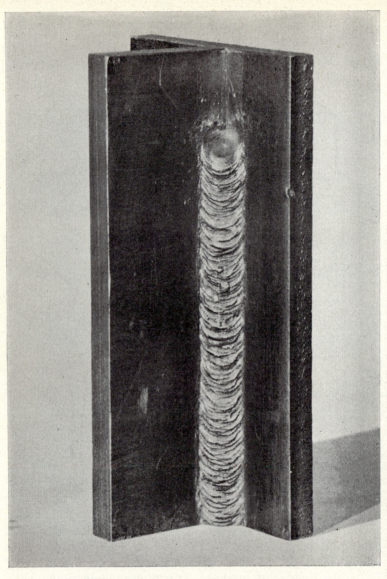

Figure 153: Satisfactory vertical fillet weld.
The weld metal is evenly deposited on both plates, and crater is centered between plates.

bility of slag inclusions between beads. The beads of the second layer should be laid along the lines of overlap of the first layer. The succeeding layers are applied in the same manner as the first.

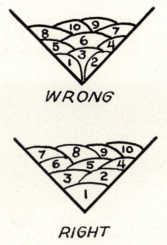

WRONG

RIGHT

Figure 154: Right and wrong methods of building up a vertical fillet weld.

Vertical Fillets. The welding of vertical fillets will require more heat than that used for vertical padding. It will also require a slight variation in the manipulation, which resembles that shown for flat welding; the actual path is shown in Figure 152. In order sufficiently to penetrate the root of the joint, the electrode should be lifted slightly, in the direction of travel. This should not be high enough for the electrode completely to leave the puddle. The succeeding beads may be put in with the same manipulation, or they may be put in with manipulation shown for vertical padding.

If the size of bead specified does not exceed ¼″, a single pass will be sufficient (Figure 153). If the size of weld is larger than ¼″, it should be put in with a number of beads as shown for the flat fillet. Figure 154 shows the right and wrong procedure of building up a weld in a number of passes. Each bead must be fused into the previous one, with no space or crevices left between beads. Any space or crevices may cause slag to be trapped. The procedure of laying in the beads is the same for all sizes of fillets in any position. Figures 155-160 inclusive show some examples of poorly welded vertical fillets.

Figure 155A: Cross section of Figure 155. Note undercut, lack of proper penetration, poor bead contour.

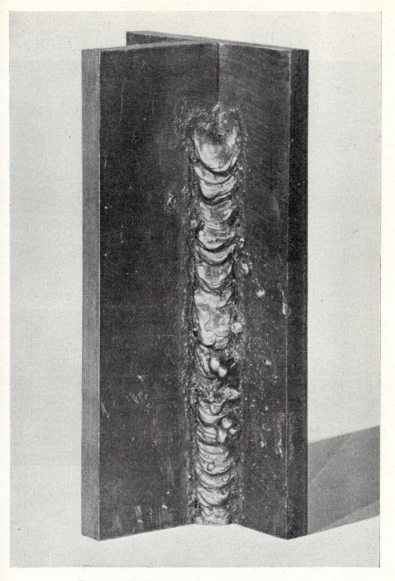

Figure 155: Unsatisfactory vertical fillet weld.
Fault: Rough, spattered appearance. **Reason:** Arc was too long.

Figure 156A: Cross Section of Figure 156. Note lack of penetration and poor contour of bead.

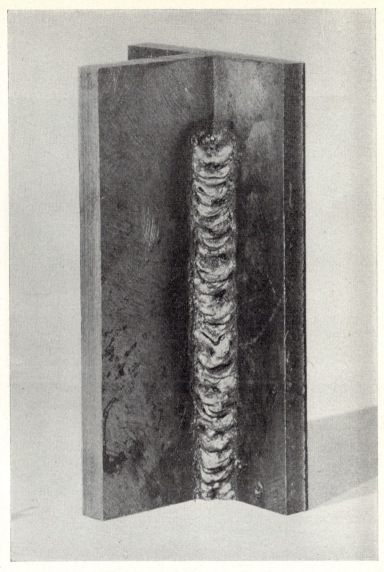

Figure 156: Unsatisfactory vertical fillet weld.
Fault: Rough appearance, holes, poor penetration. **Reason:** Arc was too short.

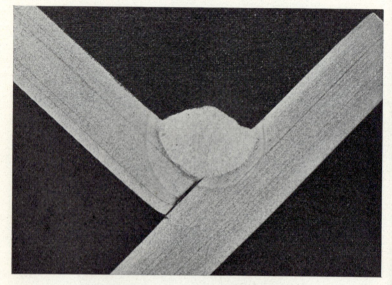

Figure 157A: Cross Section of Figure 157. Poor bead contour. Note how metal piles up in center of bead.

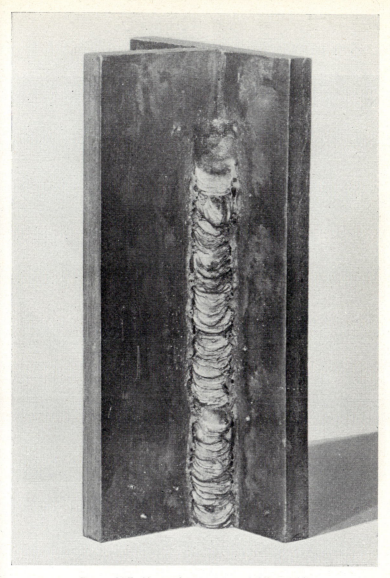

Figure 157: Unsatisfactory vertical fillet weld.
Fault: Rough, lumpy appearance. **Reason:** Too much heat.

285

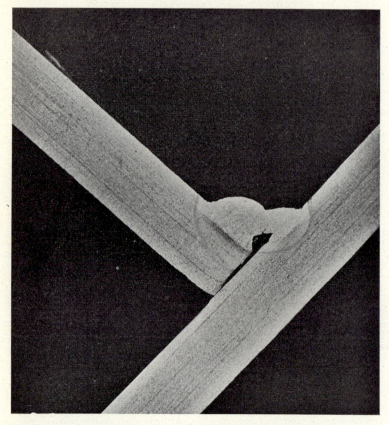

Figure 158A: Cross section of Figure 158. Note poor penetration, particularly at root of joint. Also poor contour of bead.

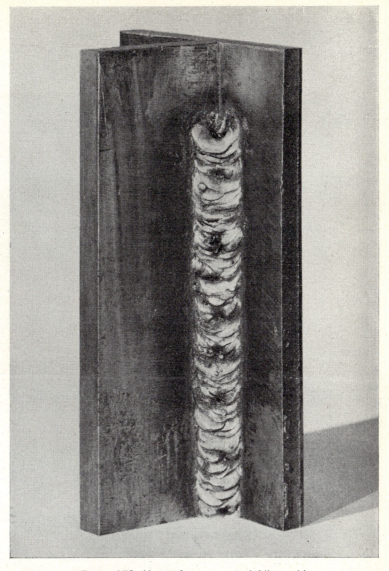

Figure 158: Unsatisfactory vertical fillet weld.
Fault: Holes, slag inclusions, and poor appearance of bead in general.
Reason: Not enough heat.

Figure 159A: Cross section of Figure 159. Note lack of penetration, particularly at root of joint.

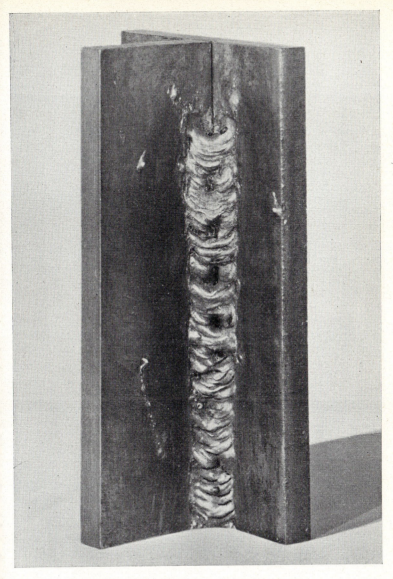

Figure 159: Unsatisfactory vertical fillet weld.
Fault: Holes, slag inclusions, lack of penetration and generally poor appearance. **Reason:** Welding speed was too fast.

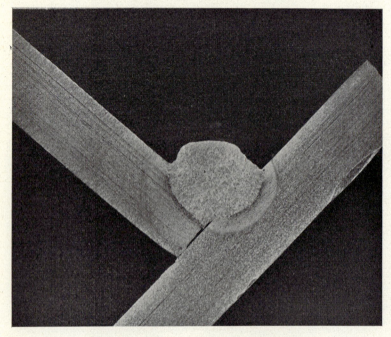

Figure 160A: Cross section of Figure 160. Note contour of weld.

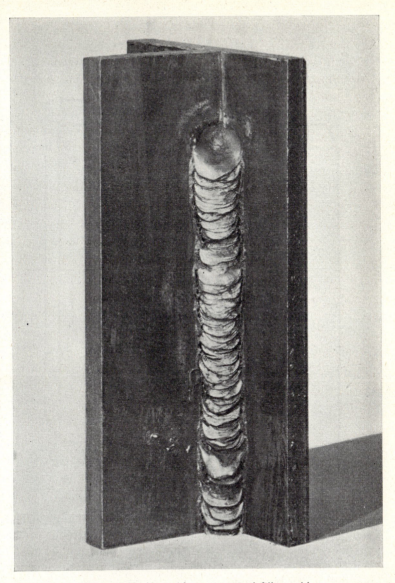

Figure 160: Unsatisfactory vertical fillet weld.
Fault: Rough appearance, piling up of metal in center of weld. **Reason:** Welding proceeded too slowly.

Vertical Laps. Figure 161 shows a vertical lap weld made up of three passes. The first bead is fused well into the root of the joint in the same manner as shown for vertical fillet. The succeeding beads may be put in with the same manipulation, or

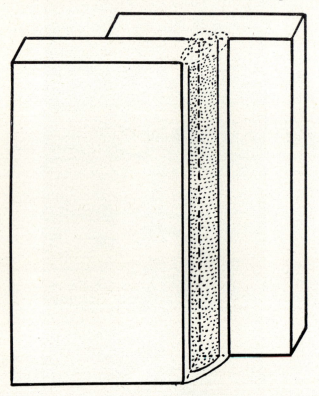

Figure 161: Vertical lap weld. Note formation of beads.

they may be made with the manipulation shown for vertical padding. Care must be taken to avoid cutting the edge of the outside plate and undercutting the surface of the inner plate. With proper hesitation at the sides of the weld this cutting possibility can be avoided.

Vertical Butts. Figure 162 shows a bevelled butt partially

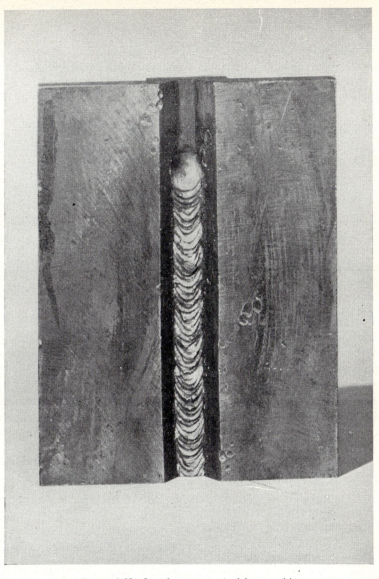

Figure 162: Satisfactory vertical butt weld.
This shows the first pass of a single vee joint welded in the vertical position. Note how metal is equally deposited on both plates and backing strip. Depth of crater shows good penetration into backing strip.

welded in the vertical position. The first pass must take in all three pieces of metal, the back strip, and the bevelled edges of both plates. The root bead should be put in with the lifting technique, as described for vertical fillets. The remaining beads may be put in with the technique described for vertical padding. In any bevelled butt, the root bead is of prime importance. It must penetrate into the back strip. The remaining beads will be easier to apply than the first.

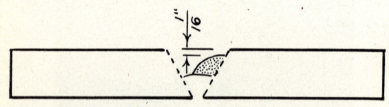

Figure 163: Proper method of depositing second bead of vertical butt when using stringer beads.

A good root bead is half the job. As the weld progresses upward, the welder should be able to see the edges of the plate being cut away by the heat of the arc and these edges being replaced by weld metal. After the root bead is completed, the remaining beads must be laid in the proper sequence to avoid possibility of slag inclusions.

It will be noted that the root bead comprises a layer of metal in itself. The second layer is made up of two beads. The first of these two is welded into one of the plates and the root bead. The next bead, which is the third bead in the butt, overlaps the previous one and welds into the other plate. The root bead is now completely covered and the face of the weld is flat. There should be no spaces between the two beads comprising the second layer. This second layer comes almost but not quite flush with the plates. The reason for staying below the surface of the plates is to use the edges of the plates as a guide for the third layer.

The third layer will consist of four beads. The first bead of this layer will be burned into the juncture of the plate and second layer, the second bead will overlap this first bead as shown in Figure 163. When completed, the third layer should overlap each side of the butt by at least ⅛″, and be ⅛″ above the surface of the plates.

There should be no space or crevices between the beads of any layer. If each bead overlaps properly, there will be no space, and the surface of the layer will be flat.

Overhead Welding. In welding in the overhead position the manipulation is practically the same as for flat welding. It must be remembered, however, that gravity is working against the welder rather than with him, as in flat welding. The greatest difficulty a beginner is likely to encounter is a bunching up of the metal. There are a number of reasons, any one or combination of which will cause this difficulty:

1) Excessive heat
2) Arc too long
3) Rate of travel too slow

1) The heat used for overhead should be the same as that used for flat welding.

2) The arc should be short, just as in other positions.

3) The rate of travel is faster than that for flat or vertical welding.

It can be seen that if the same amount of heat is used but the rate of travel is faster than for flat welding, the overhead bead will not be as heavy as a flat bead. After some experience the welder will be able to run heavier beads in the overhead position just as easily as in the flat position. At first it is advisable to run light beads in this position.

The position of the electrode should be as shown in Figure 164a. That is, tipped slightly into the puddle but straight up and down from an end view.

Overhead Padding. When running an overhead bead on the surface of a plate, as is required in padding, there is a tendency for the metal to flow into the center. This is shown in Figure 164b. To avoid this, and deposit a uniform bead of the desired shape and size, the manipulation should be that de-

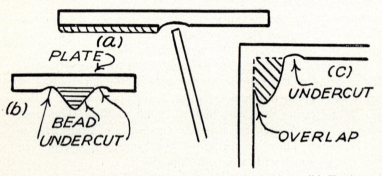

Figure 164: (a) Position of electrode for overhead welding. (b) Tendency of metal to run when welding in overhead position. (c) Overlap of weld metal.

scribed for flat padding. The speed should be increased slightly. Particular care must be taken in hesitating at the sides, as undercutting in the overhead position is more difficult to prevent than in the flat position. The formation and procedure of interlocking the beads are the same as for the flat and vertical padding previously described.

Overhead Fillets. The technique for overhead fillet welding is of necessity slightly different from any other previously described. The reason is that there is a tendency for the horizontal member to be undercut, while that portion of the weld on the vertical member is likely to be rolled or overlapped, as shown in Figure 164c.

After striking the arc and establishing the puddle, the path of travel for the electrode is as shown in Figure 165. The electrode hesitates on the upper or horizontal member to prevent possibility of undercut and to give a full-size bead; it then travels to point (2), depositing metal as it travels. Upon reaching point (2), the coating of the electrode should be in actual contact with the vertical member, Fig. 186, p. 323. From (2), the electrode is scraped quickly along the vertical plate to

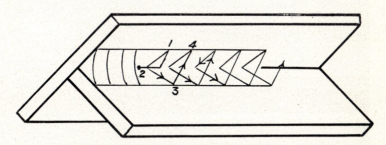

Figure 165: Path of electrode travel for overhead welding.

point (3) where it is quickly whipped up to point (4), from where the process continues. The tip of the electrode is constantly in the puddle. The reason for moving quickly on the vertical plate is to eliminate an excess deposit of metal, which will flow over and make an overlapping bead. The same care must be taken to penetrate into the root of the joint as was described for fillets in the other positions.

Figures 166-174 inclusive show fillet welding examples in the overhead position.

Overhead Lap. The manipulation of the electrode for welding overhead lap joints is the same as for overhead fillet welding. To eliminate the possibility of cutting the under edge of the bottom plate, the last bead may be put in with slightly less heat. Where the stock is thin, ⅛″ or less, the technique used for overhead padding will be the best.

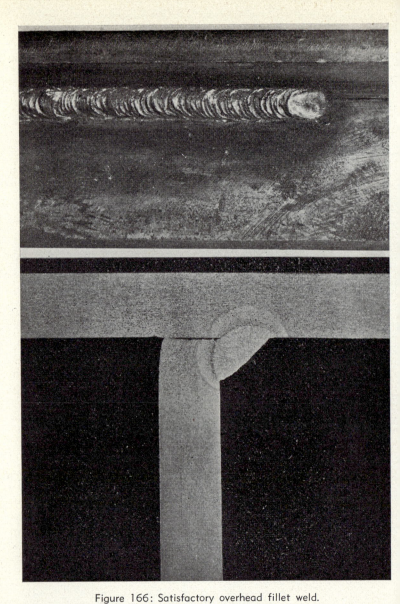

Figure 166: Satisfactory overhead fillet weld.
This shows the first pass of a two-layer fillet weld. The metal is equally deposited on both plates. The weld is free from holes and undercut. Note in the cross section the penetration at root of joint and smooth, even contour of bead.

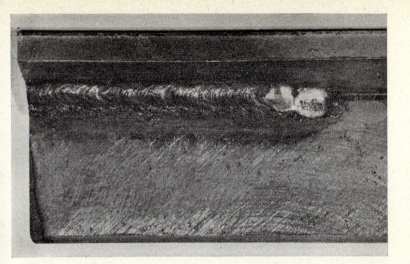

Figure 167: Satisfactory overhead fillet weld.
This shows the first two passes of a two-layer fillet. Note how second pass overlaps and cuts into first pass.

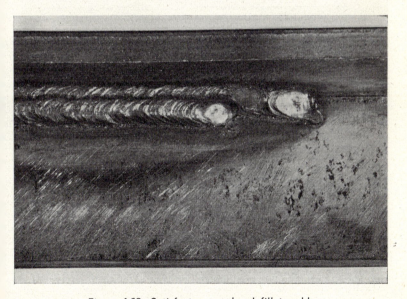

Figure 168: Satisfactory overhead fillet weld.
This shows the two-layer fillet weld completed with three passes. Note that first pass is entirely covered by the second and third.

Figure 169: Unsatisfactory overhead fillet weld.

Fault: Spatter, rough appearance, poor penetration. **Reason:** Arc was too long.

Note in cross section the undercut on both sides of bead, poor penetration, uneven contour of bead.

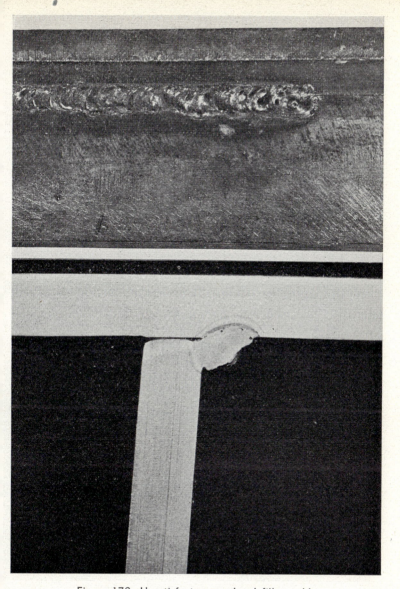

Figure 170: Unsatisfactory overhead fillet weld.
Fault: Rough appearance, holes, metal not deposited equally on both plates. **Reason:** Arc was too short.

Note in cross section the contour of weld, slag inclusions in horizontal plate and overlap on vertical plate.

Figure 171: Unsatisfactory overhead fillet weld.
Fault: Lumpy, uneven appearance, uneven deposit of metal on plates.
Reason: Too much heat.

Note in cross section excessive penetration in horizontal plate, lumpy contour of bead.

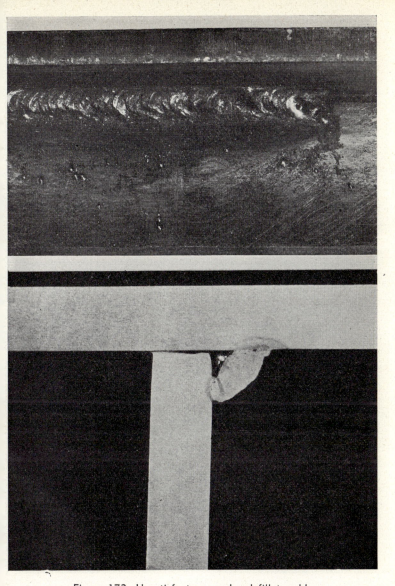

Figure 172: Unsatisfactory overhead fillet weld.
Fault: Poor appearance of weld and spatter. **Reason:** Not enough heat.
Note in cross section lack of penetration in root of joint and plates, overlap and generally poor shape of bead.

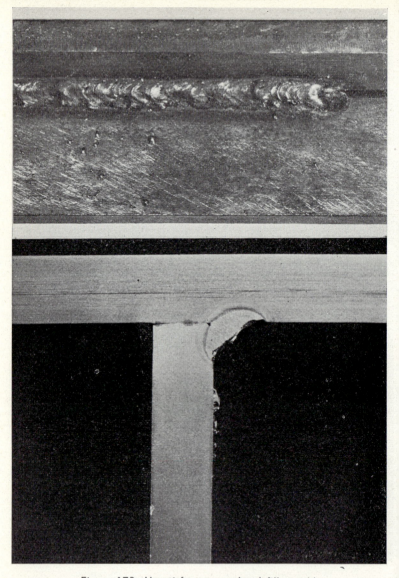

Figure 173: Unsatisfactory overhead fillet weld.

Fault: Rough, lumpy appearance and spatter. **Reason:** Welding speed was too fast.

Note in cross section the undercut and uneven metal deposit.

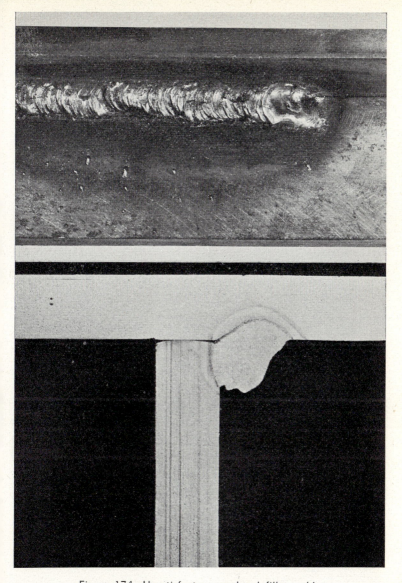

Figure 174: Unsatisfactory overhead fillet weld.

Fault: Poor appearance, irregular crater, metal is not deposited evenly on both plates.

Note in cross section the excessive penetration on horizontal plate, and not enough penetration in vertical plate. Contour of bead is very poor.

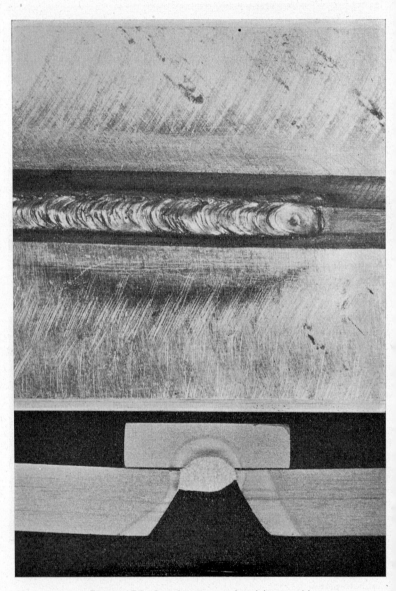

Figure 175: Satisfactory overhead butt weld.
This shows a properly deposited root bead of an overhead butt weld. Note in cross section how bead cuts into back strip and edges of both plates.

Overhead Butt. The greatest difficulty in welding any butt joint seems to be an unequal distribution of metal when putting in the root bead. This is particularly true in an overhead butt. The metal seems to deposit on one plate only instead of on both. The reason for this is that when the arc is struck and the puddle formed, the arc has been played on one plate only, so the puddle is formed on this plate and the metal continues to deposit on this plate. To overcome this difficulty, it is necessary to play the arc mainly on the backing strip and, with a slight sidewise motion, equally on both plates. Use the same manipulation and hold the electrode in the same position as for overhead padding. The root bead must penetrate the backing strip and actually cut away the bevelled edges of both plates. The pocket so formed will allow easy deposit of metal and give a good appearance. The procedure and formation of the beads is the same as for flat and vertical beads, and should appear as in Figure 175.

WEAVING METHOD

By weaving a bead is meant depositing a heavy, wide bead in such a way that the electrode is weaved from side to side. This method of welding is used extensively on piping systems, boiler manufacture, and other heavy sections. Figure 176 shows three general paths of travel for weave welding. The particular type of weaving done is up to the individual welder, and he should use the type with which he can accomplish the best results.

The width of the weave should not exceed four times the diameter of the electrode. The reason is that when too wide a weave is made, the time that elapses while the arc is traveling across the bead is enough to allow the puddle to cool too much on one side. As the puddle cools, the slag hardens. The result is that slag is trapped in the metal and the metal is poorly fused. This in turn causes a porous and generally undesirable job.

To the beginner, the greatest difficulty will probably be undercutting. In order to overcome this, the welder should hesitate at both edges of the weld long enough to allow the electrode metal a chance to fill all the area cut away by the arc.

Another difficulty may be holes in the center of the weld, caused by trying to move too fast across the face of the weld.

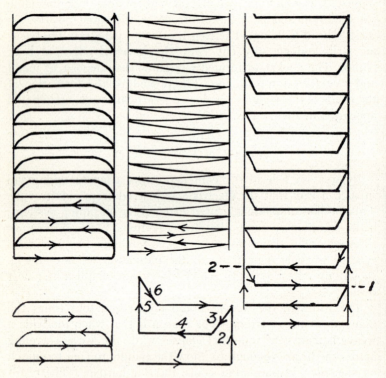

Figure 176: Paths of electrode travel for weave welding.

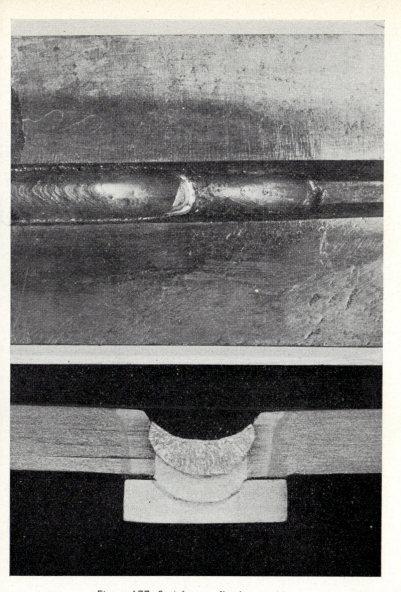

Figure 177: Satisfactory flat butt weld.
This shows the first and second passes of a flat butt weld properly made.
Note in cross section the solid, even penetration into plates and backing
strip.

It must be remembered that a great deal more metal is being deposited in one place than when the stringer bead method is used. Therefore, in order properly to deposit this metal, the rate of travel must be slower.

Flat Butt Weaving. Figure 177 shows a single vee joint partially welded in the flat position. The path of electrode travel is shown by the arrows. The electrode should:

1) Not be tipped from side to side but tipped slightly into the puddle.

2) Travel across the width of the bead slowly enough to insure good penetration.

3) Hesitate long enough to deposit enough metal completely to take care of any possible undercutting.

In the root bead of a joint of this type, penetration is extremely important. The bead must penetrate into the bevelled edges of both plates, and all the way through the gap as shown. There must be no undercut on the bevelled edges from the root bead, as slag inclusions are likely to result. While this first bead will require only a narrow weave, care must be taken to hesitate long enough on both sides to prevent any possibility of

Figure 178: Undercut, due to pulling electrode away from sides too quickly.

undercutting as shown in Figure 178. The second layer should thoroughly fuse into and completely cover the first, as shown in Figure 177. It should come up to between $\frac{1}{16}''$ and $\frac{1}{8}''$ of being flush with the top of the plates. The third bead will fill the butt and be heavy enough to reinforce it by $\frac{1}{16}''$. This last bead is known as the face or finish bead. The appearance should be smooth and uniform, no undercut, and the reinforcement should be of whatever is called for in the specifications, usually up to ⅛".

Fillet Weaving. In weaving a tee joint, as shown in Figure 179, the angle of the electrode is very important and should be carefully observed. The path of electrode travel is shown by the arrows. When the electrode is brought upward on the vertical plate, it should be held at the topmost point of the weld

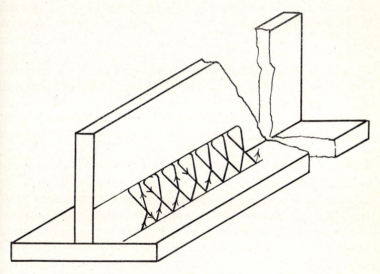

Figure 179: Electrode path of travel when weaving a horizontal fillet.

long enough for the metal to burn into the plate. If this hesitation is not made, the metal will not thoroughly fuse with the vertical plate, resulting in heavy undercut and also in the molten metal running down. As the electrode is brought down, the base metal should be thoroughly penetrated, and when the electrode gets to the bottom edge of the weld, it should be whipped quickly into its next upward stroke. The point in whipping quickly away from the bottom side is to prevent overlap on the horizontal member. There is no metal deposited on the upward stroke.

The electrode should be at an angle of approximately 30° with the horizontal when at the topmost point of the bead, and approximately 45° with the horizontal when the arc is on the horizontal plate. The angle varies between these two points as it progresses across the face of the weld. If undercut continues on the vertical plate, the angle of the electrode should be changed to a position more perpendicular to the vertical plate; at the same time, the arc should be choked when playing on this plate. When the size of the weld is such that more than one pass is required, it is necessary for each pass to cover completely the preceding one and be well fused into the base metal at the edges of the preceding pass. Unless care is taken, it is possible in this type of fillet welding to have a bead with a good outward appearance but poor root penetration. To avoid this possibility, it is necessary to hold the arc for an instant on the root of the joint during the downward stroke of the electrode.

Lap Weaving. Weaving a lap joint is practically the same as weaving a fillet weld. The same manipulation of the electrode is used, and the same precautions regarding root penetration hold for lap joints as well as the method for eliminating undercut. The only difference is that on the final pass of a fillet weld there is a possibility of leaving undercut on the vertical plate, while on a lap weld this possibility is changed to that of cutting away the top edge of the upper plate. If the electrode is held for an instant and the arc choked at the top edge, this cutting away will be eliminated.

Vertical Butt Weaving. In weave welding a vertical "V" butt joint, there is one important point to bear in mind. Go slowly enough to allow the arc to melt a pocket in the base metal. If this is properly done, there will be little or no diffi-

culty experienced. In order properly to do this, a very close
arc must be held. The complete technique is as follows:

Strike the arc and travel slowly from left to right and back
again to form a puddle approximately $\frac{5}{16}''$ deep. This forms

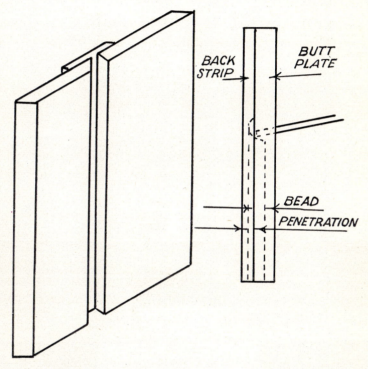

Figure 180: Proper position of electrode for weaving a vertical butt.

a foundation upon which the rest of the weld may be built.
Note that both plate bevels and the back strip are actually cut
into, forming a pocket to hold the deposited metal. After the
puddle is formed, the electrode follows a sidewise and slightly
upward circular path; and as each side is reached, the electrode

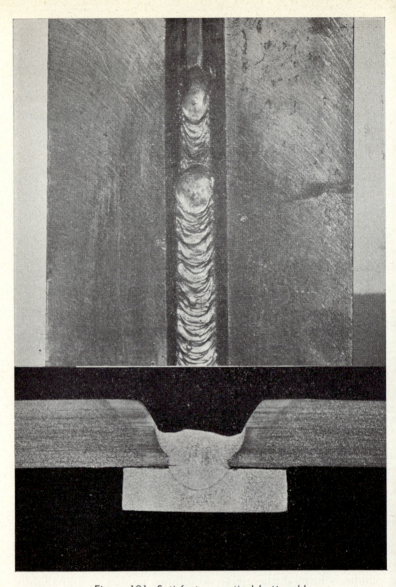

Figure 181: Satisfactory vertical butt weld.
This shows the first two passes of a vertical butt weld made with a weaving technique. Note in the cross section the good penetration of first pass into backing strip and plates, and of second pass into first pass and plates.

hesitates. This allows the arc a chance to cut into the bevelled edges of the plates and back strip. The action is that of continually cutting and filling a pocket in the bevel of the joint. If the electrode does not hesitate sufficiently long at the edges, the resultant bead will be undercut at the edges. This same thing will happen if an excessively long arc is held. The proper position for the electrode is shown in Figure 180. When the electrode is held in a **slightly** downward position, proper root penetration is assured with the first bead and proper penetration throughout the entire weld is assured with subsequent beads. Another feature of tipping the electrode to a downward position is that the arc is easier to control.

The second pass should completely cover the first, as shown in Figure 181. It should also be thoroughly fused into this first pass as well as into the edges of both plates. This can be accomplished by making a pocket as described for the root bead. The second bead will, of course, require a wider weave than the first bead. If the second bead is not properly fused into the junction where the edges of the first bead meet the plate, it is possible that bits of slag remaining at this point will not be removed. The result will be slag inclusions at weld edges. The third bead is made in the same manner as the preceding ones. The same care in fusing the metal is necessary. This third bead should come up to approximately $\frac{1}{16}''$ of being flush with the plate surface. Leaving this space of $\frac{1}{16}''$ provides a guide for the face bead. The fourth bead should overlap the butt edges by a distance equal to the diameter of the electrode being used. The fourth bead will also furnish the desired amount of reinforcement. In heavier butts the number of passes required may be greater. All beads should be made in such a way that they present a flat appearance across the face.

Vertical Fillets. The technique of weaving a vertical fillet differs from that used for a flat fillet. In the vertical fillet the metal is deposited as the electrode goes from right to left and also as it goes back again. After the puddle has been formed in the same way as in the vertical butt, the electrode travels from side to side, hesitating at each side to be sure of proper fusion on both plates. Do not move the electrode quickly from

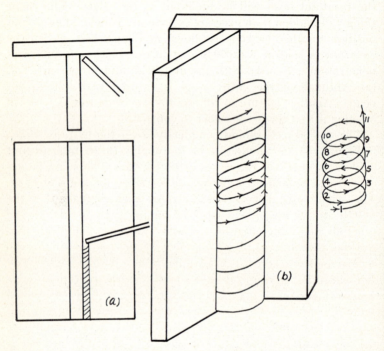

Figure 182: (a) Electrode position when weaving a vertical fillet. (b) Path of electrode travel when weaving a vertical fillet.

the sides. After leaving the sides of the weld, the electrode should travel fast across the face of the weld. This will prevent the face from being rounded out too much. The electrode should be tipped down at an angle of from 5°–10° as shown in Figure 182a. The arc should be held very close, and the

weaving lines should be close together. There should be no
fast or sudden upward motion. It will be noticed in Figure
182b that each time the electrode moves from one side to the
other, it overlaps its previous trip. This must be so to insure
a solid clean metal deposit.

Undercutting on a vertical joint of this type can occur on
both sides if the electrode leaves the weld edges too quickly.
For this reason both sides of the weld have to be carefully
watched. The upward distance of each path across is about
equal to the diameter of the electrode being used. The electrode is then brought back below this line as shown. If the
arc is held close enough and the manipulation is slow enough,
the arc can be seen actually to dig into the metal being welded.
This digging or cutting action can be used as a guide and an
indicator of the results of the finished bead. If the arc makes
a clean cut into the previous bead, it is fairly certain to remove
any slag inclusions or holes that may be present. Figure 183
shows a properly made fillet weld of this type.

Vertical Laps. In welding a vertical lap joint, the procedure
is the same as that outlined for vertical fillet welding with the
exception of the last pass. On this final pass care must be taken
not to cut the edge of the outside plate. The method of eliminating this possibility is the same as for the flat lap joint. That
is, choke the arc and hold it for an instant just as the edge is
reached. As the electrode is held at this point, it should be
actually pushed into the metal in such a way that the arc is
very short.

The main points of vertical weaving are:

1) Hold a close arc.
2) Travel slowly when coming away from the weld edges
and increase the rate of travel across the weld face.
3) Keep the electrode tipped downward.

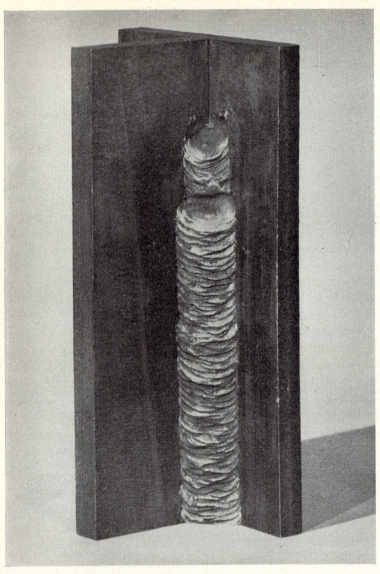

Figure 183: Satisfactory vertical fillet weld.
Note how first pass cuts into plates and root of joint. Second pass cuts into first pass and both plates.

4) Each bead must cover the previous one completely and penetrate into the base metal on each side of the previous bead.

5) Keep the electrode constantly in the puddle.

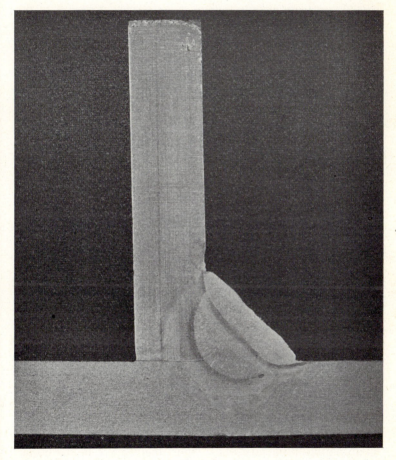

Figure 183A: Cross section of Figure 183. Contour of bead is smooth and penetration is even.

6) Do not weave a bead wider than four times the diameter of the electrode being used.

Overhead Weaving. While flat and vertical weave welding is comparatively easy to master, the overhead weave may present some difficulty because of the large amount of metal being handled against the attraction of gravity. The beginner, rather than attempting to weave a wide, heavy bead at first, should make narrow beads. There will be a tendency for the metal to flow to the center of the bead as shown in Figure 184, leav-

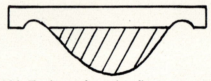

Figure 184: Tendency of metal to flow to center of bead.

ing an undercut on both sides of the bead. The reason for this is the natural tendency of the molten metal to flow downwards. This tendency is, of course, more pronounced in the overhead position than in any other. To overcome this effect, most of the metal should be deposited at the sides of the bead and very little on the face of the bead. To accomplish this, hold the electrode at both sides sufficiently long for a good full metal deposit to be made, then quickly move the arc across the face of the weld to the other side, where it is again held for the same length of time. The arc must be maintained across the face, but as some of the metal will flow from the sides, very little metal from the electrode should be deposited on the face. (See Figure 185.)

In using this particular technique on an overhead weave, it is absolutely necessary that a short digging arc be maintained across the face of the bead. The reason is that in order for the excess metal to flow properly from the sides, the line of travel

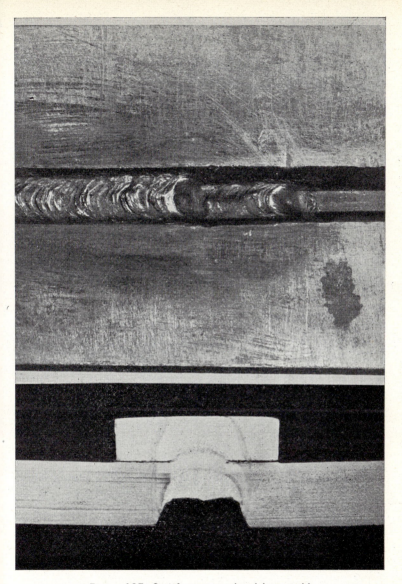

Figure 185: Satisfactory overhead butt weld.
This shows the first two passes of an overhead butt weld made with a weaving technique. Note how second pass penetrates into and completely covers first pass. The cross section shows smooth contour of bead face and bevelled edge of plates.

of the electrode across the face must be kept hot. If the arc is extinguished, the result will be a lumpy weave, because the metal will have started to solidify before it has completed its flowing action across the face. The idea is to have the excess metal which was deposited at the sides follow the arc as the arc travels across the width of the bead.

The success of this method hinges on four points:

1) Deposit an excess of metal at each side.

2) Keep the puddle in a hot and molten state so the excess metal may flow across the face.

3) Deposit little or no metal from the electrode on the weld face.

4) Maintain a short arc at all times.

Overhead Fillet. The overhead weaving of a tee joint will vary in the action of the electrode against the vertical plate, from any of the previous joints explained. The end of the electrode should actually scrape the vertical plate as shown by the arrows in Figure 186a.

The position of the electrode is shown in three steps in Figure 186b. It is tipped at an angle of from 20°–30° when scraping the vertical plate, perpendicular to the horizontal plate when the arc is playing on this member, and tipped into the root of the joint at about 30°–40° as it travels downward. The scraping action on the vertical plate should be done slowly so as to allow the proper penetration at this point. The arc should then quickly traverse the face of the weld at an angle inclined toward the joint root, as shown at C. There is no metal deposited when the arc goes from the vertical to the horizontal member. When the arc reaches the outer edge of the bead on the horizontal plate it hesitates long enough to make a good, heavy deposit, and moves across the face of the weld to the vertical plate. Metal is deposited as the arc goes from the horizontal to the vertical member.

Overhead Lap. The welding of this type of joint requires the same techniques as that for the overhead fillet. Care must be taken not to cut away the bottom edge of the upper plate.

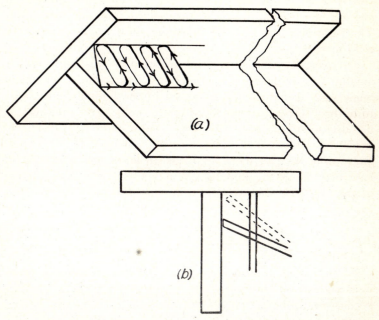

Figure 186: (a) Path of electrode travel for overhead fillet weaving. (b) Position of electrode for overhead fillet weaving.

To avoid cutting this edge, the arc must be choked hard and metal deposited, as in the case of the vertical lap.

GALVANIZED METAL

Galvanizing is a process where a thin coating or layer of zinc covers the surface of a piece of metal. Sometimes a slight difficulty arises in welding this galvanized metal, especially for the beginner; the reason being that the zinc melts at a much lower temperature than that required for welding. The result is that, as the zinc is being burned off, it will cause a great deal of smoke which may interfere with the welder's ability to see clearly what he is doing. The heat of the arc causes rapid melting of the zinc, which in turn causes the zinc to spatter. This spattering action may interfere with proper deposit of weld metal.

To overcome the difficulties mentioned, a slightly larger amount of current, approximately 10 amps. more, will help. Some welders flip the electrode out of the puddle continually, to burn off the galvanize ahead of the weld. This, however, is not necessary and generally causes more harm than good, because the chances of slag inclusions and gas pockets are greater. Only on a piece of metal that has an extra heavy coating of galvanize should this flipping action be used. The manipulation of the electrode for each position should be the same as that explained previously.

DOWN-VERTICAL WELDING

When a vertical weld starts at the top and progresses down, it is known as down-vertical. This type of vertical welding, because of construction specifications, has limitations placed upon it. In general, it is not allowed on naval ship construction. This type of welding should be confined to lap joints, seams, and corner welds where the thickness of the material does not exceed $\frac{1}{4}''$. It should not be used in bevelled butts of any size.

The bead produced with this type of welding will be a light one, although the width may be of any desired size. It will be exceptionally smooth.

In addition to general welding of the kind already described, down-vertical welding has two more uses.

1) Seal Beads: Where speed, tightness and a smooth appearance are necessary with a light deposit of metal.

2) Dress Beads: Where a butt or fillet weld has been made and the appearance is rough, it is possible to smooth it out by putting a final layer of metal on by running down-vertical beads.

This method of welding will not produce undercut. For best results the type E-6012 electrode should be used. When welding laps or fillets, the electrode should be pushed into the root of the joint. A very slight hesitation is necessary at the sides. This hesitation is not as much as for welding from the bottom upwards. The greatest difficulty will be to keep the slag from rolling into the puddle. If the electrode is held tipped up and into the puddle at an angle of about 30°, the force of the arc will usually remedy the difficulty. The electrode must move very fast in both directions. That is, it must be weaved sidewise and also travel downward quickly. The heat must be increased to even more than that used for flat welding.

SPEED FILLET TECHNIQUE

The speeding up of production in the war emergency has created a need for a more rapid process of welding, and considerable experimenting has been done to find a faster method for war production plants. The Lincoln Electric Company of Cleveland, Ohio, has been a pioneer in this field, and the speed fillet technique described here is the result of this company's research.*

Introduction. One main objective in the development of arc welding application is to find ways to meet the different conditions with fewer types of electrodes and with fewer welding techniques.

The ideal would be to find the one best way with one elec-

* The methods discussed in this section are based on advanced experimental findings and are not to be considered as final recommendations for arc welding procedure.

trode to join two pieces of steel—to obtain the required strength at the lowest possible cost.

For example: At the present time, there are five types of electrodes which are designed for fillet welding of mild steel plate. The ideal would be to have one electrode and one welding procedure to meet all conditions and all problems of fillet welding. At the present time, this is a remote possibility; however, much research and development effort is being pointed that way.

In an effort to find the ideal technique or method for fillet welding with maximum speed under all conditions, a procedure has been developed which materially increases the speed and lowers the cost of welding this type of joint.

First, let us consider the history of fillet welding.

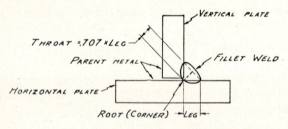

Figure 187: General welding terms.

Background. In the late 1920's, the arc speed of welding of a ⅜" horizontal fillet with bare or washed electrode was about 12' per hour. In the 1930's, the arc speed of production of a ⅜" horizontal fillet weld was increased about 68% to 20' per hour, through the development of the shielded-arc process. By 1940 this had been further increased, through improved electrodes and techniques, about 50% to an arc speed of 30' per hour.

Now, with arc welding playing such a vital part in war production, it is necessary that former welding speeds be considered inadequate and steps be taken to increase them still further.

The logical way to bring about a radical improvement in anything—whether it is a welding process or the design of a product—is to get back to fundamentals, to erase the thought of everything that has gone before and get a fresh start.

Figure 188: The ideal fillet weld with complete penetration.

Following this reasoning, a new speed-fillet technique has been developed which has increased the arc speed for the equivalent of the above-mentioned ⅜″ weld to 65′ per hour.

Objective. The ideal fillet weld would be one which is completely fused at the joint as shown in Figure 188. This type of joint with complete fusion can be made, but it is uneconomical for the majority of applications.

This type of fillet weld with deep penetration is desirable because it would require the deposit of far less weld metal than conventional welding practice for a given effective size or strength. In this type of weld, a greater amount of the parent metal would comprise the fillet.

A Practical Improvement. Even though it is not economical to produce complete fusion as shown in Figure 188 in the majority of applications, it is entirely practical to strike an average

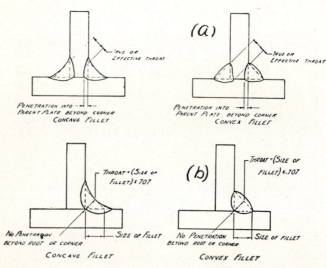

Figure 189: (a) A practical, improved type of fillet weld with deep penetration at the root or corner. (b) The conventional fillet weld has no penetration beyond root or corner.

between this ideal fillet and the conventional fillet. Two practical examples are shown in Figure 189a. Here, penetration is obtained beyond the corner of the joint (see Figure 187 for fillet terms), making it possible to maintain the same true or effective throat size of weld with less deposited metal. Compare this to Figure 189b, where the conventional procedure does not give penetration beyond the root or corner of the joint. A more direct comparison is shown in Figure 190. Note the net results:

A considerable amount of deposited metal is saved in producing a fillet of approximately the same effective size or strength.

How about the strength of this type of weld, which from all appearances is smaller than the conventional fillet?

The strength of a fillet weld is now considered proportional to the "outward" or apparent size of the weld. This is measured by gaging the length of the leg of the largest isosceles triangle contained in the weld. This is shown in Figure 189b. Note the relation of the "throat" to the apparent size and strength of the fillet.

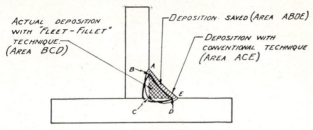

Figure 190.

However, the true or effective strength of the fillet weld is determined by the total size, including both the outward and inward weld metal. In other words, it is a measure of the true or effective throat, as indicated in Figure 189a. Hence, with other conditions equal, a small weld with deep penetration at the root and equal effective throat size will be as strong as or stronger than a large weld, piled on the outside of the plate, and not penetrated into the corner. Results of comparative tests given later in this discussion bear out these statements.

Two pairs of fillets, one made by the conventional technique, and the other by the speed-fillet technique, are incorporated in the specimen shown in Figure 191. The fillet made by the speed-fillet technique has 70% as much deposited metal as the other, yet it has 15% greater strength.

Explanation of Technique. Penetration at the root of a fillet weld can be obtained by using:

1) A short arc
2) High speed of travel
3) Sufficient welding current

Speed of travel is the one unique factor affecting these results.

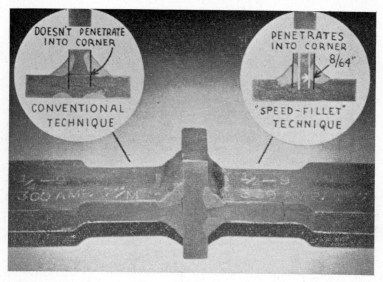

Figure 191.

For single-pass, horizontal and flat fillet welds in mild steel (see Figure 187 for fillet terms), highest speeds and lowest costs with this new technique are obtainable with A.W.S. 6030 —a Type "C" electrode.

The new speed-fillet technique employs this electrode for single-pass fillet welds in either horizontal or flat positions with d.c. and with electrode negative polarity. Also, a.c. may be used with the speed-fillet procedures. In general, 10% to 15% more current is required to obtain a given effective throat with a.c. than with d.c. Horizontal plate should be practically flat.

In conventional welding procedures for this type of joint, the

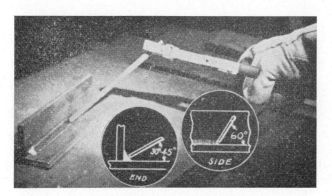

Figure 192: Angle of electrode for conventional fillet welding.

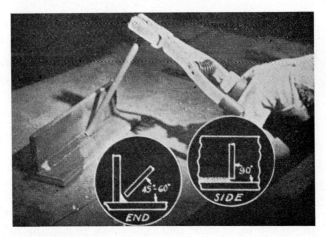

Figure 193: Angle of electrode for speed fillet welding.

electrode is held at approximately 45° with the horizontal plate and at approximately 60° to the line of weld with the end pointing backward. (See Figure 192.) The arc is held short,

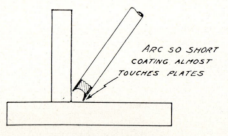

Figure 194.

but the travel speed is generally so slow that the electrode must be held out from the two plates in order to keep the end of the electrode from dipping into the molten pool.

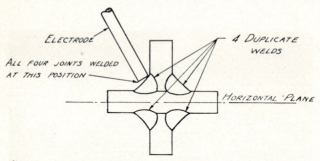

Figure 195: Set-up for making horizontal fillet samples.

In the new speed-fillet technique, the average position of the electrode should be about perpendicular to the line of the weld at from 45° to 60° with the horizontal plate. (See Figure 193.) The arc should be so short that the coating practically touches the plate. Lightly resting the coating against both plates is not objectionable. If the coating is forced against the plates, a rough bead is likely to be obtained. (See Figure 194.)

It has been found that, in producing this type of weld, the increase in speed of travel increases the penetration. The speed of travel should be such that the slag and molten pool stay just behind the electrode when it is almost touching the two plates. If the speed of travel is too high, the slag will form in islands rather than as a continuous sheath over the bead. If the speed of travel is too slow, the molten pool and slag will touch the electrode.

An increase in amperage makes possible greater penetration into the root, resulting in greater strength.

Figure 196: Four fillet welds made with conventional method at 300 amps. and arc speed of 7″ per minute.

Comparison Tests. Three ½″ plates were joined with fillet welds using various procedures with a setup as shown in Figure 195 (for horizontal position welds). The cross formed by these three plates was then sawed at right angles into small crosses about 1½″ long to produce test specimens representing the various procedures. All specimens were welded with the same type of electrode; however, the conventional fillets were made with the conventional 60° slant of electrode as shown in Figure 192.

The specimen shown in Figure 196 was produced according to conventional practice, welded at a speed of 7″ per minute.

Figure 197: Four fillet welds made with speed fillet technique with 300 amps. at arc speed of 10″ per minute.

Figure 198: Four fillet welds made with speed fillet technique with 360 amps. at arc speed of 12″ per minute.

The size of the fillet weld is ⅜″. This size fillet weld was used because it is supposed to be not as strong as ½″ plate, and it was desired to produce failure in the weld in order to compare weld strengths.

The specimens shown in Figures 197 and 198 were made by the speed-fillet technique. The specimen in Figure 197 was welded with the same current (300 amps.) as the conventional fillet, but at a higher rate of travel (10″ per min.). The specimen shown in Figure 197 was welded at both a higher current (360 amps.) and at a higher rate of travel (12″ per min.).

Similar tests have been made with single-pass, flat (positioned) fillet welds. Size of the plate and welds were the same as for the horizontal fillet-weld specimens. This setup was ar-

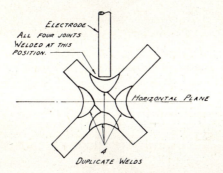

Figure 199: Set-up for preparing specimens by flat-position welding, speed fillet technique.

ranged as shown in Figure 199. Here again, it is interesting to note how much smaller the welds are that are produced by the speed-fillet technique; yet, in spite of the reduction in over-all size, the effective throat dimension remains about the same. A general view of four specimens welded by conventional and speed-fillet techniques and close-ups of the four joints are shown in Figure 200 (conventional, 300 amps.); Figure 201 (speed-fillet, 300 amps.); Figure 202 (conventional, 400 amps.); and Figure 203 (speed-fillet, 400 amps.).

In the case of fillets produced in flat position, it is interesting

Figure 200: Four fillet welds made with conventional technique with 300 amps. at arc speed of 6″ per minute.

Figure 201: Four fillet welds made with speed fillet technique with 300 amps. and arc speed of 10″ per minute.

to note that by the speed-fillet technique, without changing the amperage, but by increasing the welding speed from 6″ to 10″ per minute, the same effective throat of the weld and the same tensile strength were obtained. Measured by the conventional method, the apparent size of the fillet decreased from $2\frac{4}{64}$″ (Figure 200) to $1\frac{8}{64}$″ (Figure 201). The one made at 6″ per minute lacked fusing to the corner on the horizontal plate by $\frac{4}{64}$″. The one at 10″ per minute penetrated into the root or corner by $\frac{2}{64}$″. Cost was reduced from 15.8c. to 9.5c. per foot.

By increasing the amperage and keeping the same 6″ per

Figure 202: Four fillet welds made with conventional technique using 400 amps. and arc speed of 6″ per minute.

minute speed of travel (Figure 202), the effective throat dimension was increased and the bead fused into both plates up to the corner but did not penetrate beyond.

Here, we simply piled on more metal and increased the cost from 15.8c. to 16.6c. per foot.

Note, however, that in the case of Figure 203, where both welding current and welding speed were increased, a penetration of $\frac{8}{64}$″ was obtained beyond the root of the joint, without diminishing the effective throat size or strength of the joint. Speed was increased 100% and costs were cut from 15.8c. to

8.3c. per foot. Comparing these tests of horizontal and flat single-pass fillet welds, it is interesting to note the following:

1) For a given amperage, the effective throat is slightly larger for a horizontal fillet than for a flat fillet.

2) For a given current and travel speed, the penetration into the corner is greater on a horizontal fillet than on a flat fillet.

Figure 203: Four fillet welds made with speed fillet technique using 400 amps. and arc speed of 12″ per minute.

3) For a given amperage, the strength of a horizontal fillet is practically the same as that of a flat fillet. The smaller effective throat of the flat fillet is compensated for by the smoother contour of the bead which tends to reduce stress concentration.

4) It is possible to obtain welds of greater strength with a flat fillet than with a horizontal fillet because higher currents can be used in welding flat fillets.

Current. Since the strength of a fillet weld is directly dependent on the current that is used in welding the joint, it is important to have an accurate method of determining the current. Two methods have been used in the past, namely, meters, and calibrated dials on the machine. Meters, regardless of how accurate they are when new, eventually become inaccurate or broken, due to continual oscillations of the pointer under welding service and vibration. Dial calibrations, although quite accurate with the standard length of leads supplied with the welding machine, may not be accurate with long leads which have poor connections.

One method of determining accurately the current at the arc is by measuring the number of inches of electrode burned off or consumed in one minute of welding. For a given size and type of electrode, the electrode burn-off in inches per minute always is the same for any given current.

In general, for best possible results with the speed-fillet technique, the following electrodes and conditions are recommended:

A.W.S. 6030

1) For single-pass fillets in flat, tilted or horizontal position with good or average fit-up.

A.W.S. 6012

1) For applications of A.W.S. 6030 when this electrode is not available.

2) For intermittent welds less than 4″ long.

3) For single-pass fillets where fit-up is poor.

4) For multiple-pass fillets.

For horizontal fillets, the basic technique as outlined for A.W.S. 6030 electrodes is to be used for A.W.S. 6012 electrodes, except that the electrode is held perpendicular to the line of travel and at an angle of 45° or less with the bottom plate. (See Figure 204.) When a large gap is encountered, it is often desirable to increase the angle the electrode makes with the bottom plate to more than 45°, in order to prevent excessive digging and undercutting of the vertical plate.

In welding fillets in flat position (see Figure 187), all types of electrodes are held the same. The electrode is held to make the same angle with each plate and at approximately right angles to the seam. In other words, the electrode is held in a vertical position.

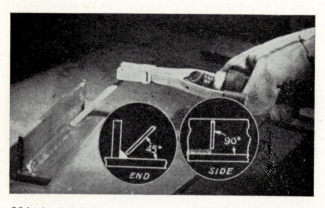

Figure 204: Angle of electrode for speed fillet welding with A.W.S. 6012 electrodes.

When A.W.S. 6012 is used, approximately 10% more current is required to produce the same effective throat as that obtained with A.W.S. 6030.

The arc speed or welding speed in each case is the maximum that will be obtained normally. Any speeds slightly below or above the ones given will produce the desired effective throat, provided the weld is free of undercut and is equally fused to both legs of the joint.

Tilting. There are many instances where the horizontal and flat fillet mentioned above are not the most economical positions in which to make a fillet weld. An additional factor of tilting the axis of the weld should be considered.

When making a fillet weld, it may be desirous to make the strength of joint equal to, or greater than the strength of the parent plate in many instances. Then again, the weld may be only a sealing bead or one where it is not necessary to make the joint as strong as the parent plate.

The minimum satisfactory amount of electrode and time should be used in making a joint. By proper positioning of the joint, any desired section or strength of joint can be obtained with optimum welding speed.

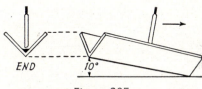

END   10°

Figure 205.

It is true that any desired strength of joint may be obtained without positioning of the work, but in many instances tremendous speed increases can be obtained by positioning.

For example, it is desired to make a "T" joint equal to the plate strength with two ¼″ plates. If the joint is welded, either as a horizontal fillet or flat-positioned fillet, the welding speed will be 13″ per min. with an electrode consumption of .17 lb. of electrode per foot of weld, with a welding current of 250 amps. If higher current is used with the joint in the above-mentioned positions, the speed of welding cannot be increased without sacrificing appearance or quality.

If the weld is positioned and the axis of the seam is tilted so that the welding is done downhill at an angle of 10° (Figure 205), the arc speed will increase from 13″ per min. to 20″ per min., with an electrode consumption of .16 lb. of electrode per ft. of weld, with welding current of 350 amps. This represents an increase of 54% in welding speed and an electrode consumption equal to 94% of that required before the joint was tilted.

If the joint had been tilted 20°, the welding speed would

have been 26″ per min., with an electrode consumption of .12 lb. per ft. of weld. The strength of the joint would still be 85% of the strength of the plate.

Increasing the angle of tilt of the seam by over 20° downhill, does not increase the speed of welding but generally produces a poorer looking bead.

It must be remembered that, as in discussion of horizontal and flat fillet welds, arc speed does not affect the strength of the weld, provided the weld is smooth, free of undercut, and is equally fused to both legs.

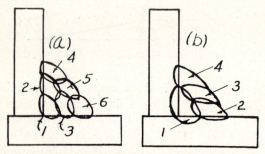

Figure 206: (a) Sequence of passes with conventional technique. (b) Sequence of passes with speed fillet technique.

When welding heavy sections, it is sometimes impossible to obtain sufficient strength of weld metal in one pass when the joint is positioned with the axis of the seam flat (no tilt of the seam up or downhill). However, if the axis of the seam is tilted so that the welding is done uphill by an angle of 4°, 15% to 20% increase in strength for a given current is obtained.

For example: A ¾″ "T" joint, welded with ¼″ electrode at 400 amps. with the axis of the seam flat, will carry an ultimate load of 37,000 lbs. per in. of joint. If the axis of the seam is tilted uphill by 4°, the ultimate load the joint will carry when welded at 400 amps. with ¼″ electrode is 44,000 lbs. per in. of joint.

Multiple-Pass, Horizontal Fillets: A.W.S. 6012 electrodes are preferable for multiple-pass welds with the speed-fillet technique, because their metal does not spread out so easily and can be built up into a more uniform weld structure.

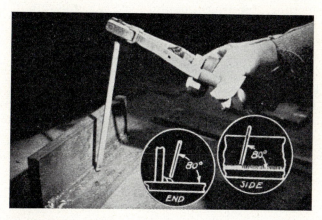

Figure 207: Angle of electrode for beads not against vertical plate.

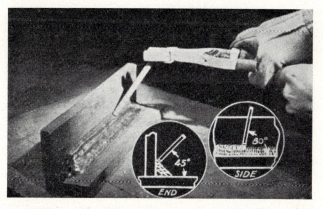

Figure 208: Angle of electrode for beads against vertical plate.

The conventional method of building up a multiple-pass horizontal fillet is shown in Figure 206a. Here the beads are laid from the top downward.

By the speed-fillet method, the first bead is laid in the corner at a fairly high current and speed, with little attention paid to undercutting. Subsequent beads should be put in with the electrode held at an angle of 70° to 80° with the horizontal plate and the line of weld, except the beads against the vertical plate, in which case the electrode should be at about a 45° angle. (See Figures 207 and 208.) In the new technique, the beads are laid from the bottom upward, as shown in Figure 206b. The idea here is to provide a flat horizontal surface upon which to place succeeding beads, permitting higher currents, resulting in faster welding.

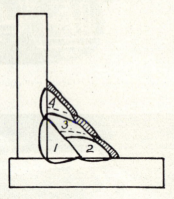

Figure 209: Dotted line above bead 2 shows where slag was before bead 3 was put on; dotted line above bead 3 is where slag was before bead 4 was put on. Cross-hatched area shows slag after completion of weld.

Another point of note is that the slag is to be left on the bead in order to provide a dam to keep the metal from running off the edge of the previous bead. This is illustrated in Figure 209. The slag is not removed until after each layer of beads is completed. In other words, for the weld shown in Figure 209, the slag is removed after completion of bead (1) and bead (4). This procedure not only saves man-hours in cleaning the weld, but it facilitates and speeds up the welding operation and makes possible a smoother weld. Any number of layers of beads may be built up in this manner.

Figure 210: A 16-pass fillet weld made with A.W.S. 6012 electrode. Plate is 1¼" thick.

A weld containing 16 passes with 1¼" plate is shown in Figure 210.

When a weld of two passes is required, the first bead can be put in as shown in Figure 211. Here, the first bead is deposited mostly on the bottom plate, then the second bead is applied without removing slag from the first bead. The electrode is held at about 45° and fused into vertical plate and the first bead.

The slag may be removed after each bead, if desired.

Summary. Advanced experiments with speed-fillet technique show increases in welding speeds of 20% to 100% for single-pass fillets in flat and horizontal positions. This weld penetrates into corner of joint. It requires deposition of only ½ to ⅔ as much metal as conventional fillet, yet is just as strong.

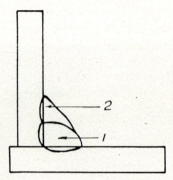

Figure 211: Location of beads for two-pass fillet.

The Speed-Fillet Technique

Example A: Single-pass horizontal fillet. It is desired to "T"-weld together two ⅜" plates so that the joint is as strong as the plate.

1) Use ¼" A.W.S. 6030 electrode.
2) Use 275 to 300 amps.
3) Hold electrode perpendicular to line of travel and at about 60° with horizontal plate. (See Figure 193.)
4) Maintain shorter arc than with conventional technique —so short that coating of electrode almost touches the plates.
5) Advance the electrode at a speed of about 12" per min. (compared with about 6" per min. for conventional fillet welding). Speed of travel should be such that slag and molten pool stay just behind the electrode.

Example B: Single-pass horizontal fillet. It is desired to re-place a conventional ⅜″ fillet weld with a fillet weld made with speed-fillet process having exactly the same strength.

1) Use A.W.S. 6030.

2) Use about 325 amps. (compared with about 300 amps. with conventional fillet welding).

3) Hold electrode perpendicular to line of travel and at about 60° with horizontal plate. (See Figure 193.)

4) Maintain shorter arc than with conventional technique—so short that coating of electrode almost touches the plates.

5) Advance the electrode at a speed of about 12″ per min. (compared with about 6″ per min. for conventional fillet welding). Speed of travel should be such that slag and molten pool stay just behind the electrode.

Example C: Multiple-pass horizontal fillet in 1″ plate (¾″ effective throat) with 9 passes. Good fit-up of plates.

1) Use A.W.S. 6012, 5/16″ size.

2) Use about 450 amps.

3) For beads next to vertical plate—Passes (1), (4), and (9)—hold electrode perpendicular to line of travel and at about 45° to horizontal plate. For other beads—(2), (3), etc.—hold electrode almost straight downward.

4) Maintain arc as short as possible without touching coating to molten metal or plate.

5) Build beads from bottom upward. In other words, put Pass (1) in corner, then Pass (2) on horizontal plate, Pass (3) on Pass (2), then Pass (4) on Pass (3) and against vertical plate.

6) Advance electrode at a speed of about 8″ per min. per bead.

7) Remove slag after each layer of beads only; i.e., after Passes (1), (4) and (9).

Part 7

Effects of Heat

EXPANSION AND CONTRACTION

When a piece of metal is heated, it will expand. This expansion will take place in all directions—length, width, and thickness. The amount of expansion will depend on three things: the particular type of metal being considered; the amount of temperature rise; and the size of the piece of metal.

Each metal has its own coefficient of expansion. That is, each metal will expand a different amount when heated. The coefficient of expansion may be defined as the expansion per unit measurement per degree Fahrenheit. The coefficient of expansion for steel is .00000636. In other words, for each degree Fahrenheit rise in temperature, the length will increase .00000636 of its initial length. The same increase applies to width and to thickness. For each degree rise a 1″ piece of steel will increase .00000636 of an inch. If, then, a piece of steel is 1″ long and heated 1000° F., the increase will be 1 × .00000636 × 1000 or .00636 of an inch. The final length, while under this heat of 1000°, will be 1.00636″. If a bar of steel was originally 100″ long, the total expansion would be 100 times as great. Therefore, the length of a 100″ piece of steel which is heated 1000° F. would expand a total of 100 × 1000 × .00000636 = .636″, making its length while under this temperature 100.636″. In other words, the amount of expansion is proportional to two things—temperature increase and size of material.

To find the actual expansion the following equation may be used:

$$\Delta L = KLT \qquad \text{(Formula 1)}$$

Where ΔL is the increase in length due to expansion, K is the coefficient of expansion, L is the original length, and T is the increase in temperature.

From the above example, it can be seen that provisions of some sort must be made for expansion when metal is subjected to heat. If proper allowances are not made and there is no way for this metal to expand, the metal itself will take care of this condition in the following ways:

1) If the material is ductile enough, it will buckle.

2) If the material is hard and brittle, it will break.

3) If the material neither buckles nor breaks, high internal stresses may result.

It can be easily seen that all three of these results are undesirable, and must be taken into consideration on a welded job.

Suppose the 100″ bar just mentioned was anchored rigidly in such a way that it could not expand lengthwise, and then heated so that its temperature was increased 1000° F. The force of expansion would be such that something would have to give way. The force would relieve itself by forcing the bar to bulge out in the center, thus deforming the bar.

As a piece of heated metal cools, it contracts and approaches its original dimensions. Suppose the 100″ bar previously referred to was free to expand and was heated up 1000° F., and while under this temperature the ends were securely anchored so that no contraction could take place. When the heat is removed and cooling takes place, the condition is that of a bar 100.636″ long attempting to shrink back to its original size of 100″. The result would be a broken bar, because the force exerted due to contraction would be greater than the steel could stand. While all cases will not go to such extremes as actually to break or deform the steel, serious internal stresses may be locked up in a welded joint. These locked-up stresses may be of such magnitude that they approach the extreme cases, and with very little additional load will cause failure of the job. In other words, the job might fail under a great deal less stress than that for which it was designed.

ELASTICITY

If an elastic or rubber band is stretched, it will return to its original shape as soon as the stretching force is removed. In other words, it has the property of returning to its initial shape and size after being deformed. Like the rubber band, other materials, too, can withstand a certain deforming load, and when this load is removed the material will return to its original shape and size. The greater the load a material can take and still return to its original shape and size, the greater is the elasticity of the material. There will be a limit to this load, after which the metal under load will not return to its original size and shape but will be permanently deformed. The elastic limit of any material, then, will be the maximum load per unit of cross-sectional area that the metal can take without being permanently deformed. For example, the elastic limit of cast iron is anywhere from 5,000 to 20,000 lbs.; that of steel from 25,000 to 55,000 lbs., the exact figures depending on the grade of the metal. This means, then, that a piece of steel, the elastic limit of which is figured at 55,000 lbs., can withstand a pull of 55,000 lbs. per sq. in. of cross-sectional area, and when this pulling force is removed, the piece of steel will return to its original shape and size. The piece of cast iron with an elastic limit of only 5,000 lbs. cannot withstand over 5,000 lbs. per sq. in. if it is to resume its original shape after the load is removed.

STRESS

Stress may be defined as the load exerted per unit of cross-sectional area. A bar, the cross-sectional area of which is 2 sq.

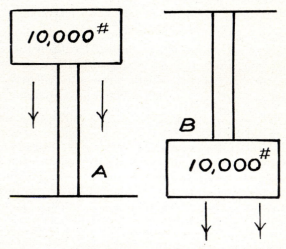

Figure 212: A—Bar in compression.   B—Bar in tension.

ins., supports a load of 10,000 lbs. as shown at A in Figure 212. The stress may be calculated by:

$$S = \frac{F}{A} \qquad \text{(Formula 2)}$$

where S is the stress, F is the total force or load, and A is the area of the cross section. From the above formula, the stress,

S, will be 5,000 lbs. per sq. in. The stress in this particular case is known as a compression stress, because the force tends to compress the bar. At B in Figure 212, the load is attached to the bar in such a way as to tend to stretch the bar. The numerical value of the stress will be exactly the same in both cases. When the force tends to stretch, the stress is known as a tensile stress.

It has been shown that when a piece of metal is heated, it attempts to expand, the amount of expansion depending on the amount of temperature change and the length of the piece. If this expansion is not allowed, there will be stresses involved. Suppose the bar of 100″ length, previously referred to, was restrained in some way so that it could not expand or move in any direction. Now, if the temperature of this bar is increased 100° F., its length would attempt to increase .0636″, but because it is restrained it cannot expand. The result is that it is pushing against the restraint in an attempt to expand. The actual amount of push or force can be figured. When this force is figured per square inch of cross-section area, the answer will be the stress involved. To find the stress directly, the following formula may be used:

$$\text{Stress} = L_1 \times E \qquad \text{(Formula 3)}$$

where L_1 is the amount each inch will increase, or .000636″, and E is what is known as the modulus of elasticity and has a definite value for each material. For steel, the value of E may be taken as 30×10^6 or 30,000,000. Substituting values in Formula 3, the result is:

$$S = .000636 \times 30,000,000 = 19,080$$

The stress, then, is 19,080 lbs. per sq. in. In other words, there is a force of approximately 9½ tons acting on each square inch of cross-sectional area, attempting to make the bar expand. This is a compression stress. If the stress involved in a case of this type comes within the elastic range of the steel, there will be no permanent change in the steel after it cools. If, however, the stress exceeds this range, there will be a permanent change.

When the heat is removed, the bar will contract. Suppose the reverse happens; that is, the bar, while being heated, is free to expand. After expanding, the ends are anchored in such a way that it is impossible for the bar to contract on cooling. The internal stresses will be acting in such a way as to pull the bar together. Or it may be considered that the anchoring device is pulling the bar. In either case, the action is that of stretching the bar, so the stress is a tensile stress. If the stress, either tensile or compression, is great enough to exceed the elastic limit, there will be a permanent change in the shape and size of the bar.

STRAIN

Strain is the effect produced by stress. There are no dimensions to strain and it is expressed only as a ratio.

The formula for finding the value of strain is:

$$\text{Strain} = \frac{\text{Stress}}{E} \qquad \text{(Formula 4)}$$

Or if ΔL, the increase in length, is known, the following may be used:

$$\text{Strain} = \frac{\Delta L}{L} \qquad \text{(Formula 5)}$$

where L is the original length. If a 100″ piece expands to 100.25″, the .25 is the value of ΔL.

To find the strain in this particular case, substitute in Formula 5:

$$\text{Strain} = \frac{.25}{100} = .0025$$

Each unit of length, then, will expand by an amount equal to .0025 times its original length. That is, a 1″ length will increase to 1.0025″; while a 1′ length will increase to 1.0025′.

By the use of Formula 4, the stress may be found. According to Formula 4:

$$\text{Strain} = \frac{\text{Stress}}{E}$$

therefore:

$$\text{Stress} = \text{Strain} \times E \qquad\qquad \text{(Formula 6)}$$

$$\text{Stress} = .0025 \times 30 \times 10^6 = 75{,}000 \text{ lbs. per sq. in.}$$

PROBLEMS IN WELDING STRESSES

In the following problems use:

Coefficient of expansion $K = .00000636$
Modulus of elasticity $E = 30 \times 10^6$ or $30{,}000{,}000$

1) A steel bar expands from 10″ to 10.00636″. What is the temperature increase?

$$\text{Formula 1: } \Delta L = KLT$$

all factors except T are known.
To solve for T:

$$T = \frac{\Delta L}{KL} = \frac{.00636}{.00000636 \times 10} = \frac{.00636}{.0000636} = 100° \text{ F.}$$

2) If the above bar was originally 100″ long, what would be its increase in length after being heated?

$$\Delta L = KLT = .00000636 \times 100 \times 100 = .0636″$$

3) A steel bar 2″ wide and ½″ thick is subjected to a tensile load of 30,000 lbs. What is the stress? What is the strain?

$$\text{Stress} = \frac{F}{A} = \frac{30,000}{2 \times .5} = \frac{30,000}{1} = 30,000 \text{ lbs. per sq. in.}$$

$$\text{Strain} = \frac{\text{Stress}}{E} = \frac{30,000}{30,000,000} = .001$$

4) To apply the above directly to welding, consider Figure 213. Here are two steel plates rigidly anchored at A and B.

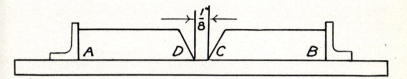

Figure 213.

If they are heated, the linear expansion can be in one direction only. Both pieces must expand toward one another. Each plate is 20″ long, 2″ wide, and ½″ thick. The space between the plates is ⅛″. Both plates are equally heated until the expansion causes them to meet. As soon as the ends C and D meet, they are immediately welded together. When the heat is removed and cooling starts to become effective, the plates tend to shrink back to their original size. The weld resists this shrinking effect and a stress is set up. To find this stress it is first necessary to find the strain—by Formula 5.

$$\text{Strain} = \frac{.125}{40} = .003125$$

According to Formula 6:

$$\text{Stress} = .003125 \times 30 \times 10^{6} = 93,750 \text{ lbs. per sq. in.}$$

To find the increase in temperature necessary to cause this expansion, divide the expansion per inch by K, the coefficient of expansion. This gives

$$T = \frac{L_1}{K} = \frac{.003125}{.00000636} = 491.3° \text{ F.} \qquad \text{(Formula 7)}$$

This is the equivalent of using Formula 1, which is $\Delta L = KLT$. By solving for T, the equation becomes $T = \frac{\Delta L}{KL}$, but $\frac{\Delta L}{L}$ is L_1.

L_1 is the actual expansion per unit length, ΔL is the total expansion of the piece in inches. L is the original length of the piece in inches. When the total expansion is divided by the original length, the result is L_1. In other words, the strain divided by the coefficient of expansion gives the temperature change. There are two things to take into consideration regarding the above problem. In order that the specified expansion take place, the temperature of both plates must be increased by 491.2° F. for their entire length at the same time and without distortion of any kind. In the second place, the stress, if great enough, can cause the joint to fracture. This fracture may or may not take place in the weld. If the base material is inferior to the weld metal, the break will be in the base metal. In any case, the weakest section will give. If the metal in the above problem was capable of standing the 93,750-lb. stress, what would be the total force acting, according to Formula 2?

$$S = \frac{F}{A}$$

therefore:

$$F = S \times A = 93,750 \times 2 \times \frac{1}{2} = 93,750 \text{ lbs.}$$

The cross section is 2″ by ½″ or 1 sq. in. Thus, the total force is also 93,750 lbs.

5) Figure 214a shows a single vee butt weld. To find the

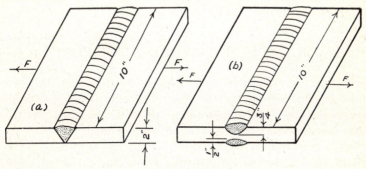

Figure 214.

stress acting on the weld, use Formula 2. In this case A is $2 \times 10 = 20$ sq. ins., $F = 150,000$ lbs., so the numerical values will be:

$$S = \frac{150,000}{20} = 7500 \text{ lbs. per sq. in.}$$

On every sq. in. of this weld cross section, there is a pull of 7500 lbs.

6) In Figure 214b the situation is slightly different. The weld does not penetrate the complete thickness of the plate. Therefore, there is not as much weld to take the load. In this case the stress will be greater than in Figure 213, even though the total load is the same. The substitution for Formula 2 for this case is as follows:

$$S = \frac{150,000}{12.5} = 12,000 \text{ lbs. per sq. in.}$$

The denominator of 12.5 is the total welded cross-sectional

area. One section is ¾″ deep and one section is ½″ deep. This is the equivalent of 1¼″ depth. When multiplied by 10, the total welded cross-sectional area is 12.5 sq. ins. This means, then, that each sq. in. of cross-sectional area has to withstand a pull of 12,000 lbs.

ALLOWABLE WELD STRESSES

In figuring weld stresses the size of the throat of the weld must be considered. In the case of a butt weld, the throat usually has the same dimension as the plate thickness. If two plates of unequal thicknesses are butt-welded together, the throat measurement is usually equal to the thickness of the smaller plate. In the case of fillet welds, the throat measure-

TABLE 23. SAFE ALLOWABLE STATIC LOADS ON SECTION
THROUGH WELD THROAT

(Based on A.W.S. Structural Code—1937)

Type of Weld		Butt		Butt		Fillet	
Kind of Stress		Tension		Compression		Shear	
Type of Electrode		Bare	Coated	Bare	Coated	Bare	Coated
Unit Stress— Lbs. per sq. in.		13,000	15,600	18,000	18,000	11,300	13,600
Calcu- lated loads per lineal inch of weld	Size of Weld ⅛″	1,625	1,950	2,250	2,250	1,000	1,200
	³⁄₁₆″	2,438	2,925	3,375	3,375	1,500	1,800
	¼″	3,250	3,900	4,500	4,500	2,000	2,400
	⁵⁄₁₆″	4,062	4,875	5,625	5,625	2,500	3,000
	⅜″	4,875	5,850	6,750	6,750	3,000	3,600
	½″	6,500	7,800	9,000	9,000	4,000	4,800
	⅝″	8,125	9,750	11,250	11,250	5,000	6,000
	¾″	9,750	11,700	13,500	13,500	6,000	7,200

¼″ should be added to calculated length of each weld to compensate for starting and stopping the arc and all craters in the welds should be filled.

ment will be equal to the leg dimension multiplied by .707. This relation between leg and throat dimensions is only true where both legs of the fillet weld are equal. If, for instance, one leg is ¼″ and the other leg is ⅜″, the throat dimensions would not be the same as though both legs were ¼″. It is, however, generally assumed that both legs of a fillet weld are equal and the throat is .707 times the leg. Only in a comparatively few cases are the legs of different sizes.

To set a standard for safe allowable loads for welding, the American Welding Society has made up Table 23.

These values are for general purposes only, and in specific cases the values may be changed. The safe allowable load in any particular case will be determined by the designer of the job. Consider a double-vee butt joint, 1″ thick, welded completely. According to Table 23 the safe allowable load for this joint in tension is 13,000 lbs. per in. length when welded with bare electrodes, and 15,600 lbs. when welded with coated electrodes. These load values are based on the cross-sectional area of the weld. If the butt is 1″ deep, then the cross section of a piece 1″ wide will be 1 sq. in. If the material making up the butt were ⅛″ thick, then a section 1″ wide, according to Table 23, could safely take a load of 1,625 lbs. in tension. Now suppose there is a butt 6″ wide and ½″ thick, the allowable load will be 6,500 lbs. for bare electrodes, or 7,800 lbs. for coated electrodes per lineal inch of weld. This will be for coated electrodes 7,800 × 6 = 46,800 lbs. for the entire 6″ butt. That is, a 6″ butt, ½″ thick will safely carry 46,800 lbs., provided the load is evenly distributed over the entire butt. A butt 12″ long and ¼″ deep will take a total load of 12 × 3,900 or 46,800 lbs., provided it is welded with covered electrodes. It will be noted that a 6″ butt which is ½″ thick will take the same load as a 12″ butt that is only ¼″ thick. The reason for this is that the cross section of both is the same.

The cross section of the 6″ × ½″ butt is 3 sq. ins. The

cross section of the 12″ × ¼″ butt is also 3 sq. ins. The allowable load per sq. in., according to the table, is 15,600 lbs. for covered electrodes. Therefore, 3 sq. ins. can take 3 × 15,600 or 46,800 lbs. It should be remembered that the 46,800 lbs. represents the total load. The stress is 15,600 lbs. per sq. in. In order to find what total load any butt will take, multiply the cross-sectional area of the weld that is taking the load by the unit stress of 15,600 lbs. The cross-sectional area will be the thickness of the butt multiplied by the length of the butt.

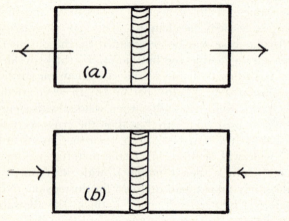

Figure 215: (a) Weld in tension. (b) Weld in compression.

If the butt is welded with bare electrodes, the value of allowable stress will be 13,000 instead of 15,600. It should be remembered that it is the cross-sectional area of the weld that determines the load that the weld can take. It makes no difference what type of preparation is used in making the butt. That is, a single-vee butt ½″ thick and 6″ long, will take the same load as a double-vee butt of the same dimensions. If a square-edged butt is properly spaced so that it can be completely welded through its entire thickness, and if the cross section of the weld is of the same dimensions, then it will take the same load as either a single- or a double-vee butt.

Suppose a square-edged butt is 6" long and 1" thick, welded from both sides, and the weld penetrates only ¼" on each side. The cross-sectional area is ½ × 6 or 3 sq. ins. The unit stress in lbs. per sq. in. is 15,600, so the total load for this butt is 3 × 15,600 or 46,800 lbs. Now if this butt is spaced so it can be welded through its entire thickness, the cross-sectional area of the weld will be 1 × 6 or 6 sq. ins., and the butt can then take 15,600 × 6 or 93,000 lbs.

So far, reference has been made only to butts having their load in tension; that is, a load tending to pull apart the pieces that are welded together. The values for welded butts in compression are slightly higher. In other words, a welded butt can take a greater load when the load tends to compress rather than stretch the weld. The compression values are also shown in Table 23. In this section of the table it should be noted that values for bare-electrode welding are equal to values for coated-electrode welding. For loads in tension, the coated electrode has a higher value than the bare electrodes.

The cross-sectional area of a fillet weld is the throat dimension multiplied by the length of the weld. As shown previously, the throat dimension is .707 multiplied by the leg dimension. To find what load a ¼" fillet weld will take, multiply ¼ × .707, which is .17675; this is the throat dimension of the weld, the legs of which are each ¼". The cross-sectional area of a ¼" fillet weld 1" long is .17675 × 1 or .17675 sq. ins.

The allowable load for fillet welds made with covered electrodes is 13,600 lbs. per sq. in. Therefore, if the cross section of a ¼" weld 1" long is .17675 sq. ins., the allowable load is 13,600 × .17675 or 2,400 lbs. This value of 2,400 lbs. is for each inch of ¼" fillet welding. If the weld is 10" long, the total load would be 2,400 × 10 or 24,000 lbs. A ½" fillet weld will have a throat dimension of .707 × .5 or .3535". The load that this size of fillet weld can take is 13,600 × .3535 or 4,808 lbs. The table gives a value in round numbers of 4,800 lbs., which is close enough. If, then, a ⅛″ fillet weld is made 10′ long, the total load will be 1,200 × 120 = 144,000 lbs. The load per in. is 1,200 lbs., and the weld is 120″ long.

In all the cases discussed, it is assumed that the load is distributed evenly in such a way that each part of the entire weld takes an equal part of the load. The values given in Table 23 are values that are considered as being safe for the type and size of welding, and contain a factor of safety. The ultimate values of the load these welds can take are a great deal higher than the values listed here. For further problems on stress of welded joints and methods of figuring stress, see Appendix II.

LOCATING WELDS

Figure 216a shows a fillet weld in what is known as transverse shear. The load is pulling in such a way that it is transverse, or across the weld. Another way of looking at it is to consider the load as pulling at right angles to the weld.

Figure 216b shows a fillet weld in what is known as parallel shear, because the load is parallel to the weld. When a weld is in transverse shear, it can take a larger load than a weld of the same length in parallel shear. Therefore, it is good engineering as well as good economy to locate welds in such a way that the load will act at right angles to the length of the weld. When the welds are located in this manner, less welding will be required.

Figure 216c shows an extremely poor design of welded joint. The load A is in a downward direction and the weld at B simply acts as a pivot for the load. Anything near a full load will cause this weld to break, regardless of how good a weld it may be. A weld at C would hold a much larger load than the weld at B.

Figure 216d shows a tee-joint weld. If the load is acting in the direction of A, the weld is well placed. If the load is acting in the direction of B, the weld is not well placed. When the load is acting in the direction of B, the weld is comparable to a weld at B in Figure 216c.

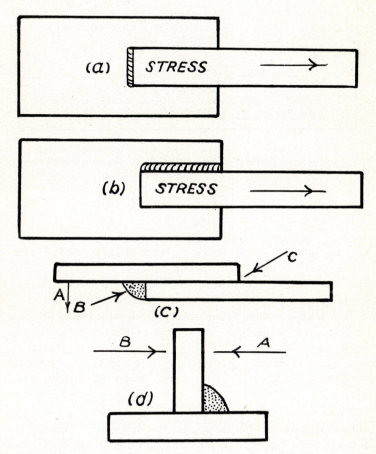

Figure 216: (a) Weld in transverse shear. (b) Weld in longitudinal shear. (c) Inefficiently located weld. (d) Tee joint weld.

In both these cases, the welds are inefficient and can take only a small part of the load they could take if placed properly.

Figure 217 shows two bevelled plates separated by a space of $\frac{1}{16}''$, and rigidly anchored in such a way that expansion can take place only in such a direction that both plates will come together at the bottom of the V. This butt joint is to be completely welded with a number of passes.

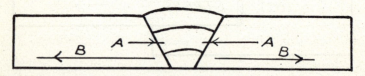

Figure 217: Upon cooling, the weld metal contracts towards the center, as shown by arrows A, while the plates tend to pull away from the center as shown by arrows B.

As each pass is made, a comparatively small area, parallel to the bead, is heated to a high degree. This heat will cause the bevelled edges to meet. As the first bead cools, the plates will attempt to contract back to their original size. The deposited weld metal is also cooling, and as it cools, it shrinks. This shrinking of the weld metal will attempt to pull the bevelled edges of the plates even closer together.

The situation, then, is one where the weld metal is attempting to pull them together. Or we may consider it as a situation where each plate, due to cooling, is attempting to stretch the weld metal. In any case, a stress is set up within the weld, and the weld metal, as well as the plates, is having a pull exerted on it.

When the second pass is made, the heat liberated will cause some expansion of the plates and the first pass. This will relieve, to some extent, the pull or tension until cooling sets in again. When this second pass cools, it will also attempt to pull the plates together. This time the pull will be exerted through the center of the plates, and some resistance to this pull will be made by the first pass. The third pass will be in the upper section of the plate, and as it cools, it will attempt to pull the top edges of the plates together.

Because 1) these plates originally were spaced, 2) they expanded by welding, and 3), due to the shrinkage of the weld metal, the plates cannot contract to their original size, it is only logical to conclude from previous examples that a stress is set up within the welded joint. This stress is acting in such a way as to pull the plates away from the deposited weld metal. Such a stress is known as a **residual** or **locked-up** stress. It is also referred to as an **internal** stress. Because the pieces shown in Figure 217 were securely anchored in such a way that, after welding was completed, the pieces were in perfect alignment, we may say that no distortion took place. Apparently in this case welding produced no bad effects. However, residual stresses which are present but not apparent are one of the greatest obstacles to welding, because they are apparent only when the welded joint breaks or fractures under the load. It is to overcome such conditions that stress-relieving, which will be discussed later, is used.

In Figure 217, if the welding had been done in such a way that expansion and contraction could take place freely instead of the pieces being anchored in place, the results after welding would be as shown in Figure 215b. In this case no resistance is offered to the expansion or contraction outside of the welded joint itself.

However, some resistance is offered inside of the joint by the deposited weld metal. When the first pass is made, the plates will contract upon cooling. The contraction in this case can take place because the plates are free to move. That is, the bottom edges of the V will still be in contact and held there due to contraction of the weld metal, but the plates as a whole will have pulled together because they are free to move. This moving together of the plates will eliminate the tension in the joint that took place in the example of Figure 217. When the second pass is made, it will attempt to pull the plates together still more, but the first pass will resist this pulling effect. This resistance takes place below the second pass. There is nothing to offer resistance above the second pass, so the result is a tipping of the plates. The third pass has a more pronounced tipping effect, the final result being that shown in Figure 218a.

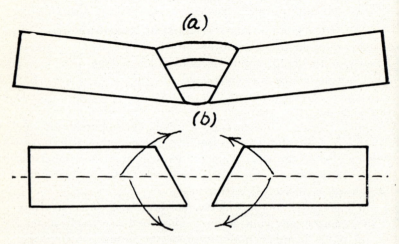

Figure 218: (a) Possible deformation of welded butt joints. (b) Distorting tendency caused by weld deposit on both sides of horizontal axis.

To visualize the effects of the deposited weld metal in a joint of this type, consider Figure 218b. All metal below the horizontal axis (1), (2), upon shrinking, will tend to pull the plates together. All welding above this axis will tend to pull the plates together and lift up the ends A, B. The ends of the joint in Figure 218a, because they were free to move during the welding, were lifted out of their original position. In Figure 217, the pieces making up the joint were rigidly anchored, no movement of the ends took place, and after welding the ends were in their original position—but residual stresses were present in the joint. In Figure 218a very little residual stress is present because there was free movement of the pieces. The residual stresses that might have been in this joint relieve themselves in lifting the ends.

In other words, residual stresses are present where no free movement is allowed during welding. Where free movement is

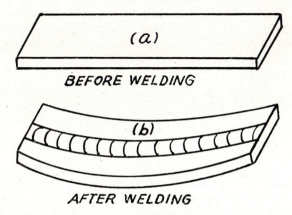

Figure 219.

allowed during welding, the stresses are absent, but the work is pulled out of alignment. When metal is pulled out of alignment, it is said to be distorted.

It can be seen that, in order to produce a satisfactory job of welding, ways and means must be found to eliminate, or at least keep to a minimum, both distortion and residual stresses. Before discussing these methods, another example of distortion (Figure 219) should be considered in order to get a more complete idea of the distorting action of welding. Here (top) is a long, narrow strip of steel. If a weld is made continuously through the center for the entire length of the piece, the contraction of the weld metal and the base metal will be such as to lift the ends and attempt to pull them together (bottom).

The contraction of metal is also referred to in welding terminology as **shrinkage.** If there were no shrinkage of metal in a welded joint, there would be no distortion or residual stresses affecting such a joint. Therefore, we may consider shrinkage responsible for both distortion and residual stresses in a welded joint. However, it has been proven that distortion and residual stresses can be held to negligible values if shrinkage is evenly distributed through a joint. This would show, then, that the real cause of distortion and joint stresses is an uneven or uncontrolled shrinkage.

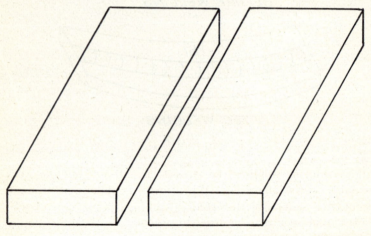

Figure 220.

Figure 220 shows two pieces of stock spaced ½″ apart. The pieces are free to move. If the face of each plate could be brought up to the melting point and at this moment the space between the two plates immediately filled with molten metal, the whole joint would be subjected to an evenly distributed shrinkage effect. The ends would not tend to lift, because there would be as much shrinkage taking place below the horizontal axis as above this axis. Refer to Figure 218b. There would be a minimum of stress within the joint because the plates were free to move. In other words, if the complete joint could be welded in such a way that the shrinking effect was evenly distributed throughout the joint, and there was sufficient free movement, the residual stresses and distortion would be minimized. The impossibilities of welding a complete joint in this way are obvious. Therefore, other methods of reducing stresses and distortion must be found.

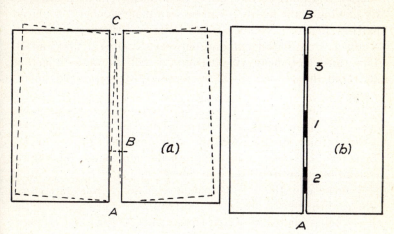

Figure 221: (a) Possible distortion of plates caused by welding. (b) Spacing the weld.

Methods of Preventing Distortion. Figure 221a shows two plates of $\frac{1}{4}''$ thickness spaced $\frac{1}{8}''$ apart. If the plates were free to move and welding started at A and continued as far as B, the position of the plates would be as shown by the dotted lines. The weld metal between A and B, upon cooling, would shrink and draw the plates together at C.

Figure 221b shows the same plates as in Figure 221a, but this time the welding, instead of starting at A and progressing continuously in one direction, will be distributed evenly over the seam. Starting at the center, a short weld, approximately 2″ in length, will be made at Point 1. Because this short weld or increment is in the center of the seam, its effect will be distributed over the entire seam. Its effect will be to pull both plates together evenly. At Point 2, another 2″ increment is made. This second increment will also attempt to pull the plates together at Point A; but Number 1 has cooled and now offers a resistance to the pulling effect of increment Number 2. By looking at the figure, it can be seen that Number 2 is placed halfway between Number 1 and Point A. Another increment, Number 3, is placed halfway between Number 1 and end B. This third increment will attempt to pull the plates together at B, but this tendency will be opposed by the previous increments.

It was said that these plates were free to move. This, however, was not entirely true after the first increment was made because, from this point on, the shrinking effect of each increment met resistance from the previous increments. Therefore, instead of an entirely free movement, the plates have a limited movement after the first increment is made. It was shown that where shrinkage takes place without free movement of the pieces being welded, residual stresses are set up within the joint. It was also shown that where too much free movement was allowed, distortion took place. Unequal shrinkage was also shown to cause distortion and residual stress. The method of depositing the increments in Figure 221b allows some free movement. It distributes evenly over a large area both the welding and the shrinking effects of the welding, and in such a way that the total stresses and distortion are at a minimum for a practical job.

To complete the welding of this seam, the weld should be

made in increments and deposited in the order indicated by
the numbers of Figure 221b. There will possibly be a tendency
to raise the edges of both plates in the same fashion as shown

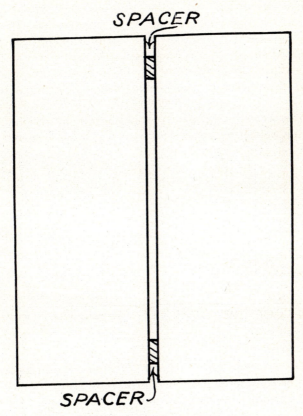

Figure 222: Use of spacers.

in Figure 218a, but much less pronounced. To overcome this
lifting effect, the ends would be clamped in place on an actual
job. If the welding completely penetrates the seam, the lifting

effect of the edges will be very small, and clamping should not be required. This is so because the same principle is involved as described for Figure 220.

Where clamping is impossible, and where no allowance can be made for movement of the plates, **spacers** are sometimes used. A spacer is a small wedge or strip of metal. The plates are spaced the desired distance apart and a spacer is placed between them, as in Figure 222. The only advantage of such spacers is to keep the ends from pulling together, as in Figure 221a.

A joint welded with spacers would have more residual stress than one welded by the method shown in Figure 221b.

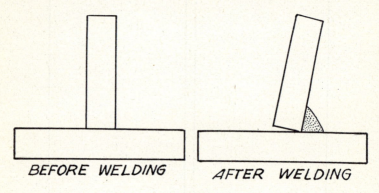

BEFORE WELDING   AFTER WELDING

Figure 223.

There are two more common examples of shrinkage that should be considered. The first is that in Figure 223. Here the vertical member was free to move before welding. As the deposited weld metal cooled, it contracted and pulled the vertical member to one side.

Figure 224 represents a large plate with a number of stiffeners welded across it. If the distance A was carefully measured before and after welding the stiffeners, the distance A would be found less than it was before welding. The greater the number of stiffeners welded across the plate, the shorter would be the distance A after welding. The distance B would also be less, by a negligible amount. In other words, shrinkage is more effective in the direction perpendicular to the line of welding than parallel to the line of welding.

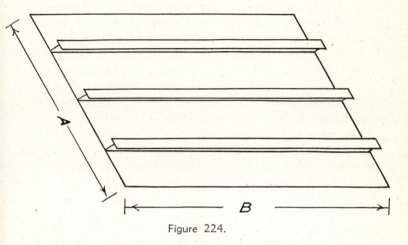

Figure 224.

So far, the stress and distortion of only single units of relatively small size have been discussed. It has been shown that either residual stresses or distortion will result from welding. Therefore, in order to weld any large structure, such as a ship, it becomes necessary to find a way in which both residual stresses and distortion can be kept to the point where they do not produce objectionable results. If each piece of metal in the entire structure of a ship is rigidly anchored and strongbacked so as to prevent any movement of the piece, distortion may be eliminated, but the resulting residual stresses would probably be such that welds would be continually breaking. On the other hand, if too much free movement is allowed, the result will be too much distortion. It should be understood that it is not the heat, but the distribution of the heat, that causes distortion, as shown in Fig. 220.

In Figure 221a the plates would not pull together at Point C if the weld could be kept hot enough to prevent the deposited metal from shrinking as it cooled. Distortion is caused by an **unequal** distribution of the heat and of shrinkage. One part being heated, attempts to expand and another part, being comparatively cold, resists this expansion. There are, then, two opposing forces, with the final result being distortion.

If two plates 10' square and ⅛" thick are to be welded together to form a single plate 20' long, it will become necessary, in order to prevent warping, to do something more than simply tack-weld the edges. The method of depositing the weld metal would have to be considered. Instead of starting at one end of the seam and welding continuously through the seam, it is necessary to deposit the metal in a skip-around fashion. After the edges are tack-welded or dogged down, the weld should be started at the center of the seam and a bead of 5" or 6" made. At a point halfway between the first bead and one end, another short bead or increment is made. The third deposit is made between the first one and the other end of the seam. This method of skipping around is continued until the seam is complete. The reason is to reduce the possibilities of distortion. Since each increment is short, its distorting effect will be overcome by the size of the plates. The distribution of the heat helps distribute the distorting forces so that they oppose one another, and distortion is either eliminated or greatly reduced.

It can be seen, then, that in order to produce the proper type of welded job, some method or procedure of metal deposit must be used in conjunction with the proper amount and method of restraint. For further discussion of the effects of shrinkage in ship welding, see Appendix I.

Special Stress Precautions. In some special types of work, special precautions are taken to avoid stresses, as indicated in the following.

a) Preheating, from 100° to 500° F., depending on the job, is resorted to in order to slow down the cooling rate.

b) Annealing is used on heat-treated steels.

c) Stress relieving is accomplished by bringing the weld to 1100°–1250° F., holding it there an hour for each inch of thickness, and then slowly cooling.

d) Normalizing before welding is required on carbon moly pipe. It is done by heating the piece in a furnace to 1650° F., and then air cooling.

e) Peening serves the purpose of stretching the weld, cutting down surface tension and stopping cracks from developing.

Summary.

a) Plan welding procedure so that the pieces have freedom to move for as long as possible.

b) Spread the heat evenly over the whole of the seam that is being welded.

c) Avoid concentrated shrinkage by putting welding increments where indicated and by doing block welding when indicated.

d) To produce the greatest amount of weld per unit of time, use the proper method for the particular job, select the largest permissible electrode, and use enough current.

e) On large jobs never leave a block of welding to cool for any long period unless the weld is up to size.

f) Protect large welded parts by asbestos covers and strip heaters.

Note. The size of stresses depends on the heat added during welding, which in turn depends on the amount of metal deposited. Therefore:

a) Select electrodes giving the least heat per unit of deposited metal.

b) Make the welding groove as narrow as good welding will permit; or build up one side of an over-wide groove progressively, to keep the smallest possible "V." This will help keep down the amount of weld metal deposited.

Part 8

Sequence

A welding sequence is a method of depositing weld metal. In planning a sequence for any given job, an attempt is made to distribute the heat due to welding in such a way that shrinkage and its resulting residual stresses and distortion will be reduced to a minimum. There are a number of terms applied to welding sequence, such as, wandering, block, and back-step. These terms signify the kind of sequence.

Wandering Sequence. A wandering sequence is any sequence where the metal is deposited in a skip-around fashion. Instead of starting at one end of the job and welding continuously, the metal is deposited in increments. An **increment** is a short weld. If a fillet weld 20′ long is to be made in a wandering sequence, the procedure may be first to make a 6″ increment at the center of the joint. At a point 2′ away on one side of this first increment, another 6″ increment is made. At another point 2′ from and on the other side of the first increment, another 6″ increment is made. This procedure is continued until the entire bead of 20′ length is made. In other words, the bead is made of sections that are deposited in a skip-around fashion.

There are a number of different ways of carrying out a wandering sequence. The specific type of wandering sequence will depend upon the job at hand. In some cases, such as welding stiffeners to a bulkhead, the first increment may be made at the center of the center stiffener, the second increment may be made on the opposite side of this stiffener, directly opposite the first increment, or it may be staggered off to one side of the

376

first increment. Both sides of the stiffener may be carried along together, or one side may be tacked and the opposite side completed in a skip-around fashion. After this, the side that was tacked would be completed. In any of these cases, the term "wandering sequence" is properly applied.

In every type of wandering sequence, it is absolutely essential to the quality of the job that each increment be carried into and fused into the increments on each side of it.

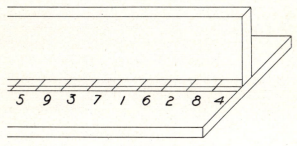

Figure 225.

Block Sequence. When a heavy weld, requiring a number of passes, is to be made, the block sequence is sometimes used. In using this method of depositing weld metal, full-size increments are deposited in a wandering fashion. This method is illustrated in Figure 225. Here a ⅜″, 3-pass weld is to be made the entire length of the joint. A full ⅜″ increment of some predetermined length, probably 8″ or 10″ long, is made at the center of the joint. This first increment is marked 1 in the figure. The remaining increments are made in the order indicated by the numbers, and are the same length. Each increment is made to its full size, with 3 passes before the next one is made. In other words, the entire weld is made up of blocks deposited in a wandering fashion.

Another method of block welding is to bring each increment up to one pass less than full-size, and when all the blocks are made, to run the last, or finish bead, either continuously or with a wandering sequence.

Back-Step. Figures 226a and 226b both show the sequence of depositing weld increments by the back-step method. The welding of the seam of Figure 226a is started at 4″ or 5″ from one end and carried out to this end. The second increment is started 4″ or 5″ from the starting point of the first increment and carried to this starting point. The rest of the seam is welded by the same method. The numbers indicate the order in which the increments are made. The arrows indicate the direction of the welding.

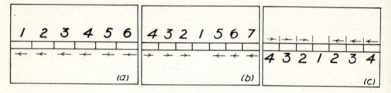

Figure 226.

The method shown in Figure 226b is in general the same as that shown in Figure 226a, with the exception of the starting point. Here the first increment is deposited at the center of the seam, and one half is completed first. After this, the second half is completed. The numbers in this figure also indicate the order of depositing increments.

Another method of welding a seam is shown in Figure 226c. Here the first increment is made at the center, and both sides are carried out together. The numbers and arrows indicate the order of deposition and direction of travel.

In the case of Figure 226a the welding proceeds toward one free end, while in Figures 226b and 226c, the welding, as a whole, proceeds toward both ends.

Single-Pass Sequence. Another method of welding the joint shown in Figure 225 is to weld one pass at a time for the entire length of the joint. Each pass would be completed in increments by the use of a wandering sequence before the next pass was started.

SHIP SEQUENCE

The general idea of welding a ship is that of starting at the center line and working outboard toward both sides at the same time, and from the midship section toward both ends at the same time. When this procedure is followed, the work continues to progress toward the free ends, allows some movement to the members being welded. This free movement of the welded members helps to reduce locked-up stresses which would occur if the members were not free to move.

From what has been said so far, it can be seen that, regardless of how good a welding sequence may be planned, some shrinkage is bound to occur in every weld made. If all the shrinkage is added up, it will total an appreciable amount, and this factor must be taken into consideration as one of the problems of welded ship construction. To help overcome the shrinkage problem, extra stock is usually left to compensate for it. If, for instance, it is estimated that a plate will shrink ½″ during the welding process, the plate will be made larger by this amount. Whatever extra stock is left after the welding is completed is burned or chipped off.

When the butt plates shown in Figure 218a, page 366 were welded without taking precautions against shrinkage, enough force was exerted by the shrinking effect to pull up both sides of the butts. The same effect is produced on a ship structure when the sequence of welding is not properly planned and carried out. The total accumulated stresses may be enough to lift the ends of the ship off the keel blocks. If this lift is excessive, the ship's lines may be thrown out, resulting in a costly job to repair the damage done. It would be possible during the construction of a ship to anchor the ends in such a way that no part of it could lift. The ends would then be on the blocks all the time, but, as was previously shown, the lack of free movement would cause an excessive amount of locked-up stresses. The resulting stresses would probably be worse than the lift. The proper solution is to leave the ends free and, by the use of proper welding sequence, permit the ends to remain down by their own weight.

A slight lift may be considered as a sign of proper welding, because it will show that the structure had some free movement during its fabrication, and because of this fact it can be reasonably assumed that the locked-up stresses are not excessively large.

PROCEDURE LETTER

Welding sequence letters will, in general, contain the following information:

a) Description of the area to be welded in regard to type of construction, weight of plating, kind and size of members used.

b) A list of the general welding notes on the plans that might be applicable to the particular structure.

c) A list of welding operations, designed so that there is always a free end toward which the welding progresses.

d) A list of all extra stock left on the material to allow for shrinkage caused by welding.

SLIP JOINTS

While it is impossible to eliminate internal or residual stresses and shrinkage entirely, it is possible, by proper methods of construction and by the use of correct welding sequences, to keep the objectionable factors of welding to a minimum.

One of the methods used in ship construction to prevent over-all distortion of a vessel, is to use slip joints. A slip joint is not actually a joint, but is simply a section of the ship that is not welded until all the welding fore and aft of it is completed. After all the rest of the ship's frames, decks, and plating are welded, the slip joint is welded. Slip joints are used to keep the ends of the ship from lifting off the keel blocks and also to keep the ship's sides from pulling in.

The application and advantage of slip joints may be understood better if we imagine a ship built in sections. Consider, for example, a ship built in three separate sections, each section fabricated completely and independently of the others. That is, the forward section would be completely built in itself, the midship and after sections built the same way. Now we have a complete ship built in three sections. If the welding in each section has been carried out correctly and each section is welded completely, without distortion, the only thing that remains is to join the three sections together. The comparatively small amount of welding required for this final operation, when carried out in the proper sequence, will not be enough to cause any serious distortion to the completed ship. The points at which the three sections are welded together to form the complete structure may be considered as slip joints. The whole purpose of slip joints is to divide the ship into sections so that each section may be welded independently of the others.

Figure 227 shows a longitudinal slip joint between two bulkheads. Between these two bulkheads is a break in the continuous members of the ship. That is, between these bulkheads from the keel up, each member, deck plate, longitudinal, and shell plating have one loose butt. There may be a number of slip joints dividing the ship into a number of sections. The welding is started at the center of the section and carried out to both ends of the section. The butts forming the slip joints

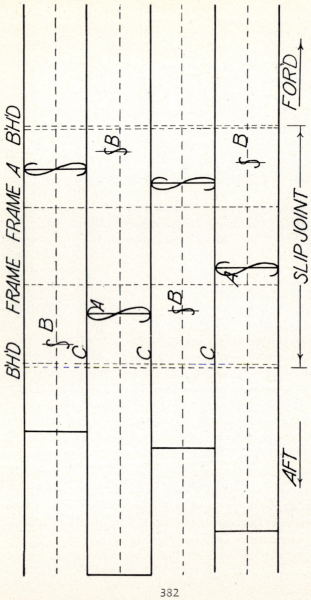

Figure 227: Section of side shell. A—Shell butts. B—Longitudinal framing butts. C—Shell seams.

are left unwelded while the welding in the adjacent sections is completed. When all sections are welded, then the slip joints are welded.

To see how a slip joint works, suppose that, due to the welding on the after side of the forward slip joint, there was a tendency to raise the bow. It can be seen that if all the members have one loose butt, the lifting cannot go beyond the joint because the force which would tend to lift will cause the various members to shift a little at the slip joint. The bow, however, will not be affected, and will remain where it belongs, which is the purpose of the slip joint. The only welding which will have a direct effect, as far as lifting the bow-end of a ship is concerned, will be that which is done forward of the forward slip joint, together with the welding of the slip joints themselves. The welding tending to lift the after-end of a ship is that which is done aft of the after slip joint, plus the welding of the slip joints. In either case the amount of welding is comparatively small, and it will not be difficult to control. The lifting of the after-end of a ship under any conditions is usually less than that of the bow-end, due to the weight of the after-end and the equipment that is installed.

The type of slip joint discussed is known as a **longitudinal** slip joint. Another is the **transverse** slip joint. In this type, the transverse members are left loose in such a way as to divide the ship into upper and lower sections. The welding is carried out from the vertical keel to the inboard side of the slip joint. The members making up the joint are left loose, and welding is carried on from the outboard side of the joint and up the side of the ship. When welding has progressed far enough so that the danger of the sides pulling in is past, the joint itself is welded. The action of this type of slip joint is comparable in every way to that of the longitudinal slip joint, except that its purpose is to prevent the sides from pulling in while the longitudinal slip joint is effective on the ends.

BULKHEADS

As a general rule, bulkheads, particularly the smaller ones, are fabricated in the shop and delivered to the ship ways ready to be welded in place. Bulkheads will vary as far as size, shape, and thickness of material are concerned, but the welding sequence described here will apply in a general way to all bulkheads. Eliminating distortion will, of course, be more difficult when working with light stock than with heavy stock. For this reason, the welder should be particularly careful to observe the sequence when welding a thin bulkhead. When a bulkhead becomes distorted, it must, of course, be straightened. The time used for straightening will be a great deal more than the time required to take precautions against distortion. A little extra time to take the proper precautions before and during welding will save time in the end.

Tack-welding the plate edges to the metal platform and placing heavy weights on the plate is a commonly used method to keep bulkhead plates from buckling. During the welding, some of these tack-welds may break, in which case they should be immediately replaced.

If a bulkhead is to be made up of two plate sections and stiffeners, the plates should be welded together first if the stiffeners are to run across the welded seam. If the stiffeners are to run parallel with the seam, each plate may have its stiffeners welded first, and then the two sections may be welded together. In either case the seam should be welded with a wandering sequence, as indicated in Figure 228.

In welding a seam, distortion will be minimized if the edges of the plates are dogged down or tack-welded to the floor. Tack-welds about 1½″ long are placed 1′ apart all around the plate. Weights, such as heavy iron blocks, should be placed along the seam, 3″ or 4″ away on either side of the seam. Starting at the center of the seam and working out in both directions, the seam is tacked. These tacks should be about 1″ long and placed 7″ or 8″ apart. The tacks should be cleaned of slag, and when this is done, the seam is ready to be welded solid.

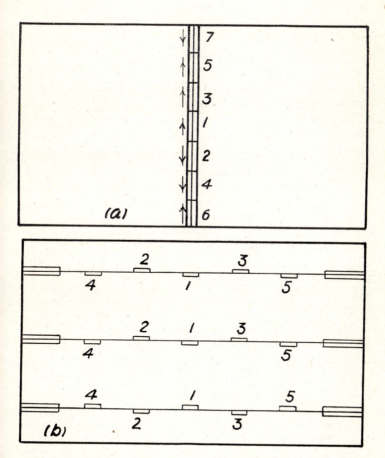

Figure 228: (a) Sequence of plate seam. Long increments at ends of stiffeners to be completed last. (b) Stiffener sequence.

The length of each increment represented in Figure 228 should not be greater than can be made with one electrode. In some cases it is policy to use only one-half an electrode to an increment. As the tack-welds are encountered, the solid welding should not be stopped at one end of a tack and picked up again at the other end. The solid welding should be carried into the tack. That is, the tack is remelted and made a homogeneous part of the finished weld.

When the welding on this side is complete, tack-welds holding the edges of the plates are chipped off, the weights removed, and the plate turned over. Where the plating is ¼″ or more in thickness, the root of the continuous welding on the first side should be coped out to clean sound metal. The second side of the seam is now ready to be welded, using the sequence shown in Figure 228.

Stiffeners must also be welded in the proper sequence, and it is generally good policy to tack-weld all stiffeners in place before completely welding any of them. In addition to tack-welding the plate edges to the welding platform, heavy wooden beams are sometimes placed across the stiffeners. When these beams are pulled down tight, they will prevent a great deal of the distortion that might otherwise take place.

On a bulkhead where the stiffeners are all parallel to one another, but do not run completely across the bulkhead, the possibilities of distortion are greater than where the stiffeners do run from end to end. The result is that, even though tack-welded, the edges may be warped. If a heavy beam or piece of flat bar is dogged down edgewise about halfway between the end of the stiffeners and the plate edges, this effect will be reduced.

Figure 229 shows a bulkhead made up of a number of plate sections. In fabricating a bulkhead of this type, all sections should first be welded together to form a single unit before welding any stiffeners. In welding these sections together, the

first step is to tack-weld them all together. The tacks should
be distributed evenly over the whole bulkhead. This can be
done by following the numerical order indicated in Figure
229. In some shipyards the tacks or increments are made 3"

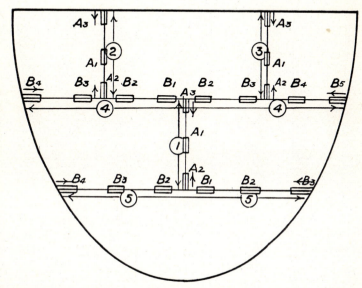

Figure 229.

or 4" long and are considered as a part of the finished weld.
That is, after these increments are all placed, the job is completed by filling in between the increments. The end increments are started at the outer end of the seams and are carried
in toward the center, as indicated by the arrows in Figure 229.
The circled numbers indicate the order in which the seams are
to be welded. After one side is completely welded, the tack-
welds, or dogs, and weights are removed, and welding is carried
out on the other side after coping.

The first step in welding the stiffeners is to tack-weld all intersections. That is, tack the stiffeners to each other and to the plate at stiffener intersections as shown in Figure 229A by A_1, A_2, and A_3. Starting at the center and working outward in all directions, deposit increments as shown by B_1, B_2, etc. In

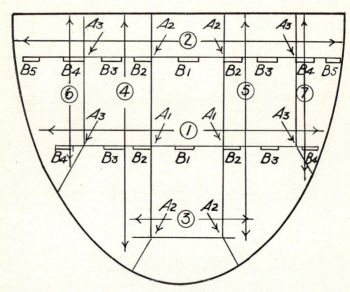

Figure 229A.

order to keep the figure from being too confusing, this depositing of increments is shown for only two stiffeners. All stiffeners will have their increments deposited in the same manner. These increments are deposited on only one side of each stiffener. Welding is completed first on the sides opposite the tack-welds, using a wandering sequence and working out from the center in all directions. After this is completed, the welding on the tack-welded sides is completed in the same manner. The circled numbers represent the order in which the stiffeners are completed.

SHELL PLATING

Sections of the bottom and side shell plating may be shop-fabricated with their framing, or bottom and side shell plating, and their framing may be welded piece by piece to the ship structure.

If a section of side shell or bottom plating is to be shop-fabricated, the use of properly designed jigs and methods of restraining the work are essential to keep the assembly free of distortion. One method of making this assembly is first to tack-weld the plate together. Where square butts are formed, the opening of these butts should be equivalent to at least one-half the plate thickness. The plates are welded with a wandering sequence, making a single unit of the plates. When this is completed, the unit is turned over and the butts chipped down to clean, sound weld metal and welded. The plate assembly may now be placed in the jig and have its framing tack-welded.

The next step is to weld all framing intersections. The transverse and then the longitudinal framing is welded in place to complete the assembly. If the plates are to be welded in the jig, the same procedure will follow along with the exception of chipping out the butts. After the plating is welded, the frame welding is completed, and then the butts are chipped out and welded as the final operation.

The ship assembly of shell plating, in general, will begin with the welding of butts and intersections of the shell framing. The transverse butts in the plating are then completed. We now have formed a solid unit of the entire shell framing in this particular section—that is, a section between two bulkheads, and all the transverse plate butts are welded. The transverse and then the longitudinal framing is welded to the shell plating; and, as the final step, the shell lap welding is completed; all welding being carried out as evenly as possible on both sides of the center line, using a wandering sequence.

The particular sequence of welding shell plating will vary in different yards. In some instances, the shell may be carried along a strake at a time to a slip joint, or a number of strakes may be carried along together. In some ship construction the shell plating through the midship section is completed from the keel to the sheer strake, while the lower strakes are completed forward and aft. The result is that the completed welding at this point is in the form of a triangle with the midship shell plating completed all the way up to the sheer strake and the bottom plating completely welded from bow to stern, the intermediate strakes being carried along in proportion. Another method is to carry along the strake laps to within 6″ of a transverse butt, weld the transverse butt complete, then go back to pick up the unwelded 6″ and continue welding the strake lap up to within 6″ of the next transverse butt, where the procedure is repeated.

DECK SECTIONS

Deck sections may be fabricated in the shop or aboard ship, depending upon conditions. These sections may be made of light or heavy stock, depending upon the type and location of the deck, as well as the type of ship. For that reason, we will consider only the general methods of deck sequence. It is to be understood, of course, that the same precautions to prevent distortion or locked-up stresses must be taken as would be with any other type of assemblies.

In general, it can be said for ship-welded deck sections that the following sequence would apply:

1) Tack the plates together, restraining the edges by dogging, clamping, or any other proper means.

2) Weld the transverse butts or laps, using a wandering sequence.

3) Weld the longitudinal butts or laps with a wandering sequence.

4) Tack the framing in place and weld all intersections.

Another method of welding the plating would be to carry both transverse and longitudinal welding together, always completing the transverse welding ahead of the longitudinal welding. In either case, the plating is completely welded together before any framing is welded. After the plate welding is completed, all the framing may be tacked in place, or only a part of it, so that as the remaining part is being tacked in place, those members which are already in place may be completely welded. In this way, tacking and welding go along together. In any case, the framing members should be welded to each other at their intersections before being welded to the deck plating. One method would be to weld completely all framing butts and intersections first, making the members continuous throughout, and then to weld this solid framework to the plating. Another method would be to carry the plate welding along with the butts and intersections, but to keep the frame butts welded ahead of the intersections, and the welded intersections ahead of the welding to the plating.

The butts in the longitudinal and transverse framing members may be carried along with the intersections and welded in turn, or they may be welded first, before any intersections are welded.

There may also be variations in the general method of welding the framing to the plating. The transverse framing may first be welded completely, after which the longitudinal members are completed. It is also possible to carry along both transverse and longitudinal welding at the same time. A deck section may be framed either transversely or longitudinally. That is, its main support may be from longitudinal framing members, or it may be from transverse members. In both cases, it is likely that there will be some intercostal framing. Or it may be that the particular deck section is framed equally by transverse and longitudinal members. Where there is auxiliary support in the form of intercostal framing, the continuous members are usually welded before the intercostal members.

Regardless of which method of fabrication is used, the whole assembly after completion should be turned completely over, and all butt roots chipped down to clean, solid weld metal, and then welded.

Fabricating the deck aboard ship follows in a general way the same procedure as that outlined for shop fabrication, with the same possible variations. For example, we can consider a section of deck between two transverse bulkheads. The framing between these two bulkheads should be welded together before any plating is welded to the framing. Starting at the center of the section between these bulkheads, and working evenly fore and aft and outboard from the center line, all butts in the framing should be welded first. The framing intersections are then welded. This makes the whole framework in this section one solid unit.

Another method is to treat framing butts as intersections and carry both along together, but keeping the butts welded ahead of the intersections. In either case, the welding is started at the center of the section, and welding is carried evenly forward, aft, and outboard. The plating is put in place, pulled tight to the frame, and tack-welded to the framing. The plating for the entire section may be tacked in place and then the transverse laps or butts welded. After this, the longitudinal welding may be completed, or both transverse and longitudinal welding may be carried along together, keeping the transverse welding completed ahead of the longitudinal welding.

Another method would be to weld the pieces of plating together as soon as they were tacked in place instead of waiting to tack-weld the entire section, if the proper sequence could be carried out.

In either case, the deck plating is now in the form of one large plate, and the deck framing is in the form of a single solid unit. All that remains to be done now is to weld the plating to the framing. This may be done by first welding all the transverse framing or by carrying both transverse and longitudinal welding along together. If both are carried along together, the transverse welding should be carried ahead of the longitudinal welding.

Instead of welding the plating in such a way as to form one large plate, and then welding it to the framing, it is also possible and correct to weld the various plates together and weld the plating to the framing at the same time. If both types of welding are to be carried along together, the transverse butts or laps of the deck plating should be welded before any framing is welded to the plating beyond these laps or butts. The longitudinal plate welding should not be carried out beyond a transverse butt until after the transverse butt is welded. That is, there should be no transverse butts or laps left unwelded between any longitudinal welds. The longitudinal plate welding should always be completed outboard ahead of the welding that welds the longitudinal framing to the deck.

METHOD OF ERECTION

Up to this point a number of different ways have been given for welding different sections or assemblies. The following pages will give the actual sequence of welding a particular ship.

The ship has 4 slip joints, dividing it into 5 sections. The forward slip joint comes between frames 8 and 9; the next one between frames 54 and 55; the third between frames 150 and 151; and the fourth between frames 179 and 180.

All welding throughout the ship is to be carried out with a wandering sequence, and all welding will be kept evenly distributed on both sides of the center line of the ship.

Construction is to be carried along simultaneously in each of the 5 sections into which the ship is divided by the slip joints. The midship section—that is, between frames 55 and 150—will be considered first. The construction of this section will start at bulkhead 104 and progress outboard from the center line, and forward and aft to the slip joints.

Here we will consider the erection as it progresses toward the forward end of this section. Weld the topside of the flat keel butt at frame 99½. The underside of this butt is now coped and welded. The vertical keel butt, which is located one frame aft of the flat keel butt, is welded next. One side will be completed first. The root of this butt is then coped and welded. After both these butts are completed, the flat keel is a continuous member in this vicinity, and the vertical keel likewise. The next step is to weld the vertical keel to the flat keel, welding the brackets when encountered, as far as the slip joints both forward and aft.

The welding of the shell plate will begin by welding the transverse butt in the A strake at frame 101½. The next step is to weld the A strake to the flat keel. This will be a longitudinal lap weld which will start at frame 104 and continue on past the transverse butt already welded in the A strake up to a point 8″ short of the second A strake transverse butt. From here the first butt encountered in the B strake is welded. The A and B strake lap is welded to within 8″ of the second transverse butt in the B strake, and the first butt in the C strake is welded. As in both previous strakes, the longitudinal lap between B and C strakes is welded to a point within 8″ of the second butt encountered in the C strake.

From this point, welding drops back to the second butt in the A strake. This butt is welded, and the longitudinal welding is picked up by welding the 8″ previously left and carried up to within 8″ of the next butt in this strake. The B and C strake welding continues in the same manner, and this general sequence is carried out forward and aft evenly on both sides of the center line as far as the slip joints.

The welding of the framing connections may be completed throughout the section before any plating is welded to the framing; or the framing connections may be carried along just ahead of the plate welding. If the welding of the framing is to be carried along with the welding of the plating, the following order would be the one to follow:

1) Weld butts in framing
2) Weld framing intersections
3) Weld transverse butts in plating
4) Weld the transverse framing members to the plating
5) Weld the longitudinal framing to the plating
6) Weld the longitudinal laps

When erection has reached this point, the welding of interior structural members and foundations should begin. The same general sequence should be used—that is, starting at the center point and working outboard and upward. The method of welding platforms will be the same as deck welding, which has already been discussed. Welding decks to the shell plating will be considered and carried along as a longitudinal strake lap. The same procedure may be carried along simultaneously in each of the sections between slip joints, and because of the break provided at the slip joints, the welding in one section will not affect another section in any way.

Tack-Welding. Due to shrinking, the tack welds that have been used to keep various parts of an assembly in place, sometimes break. A common example of this is where a bulkhead which is made up of a number of plates is tack-welded along its edges to the floor. The welding may be partially or completely finished and, due to the total shrinkage, the tacks may not be large enough to stand the pull exerted on them, with the result that they crack and give way. When this happens, the tacks should be immediately replaced.

Extra Stock. When a shell plate, deck plate, or framing member is to form part of a slip joint, the framing members will be slightly longer and the plating will be slightly wider or longer, depending upon the type of slip joint of which it is to be a part. The material of these over-sized dimensions is known as extra stock. The purpose of extra stock is to allow for shrinkage. If, after serving its purpose, the extra stock allowed has been too much, it is cut or burned off, the joint fitted in place, and the welding completed.

Stresses in Heavy Work. This section so far has dealt with material whose average thickness did not exceed $\frac{3}{8}''$. Now we will consider such structures as stern weldments, strut arms, rudders, turrets and yokes.

This type of work is heavy, has machined, well-fitted sections, can have no extra stock, and carries a tolerance for dimension. But first of all it is thick. There will be no chance for free shrinkage. Heavy residual stresses will be set up by welding, and the consequent dangers must be overcome.

The following will indicate some of the things that can be done.

Block Welding—Tacks. Tacking commonly consists of very small increments, but in work of this type it would prove unsatisfactory in many cases. First, the sections are properly aligned. Then block tacks from $\frac{1}{2}$ to $\frac{3}{4}$ the size of the V butt are placed about 12″ apart. The length of these blocks is about 4″. They are generally placed in the flat position, but if stronger tacking is needed, the opposite or overhead position should be built to the same size at the same time.

Sub-Assembly. It is advisable to weld up any small sub-assemblies that can be conveniently erected and handled before uniting the whole assembly. These sub-assemblies will usually have enough free edges so that minimum stress is obtained, at least within each sub-assembly. These units are put together, and in general the welding will start at the center, working out radially towards the edges, using block welding and wandering sequence.

Block Welding. Instead of placing $\frac{3}{8}''$ increments, large blocks of weld are deposited. These blocks are of a size more in proportion to the thickness of the stock being welded. (See page 377.)

Constant Temperature. The location in which the structure is to be welded should be kept as near a constant temperature as possible, usually about 75° F. This temperature is not too uncomfortable to work in, and at the same time is warm enough to keep the structure from cooling too rapidly after the welds are deposited. Cold drafts from outside must not be permitted to strike the unit. The sudden cooling causes quick contraction on the outside of welds, which is very apt to start a root crack, which will slowly continue up through to the face of the weld.

Peening.* Sometimes it is necessary to resort to peening to prevent cracked welds, especially if the unit is very rigid and very heavy. This is usually done before the weld metal has cooled down to room temperature. It stretches the surface metal enough to prevent a stress great enough to start a crack. Peening is usually done when a block is half size and then again when just under flush.

Preheating. For very critical work the temperature can be raised to 150° F. by means of strip heaters or oxy-acetylene torches. This will allow a longer time for the weld to cool, and thus minimize the danger of cracking. The amount of preheat will vary. Sometimes it is preferable to go as high as 400° F.

Banding. This is relatively a new term. It means the substitution of a complete length and width of good weld metal in the place of a questionable cast metal to which another heavy section has to be welded. The casting in the way of the weld before assembly is chipped down ¾₁₆″, and this groove is filled with weld metal. The whole is chipped flush and then assembled. This will allow the better ducility of the weld deposit to be utilized to its utmost.

---

* A method of stress-relieving, accomplished by the use of a pneumatic hammer and a special peening tool.

Back-to-Back Blocking. This is merely the depositing of two blocks exactly opposite each other. It is used when sections are very heavy and rigid. Care must be taken not to cope out root when metal is too hot. Also, each block must be built up continuously to flush.

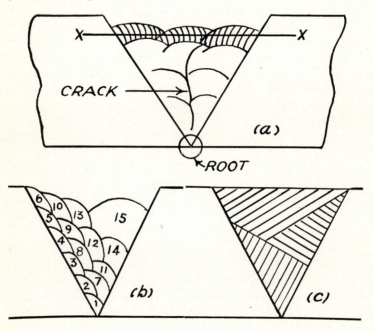

Figure 230: (a) Sudden cooling of top layer X-X may cause sufficient shrinkage to start a root crack, which might easily travel up to the face of the weld. (b) Only one bead of each layer ties to the other plate. The beads are built up on the edge of one plate, as shown. (c) The joint is built up of several wedge-shaped blocks where more initial metal is needed at the root.

Order of Depositing Beads in Blocks. There are several orders in which the beads may be deposited, and each order has a direct bearing on the possibility of cracking. Figure 230a shows the normal way in which a block could be built up. From this sketch we can see that the greatest amount of shrinkage between the two plates would come directly through the last layer, causing considerable locked-up stress.

Figure 230b shows another way in which the beads could be deposited, giving greater free surface for the shrinkage.

Figure 230c shows another way, with even a greater free surface.

Distortion. The next item to be considered is distortion. With such heavy plating and large volume of weld metal, the temporary bars that are used of the lighter structures, would be practically useless. Heavy channels and I-beams can be used at times, but for the most part it is necessary to depend on proper balance when depositing the welds.

The blocks are numbered in the order in which they are to be deposited. This serves two purposes.

a) With the welder following the numbers he is able to keep the amount of welding on each side of the connections well balanced.

b) On all bevelled connections the root of the weld must be chipped out to clean metal before the block may be started. The sequence of blocks is so arranged that after all the numbered blocks are deposited, the root of each block on both sides of the connection is left free for chipping.

Size of Blocks. The length of the blocks deposited on heavy units has been determined by experiments. The heavier the plate, the shorter should be the block. Two-inch material requires 6″ blocks.

Reinforcement. To give a neat, workmanlike appearance, the blocks are brought up to flush only, and continuous passes are made about $\frac{1}{16}$″ over the plate level. The correct fillet is applied in accordance with the specifications.

Stress Relieving. There is always some locked-up stress in every welded structure. Units which are to withstand heavy local stresses, such as rudders, stern weldments, turret sections, etc., must be free from internal stresses. To insure this condition heat treatment at about 1150° F. is given, and the unit is allowed to cool in the furnace. One hour of heat at 1150° F. is allowed for every inch of thickness. The rate at which the units are heated and cooled is determined from the thickest portion.

Part 9

Tests

METHODS OF TESTING

In order to qualify for a job and to maintain good welding quality on the job, welders must pass a number of tests. The particular type of job on which the welder is to work will determine just what test or tests the welder will have to pass. All tests may be divided into two general classifications—destructive and non-destructive. In the destructive type of testing, the piece being tested is either bent or broken. In the non-destructive type, the weld being tested is not affected in any way. On the following pages are described in detail the types of destructive testing used by the Navy Department, Coast Guard, and the Maritime Commission, to qualify welders for ship construction and repair. The tests used by the Chicago Bridge and Iron Company, which are also described, are typical of the tests used to qualify welders for general construction work.

The non-destructive types of testing include:

1) Visual
2) Radiography

Visual testing will show only the surface appearance of the weld, and perhaps should be considered a method of inspection rather than testing.

Radiographic testing means making an X-ray photo of the

particular weld being examined. In this method, any defects in the weld will show up on the X-ray photographic film. This type of testing is used not only to qualify a welder but also to test the completed job. In some places all weldments are subjected to radiographic inspection upon completion of the job, so that there is a constant check on the welder's skill and ability.

MARINE TESTS

In order to standardize qualification tests for welding operators, the United States Coast Guard, the American Bureau of Shipping, and the Bureau of Ships, have formulated a reciprocal qualification test procedure.

The Bureau of Ships has agreed to the above reciprocal qualification tests in accordance with the following:

a) Welding operators who have been qualified in accordance with the common qualification tests as set forth in the following:

  1) United States Coast Guard's Federal Register, 1942
  2) American Bureau of Shipping's Rules for Building and Classing Steel Vessels, 1942
  3) General Specifications for Inspection of Material, U.S.N., 1938

by any of the participating agencies will be accepted by the other agencies within the limits covered by those qualification tests passed. No re-qualification tests will be required unless:

  1) The welding operator has not been engaged in the actual use of the welding process for which he was qualified for a period of 3 months or more.
  2) In the opinion of an inspector of one of the participating agencies under whose cognizance the work is being done, his work is of doubtful or uncertain quality.

In the above cases the welding operator will not be permitted to resume work until he has passed the applicable qualification test.

b) A common record card will be used, which will be retained by the employer; upon request, a duplicate will be furnished the inspector of any of the participating agencies.

Welding operators who have been qualified by the former Bureau of Marine Inspection and Navigation (now Marine Inspection Section, Operations Division), United States Coast Guard, and the American Bureau of Shipping, should be considered acceptable for the common qualification tests in accordance with the following rules:

a) Welding operators qualified by the former B.M.I.N.:

1) A welding operator who qualified on plate in the vertical or overhead positions will be acceptable for welding covered by the new Tests Nos. 1 and 2 in any position. If qualified by welding a horizontal seam in a vertical plate, he will be accepted for new Tests Nos. 1 and 2 in the horizontal and flat positions, and if qualified by welding in the flat position he will be accepted for new Tests Nos. 1 and 2 for flat position welding only.

2) A welding operator who qualified in accordance with Figures W-32 and W-33 of the former B.M.I.N., September 1939 Bulletin, with the axis of the pipe in the horizontal and vertical fixed positions or the horizontal fixed position only, will be accepted for welding governed by new Tests Nos. 3 and 4, respectively, in any position.

If qualified in accordance with Figures W-32 and W-33 with the pipe in the vertical fixed position only, he will be accepted for new Tests Nos. 3 and 4, respectively, with the axis of the pipe in the vertical fixed position only.

If qualified on pipe in accordance with Figures W-32

and W-33 in the horizontal rolled position, he will be accepted for new Tests Nos. 3 and 4, respectively, in the horizontal rolled position. If qualified per Figure W-32 of the former B.M.I.N., March 1939 Bulletin, he will be accepted for new Test No. 4 in the same position or positions in which the pipe was welded.

b) Welding operators qualified by the A.B.S.:

    1) A welding operator qualified for Group H-1, B-1 or B-2 by welding a reduced-section tensile specimen, a free-bend specimen and a nick-break specimen will be accepted for new Test No. 1 in any position. (It is understood the A.B.S. formerly required qualification test specimens to be prepared in all positions.)

    2) A welding operator qualified by boiler or pressure vessel workmanship tests for Group B-1 or B-2 will be accepted for new Tests Nos. 1 and 2 for the same position or positions in which the workmanship test plates were prepared.

QUALIFICATION TESTS

General Specifications for Inspection of Material

Appendix VII, Welding
Part E, Section E-1

Qualification Tests for Fusion Welders
(Issued by the Navy Department, November 1, 1938.)

Subsection 1—Applicable Specifications.

1a. This appendix forms a part of the Navy Department General Specifications for Inspection of Material of the issue in effect on the date of invitation for bids, and bidders and contractors should provide themselves with the necessary copies.

1b. Grade EA steel (covered) electrodes.

Navy Department Specifications

22W7	Electrodes, Welding (Bare, Coated, or Covered), Iron and Steel.
48S5	Steel, Plate, Hull, Structural, Black (uncoated) and Zinc-Coated (Galvanized) (Grade M).
46S1	Steel, Shapes and Bars for Hull Construction (Grade M).
48P2	Steel, Plate, Marine-Boiler (Class b).
47S11	Steel and Iron: Sheets and Strips for Flanging, Cupping, and Drawing.
44T13	Tubing, Steel, Seamless, for Oil, Steam or Water (Type A).

1c. Corrosion-resisting steel electrodes (19 Cr-8 Ni).

Bureau of Construction and Repair Specification

SPS941	Electrodes, Welding (Covered) Corrosion-Resisting Steel.

Navy Department Specifications

47S20	Steel, Corrosion-Resisting: Plates, Sheets, Strips, and Structural Shapes (Grade 1 only of 0.07 carbon maximum).
46S18	Steel, Corrosion-Resisting: Bars, Rods, and Forgings (except for reforging) (Grade 1, Type A only).
44T27	Tubing, Steel, Corrosion-Resisting (18% Chromium and 8% Nickel) Seamless-Drawn, Round, Structural.

1d. Nickel-copper electrodes.

Navy Department Specifications

17E4	Electrodes, Welding (Covered) Nickel-Copper Alloy.
46M7	Nickel-Copper Alloy: Bars, Plates, Rods, Shapes, Sheets, Strips, Tubing (Seamless) and Wire.

Bureau of Ordnance Specification

0S628	Specification for Copper-Nickel Alloy—Monel Metal, Wrought Form.

1e. Carbon-molybdenum steel electrodes.

Bureau of Engineering Specification

SGS(1)	118-Electrodes, Welding (Covered) Alloy Steel.

Navy Department Specifications

46S33   Steel, Molybdenum-Alloy: Castings.
47S23   Steel, Plate, Boiler, Molybdenum-Alloy.
44T33   Tubing, Steel, Molybdenum-Alloy, Seamless.
  1f. Scale-resisting alloy electrodes (25 Cr-20 Ni).

Bureau of Engineering Specification

SGS(1)   137-Electrodes, Welding (Covered) Scale-Resisting Alloy
          (25% Cr; 20% Ni).

Subsection 2—Special Terms.

2a. The commandant, superintending constructor, inspector of machinery, inspector of ordnance, inspector of naval aircraft, inspector of naval material, public works officer or authorized representative will hereinafter be called the naval inspector.

2b. Fully qualified welders, regardless of whether they are rated as first, second, third class, or apprentices, will be referred to as welders.

2c. Men qualified to do tack welding only will be referred to as tack welders.

2d. Contractors, navy yards, shipyards, and subcontractors doing naval work shall hereinafter be termed contractors.

2e. The word "Bureau" shall hereinafter be used to designate the bureau concerned.

Subsection 3—General Requirements.

3a. Before being permitted to perform any production work, each manual metal arc welder, excepting those welders listed in Paragraphs 3g and 3o below, shall pass the tests required hereinafter. Any welder who is to operate or control semiautomatic or automatic welding equipment, excepting those welders listed in Paragraph 3g below, shall pass the applicable qualification tests required hereinafter, making the welds with the equipment that he is to use in production. The contractor shall direct and supervise the testing of welders and shall bear the expense of conducting these tests. The welding and testing shall be witnessed by the naval inspector.

3b. The qualification tests described hereinafter are specially devised tests to demonstrate welder's ability and may or may not conform to the requirements for production welding. The practices required in the qualification tests shall not be used as a guide for production welding; the latter shall be done in accordance with the requirements of the Bureau.

3c. The contractor shall require any welder to repeat these tests when, in the opinion of the naval inspector, the work indicates a reasonable doubt of the welder's ability. In such cases the welder shall not be permitted to resume work until he passes the retest. Any welder who has not been employed as a metal arc welder for a period of 3 months or more shall, before being permitted to perform production work, be required to pass the applicable qualification tests even though he has previously passed such tests.

3e. The qualification tests shall be conducted with the same equipment, or equipment equivalent thereto in performance and condition, in the opinion of the naval inspector, as is used in production.

3f. All qualification specimens shall be stamped, stenciled, or otherwise indelibly marked with the welder's identification number, and other applicable markings sufficient to establish the position of welding and type of specimen.

3g. Qualification of welders working on assemblies, the possible failure of which is remote and would not result in danger to the vessel, plant, or structure, may be omitted, provided this omission is authorized by the Bureau. Laundry machinery, soda fountain machinery and their motors and controllers are examples of such assemblies.

3h. The following qualification tests (see pages 408-438 for figures referred to) shall be used as directed hereinafter in qualifying metal arc welders:

3h1. Qualification test No. 1 shall be the welding of specimens in accordance with Figure 231 as directed hereinafter which after machining shall be bent in accordance with the requirements of Paragraphs 3i and 3j.

3h2. Qualification test No. 2 shall be the welding of specimens in accordance with Figure 232 as directed hereinafter, which after machining shall be bent in accordance with the requirements of Paragraphs 3i and 3j.

3h3. Qualification test No. 3 shall be the welding, hydraulic testing and visual inspection of pipe assemblies, or, as an alternate, removal of specimens for microscopic examination, in accordance with the requirements of Figure 233 as directed hereinafter.

3h4. Qualification test No. 4 shall be the welding of specimens in accordance with Figure 234 as directed hereinafter which after

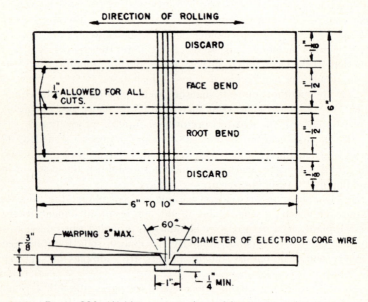

Figure 231: Welding operator's qualification test, No. 1.

Notes:

1. Weld shall be made with the maximum size of electrode permitted to be used in production for the position in which the welding operator is being qualified.

2. Machine reinforcement and backing strap flush. Do not remove any undercutting.

3. Machining shall be done transverse to the weld.

4. All specimens shall be machined or sawed from plate.

5. Backing strap shall be contiguous with plates.

6. Joints welded in the vertical position shall be welded upwards.

7. Welding shall be done from one side only.

8. Break edges of specimens to a radius of T/6 maximum.

machining shall be bent in accordance with requirements of Paragraphs 3i and 3j.

3h5. Qualification test No. 5 shall be the welding and bending

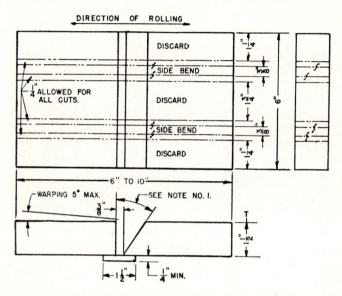

Figure 232: Welding operator's qualification test, No. 2.

Notes:

1. When welding in the flat and vertical positions of welding, the groove angle shall be 25°; when welding in the horizontal position the groove angle shall be 35° and the unbeveled plate shall be located on the top side of the joint.

2. Backing strap shall be contiguous with the plates.

3. Each pass of the weld shall be made with the same size of electrode that will be used in production for the position in which the welding operator is being qualified.

4. Joints welded in the vertical position shall be welded upwards.

5. Welding shall be done from one side only.

6. Machine reinforcement and backing strap flush. Do not remove any undercutting.

7. All specimens shall be machined or sawed from plate.

8. Machining shall be done transverse to weld.

9. Break edges of specimens to a radius of T/6 maximum.

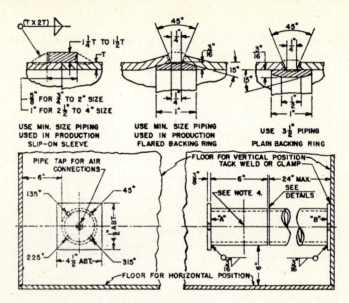

Figure 233: Welding operator's qualification test, No. 3.
Position in which specimens are welded:

One assembly in horizontal fixed position.

One assembly in vertical fixed position.

Notes:

1. When slip-on sleeves and plain type backing rings are used in production, plain type backing rings shall be used in this test. When all three types are used in production, flared type backing rings shall be used in this test.

2. Parts shall be galvanized where required.

3. Weld shall be deposited in a minimum of two layers.

4. Saw cut after pressure test for visual inspection.

5. No icicles or reduction of area of piping shall be permitted.

6. Omit plates A and B when etch test is used in lieu of the hydrostatic test.

7. Remove macro specimens from 45°, 135°, 225° and 315° points of the welded butt joints, as indicated (for etch test only).

8. Mark top and front of piping to insure proper location of specimens when etch test is used in lieu of hydrostatic test.

9. Welding shall be done from one side only.

10. Weld shall be made with the maximum size of electrode to be used in production for the position in which the welding operator is being qualified.

410

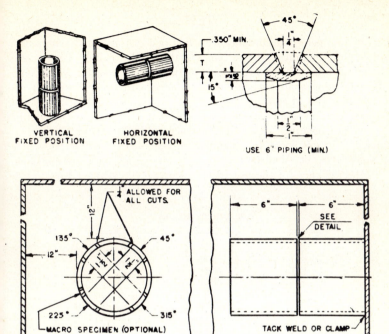

Figure 234: Welding operator's qualification test, No. 4.
One assembly in horizontal fixed position.
One assembly in vertical fixed position.

Notes:

1. Each pass of the weld shall be made with the maximum size of electrode permitted to be used in production for the position in which the welding operator is being qualified.

2. Machine reinforcement and backing strap flush. Do not remove any undercutting.

3. Machining shall be done transverse to weld.

4. All specimens shall be machined or sawed from piping.

5. Break edges of bend specimens to a radius of T/6 maximum.

6. Mark top and front of piping to insure proper location of specimens.

7. Remove face-bend specimens from 45° and 225° points, and root-bend specimens from 135° and 315° points as indicated.

8. Welding shall be done from one side only.

9. If piping of greater wall thickness than 0.380" is used in this test, piping may be machined to 0.350" to 0.380" before welding, or the bending jig (Figure 237) may be made in accordance with the actual thickness, T, of the piping used.

411

of specimens in accordance with Figure 235 as directed hereinafter.

3h6. Qualification test No. 6 shall be the welding of specimens in accordance with Figure 236 as directed hereinafter which after machining shall be bent in accordance with the requirements of Paragraphs 3i and 3j.

3i. Specimens for qualification tests Nos. 1, 2, 4, 5, and 6 shall be bent in a bending jig having the exact profile shown in Figure 237, page 415; specimens for qualification test No. 1 modified (see note No. 3, Par. 3k) shall be bent in a jig having a contour proportional to the thickness of the test plates involved as shown in Figure 237,

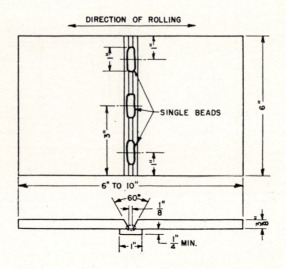

Figure 235: Welding operator's qualification test, No. 5.

Notes:

1. One-eighth inch diameter electrodes shall be used.
2. Backing strap shall be contiguous with the plates.
3. Joints welded in the vertical position shall be welded upwards.
4. Specimen shall be bent in one piece with backing strap in place, and face of weld in tension.
5. Weld fractures shall exhibit no unfused areas on backing strap or sides of groove throughout length of each tack.

page 415. Root bend specimens shall be bent with the root of the weld in tension; face bend specimens with the face in tension, and side bend specimens with that side, which is suspected of being the worse of the two, in tension.

3j. Specimens shall be bent to the angles of bend specified hereinafter. Any specimen in which a crack or opening exists before the bending, or results from the bending, exceeding ⅛″ (unless otherwise

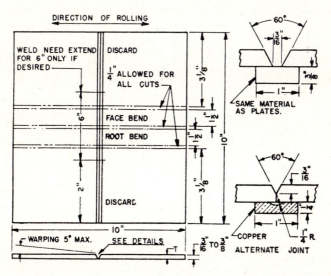

Figure 236: Welding operator's qualification test, No. 6 (for base metals of high thermal conductivity)

Notes:

1. Weld shall be made on the maximum thickness plate, within limits indicated, with maximum size electrode permitted to be used in production for the position in which the welding operator is being qualified.

2. Machine reinforcement and backing strap flush. Do not remove undercutting.

3. Machining shall be done transverse to weld.

4. All specimens shall be machined or sawed from plates.

5. Backing strap shall be contiguous with plates.

6. Joints welded in the vertical position shall be welded upwards.

7. Welding shall be done from one side only.

8. Break edges of specimens to a radius of T/6 maximum.

TABLE 24

REQUIRED QUALIFICATION TESTS

	Position in which welding is to be done on job.		
	Flat, Vertical, Horizontal and Overhead.	Flat, vertical; and Horizontal Fillets.	Flat Position only.
On material of limited thickness (¾" or less in thickness). (See Notes 1 and 3.)	Test No. 1. in vertical and overhead positions.	Test No. 1 in vertical position.	Test No. 1 in flat position.
On material of unlimited thickness. (See Note 2.)	Test No. 2 in vertical and horizontal positions.	Test No. 2 in vertical position.	Test No. 2 in flat position.
On piping or tubing (³⁄₁₆" or less in thickness).	Test No. 3, in horizontal and vertical fixed positions, provided welder has previously passed Test No. 1 in vertical and overhead positions.		Test No. 3 in horizontal position and rolled.
On piping or tubing (¾" or less in thickness). (See Note 4.)	Test No. 4 in horizontal and vertical fixed positions.		Test No. 4 in horizontal position and rolled.
For tack welders.	Test No. 5 in vertical and overhead positions.	Test No. 5 in vertical position.	
On material of unlimited thickness (for base metals of high conductivity).	Test No. 6 in vertical and overhead positions.	Test No. 6 in vertical position.	Test No. 6 in flat position.

Note 1) Where the maximum thickness of material on which a welder may have occasion to work throughout a period governed by a test is indeterminate, the naval inspector may, if desired, require welders to qualify under unlimited thickness requirements.

Note 2) Where the maximum plate thickness to be welded is between ¾" and 1½", qualification test No. 2 may, with the permission of the naval inspector, be conducted on plate or maximum thickness involved.

Note 3) Where the maximum thickness to be welded is less than ⅜",

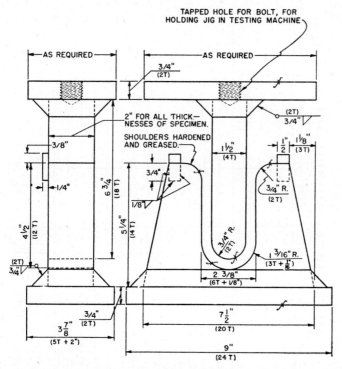

Figure 237: Jig for guided bend test—standard.

Notes:

1. T, thickness of test specimens.
2. Specific dimensions are for ⅜" test specimens.
3. Hardened rolls may be used on shoulders if desired.

---

the contractor may, with the permission of the naval inspector, use the following modification of test No. 1: The plate thickness shall be the maximum to be welded in production but shall be not less than ³⁄₁₆". The root opening shall be not more than one nominal diameter of the electrode to be used. The backing strap thickness shall be not less than ⁵⁄₃₂". The bending shall be done in a jig having a contour proportional to the thickness of the test plates involved as shown in Figure 237.

Note 4) Welders qualified under the requirements of test No. 4 will be considered as qualified to make welds governed by tests Nos. 1, 2, and 3.

NAME: _____
      (Last)   (First)   (Middle)

RECORD CARD OF WELDING OPERATOR'S QUALIFICATION TESTS

Employed by _____ Location of plant _____

Process	Test Number	Base Metal	Position	Filler Metal Type	Filler Metal Size	Date of Test	Signature of Inspector	Agency

A56365.

Figure 238: Welding operator's record card—Side A.

416

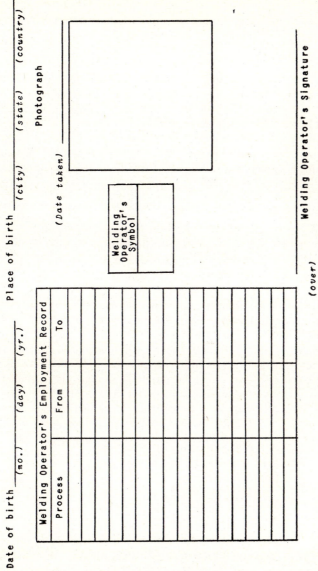

WELDING OPERATOR'S IDENTIFICATION   Check No. _____

Date of birth _____ _____ _____   Place of birth _____ _____ _____
              (mo.)   (day) (yr.)   (city) (state) (country)

Photograph

(Date taken)

Welding
Operator's
Symbol

Welding Operator's Employment Record

Process	From	To

(over)   Welding Operator's Signature

417

Figure 239: Welding operator's record card—Side B.

specified) measured in any direction, shall be rejected. No elongation data are required.

3k. All metal arc welders shall pass the qualification tests for the type and thickness of material, the kind of welding and position of work involved as specified in Table 25 and hereinafter.

3l. The results of the qualification tests, together with identification data, shall be recorded in Table No. 2, copies of which shall be filed in the office of the naval inspector.

3m. Tube specimens for Test No. 3 shall be subjected to the hoop stresses specified hereinafter. The hydrostatic pressure necessary to obtain these stresses shall be calculated by the following formula:

$$P = \frac{S \times 2t}{D}$$

where

P = the hydrostatic test pressure in lbs. per sq. in.

S = the specified hoop stress in lbs. per sq. in.

t = wall thickness of tube in ins.

D = inside diameter of tube in ins.

Wall thickness thinner than those specified shall be used when the former are authorized for production work, but wall thicknesses thicker shall not be used without the permission of the Bureau. The diameter of the tubing may be varied somewhat if desired. If the diameters or thicknesses different from those specified are used, the hydrostatic pressure shall be adjusted so that the specified hoop stress obtains. As an alternate for the hydrostatic test, four transverse specimens may be removed from the welded joint of Test No. 3 at the 45°, 135°, 225°, and 315° points for microscopic examination.

3n. The base metals listed hereinafter for use in qualifying welders may, unless otherwise specified, be either cast or wrought, regardless of the type of material upon which the production welding is to be done.

3o. For the Bureau of Aeronautics, metal arc welders shall be qualified in accordance with the requirements of Bureau of Aeronautics Specifications SR-14a, SR-43a, and PW-2.

3q. The passing of these qualification tests with direct-current equipment shall qualify welders with the direct-current equipment only. The passing of these qualification tests with alternating-current equipment shall qualify welders for welding with the alternating-equipment only. If both types of equipment are to be used by a welder, he shall be qualified with both alternating-current and direct-current equipment.

Subsection 4—Tests and Inspection.

4a. Grade EA, steel (covered) electrodes.

4a1. All metal arc welders who are to weld with grade EA electrodes shall pass qualification tests Nos. 1, 2, 3, 4 or 5, as required by paragraph 3k. Tests shall be carried out in accordance with the requirements of Paragraphs 4a2 to 4a12 below. The electrode used in the qualification tests shall be an approved electrode conforming to the requirements of Navy Department Specification 22W7.

4a2. The qualification test material shall conform to the requirements of one of the following Navy Department Specifications:

48S5   Steel, Plate, Hull, Structural, Black (uncoated) and Zinc-Coated (Galvanized) (Grade M).

46S1   Steel, Shapes and Bars for Hull Construction (Grade M).

48P2   Steel, Plate, Marine-Boiler (Class b).

47S11   Steel and Iron: Sheets and Strips for Flanging, Cupping and Drawing.

44T13   Tubing, Steel, Seamless, for Oil, Steam or Water (Type A).

49S1   Steel Castings (Class B).

Similar material may be used with the permission of the Bureau.

4a3. For the Bureau of Construction and Repair, one plate of each joint of Tests Nos. 1 and 5, one piece of tubing and one plate of Test No. 3, shall be galvanized in accordance with the requirements of specification 48S5 and 44P10, respectively. The galvanizing for Tests Nos. 1 and 5 shall be done after plate is beveled so that the weld shall be deposited on the galvanized surface. The use of galvanized plate for testing welders will not be required when the work is wholly on black material.

4a4. Welders who have passed qualification tests on galvanized material shall be considered as qualified for welding on the black material covered by the corresponding qualification tests.

4a5. For Tests Nos. 1 and 5, the thickness of the backing strap shall be not less than ¼″.

4a6. For Test No. 3, the wall thickness of the tubing shall be not greater than 0.120 in.

4a8. Temperature of previously deposited weld metal shall not be over 212° F. at time of deposition of subsequent bead or layer.

4a9. No peening shall be done in Tests Nos. 1, 3, 4, and 5. Peening may be done on each layer except the first and last layer in Test No. 2.

4a10. No stress relieving shall be done on Tests Nos. 1, 3, and 5. On Test No. 2, before machining specimens from the joint, the plate shall be stress relieved by maintaining it at 1150° F. (± 50° F.) for 1½ hrs. followed by slow cooling with the furnace to a temperature below 500° F. Stress-relieving, as outlined for Test No. 2 above, may be done on Test No. 4, provided such procedure is being carried out in production work.

4a11. Test specimens from Tests Nos. 1, 2, and 4 shall be bent to the full capacity of the jig shown in Figure 237, page 415. Specimens from Test No. 5 shall be bent to fracture in the jig shown in Figure 237.

4a12. Test No. 3 shall remain tight under a hydrostatic pressure sufficient to impose a hoop stress of 30,000 lbs. per sq. in. Microscopic examination of etched transverse weld specimens shall show complete penetration into the root of the weld and freedom from cracks, slag inclusions, porosity or other defects.

4a13. The passing of a qualification test with grade EA electrodes on the base metals listed in Paragraph 4a2 above, shall qualify a welder to make welds governed by that test with grade EA electrodes on any of the base materials conforming to the requirements of the following specifications, or any combination of these materials.

Navy Department Specifications

48S5	Steel, Plate, Hull, Structural, Black (Uncoated) and Zinc-Coated (Galvanized). (Welding quality only.)
48P2	Steel, Plate, Marine-Boiler.
47S10	Steel: Sheet, Black and Zinc-Coated (Galvanized).

47S11	Steel and Iron Sheets and Strips for Flanging, Cupping and Drawing.
47S16	Steel, Sheet, for the Manufacture of Metal Furniture.
47M1	Metal, Expanded (Steel).
47S18	Steel, Plate, Floor, Rolled (see Paragraph 4a13).
46S1	Steel Shapes and Bars for Hull Construction, including Material for drop and Miscellaneous Forgings.
46S29	Steel: Forgings for Welding.
46S2	Steel, Extra Soft, Bar.
46S4	Steel, Carbon and Alloy: Blooms, Billets, Slabs, and Bars for Reforging. (Grades M and Bw only.)
46S19	Steel, Staybolt (Boiler).
46S13	Steel, Machinery, Cold-rolled or Cold-drawn; Rods and Bars.
46S6	Steel, Carbon, Hot-rolled or Forged. (Class C1 and C2 only.)
46-1-7	Iron, Wrought (Refined): Bars.
43R1	Rivets and Rivet Rods, Steel, for Hull Construction.
49S1	Steel, Castings—Class B only—(Classes A, Bs, C, D & F when specifically approved by the Bureau).
44T14	Tubes, Boilers, Charcoal Iron, Lapwelded.
44T3	Seamless Boiler Tubes.
49T1	Tubes, Steel (Carbon, Mild), Seamless.
44T1	Tubing, Steel, for Structural Purposes.
44T11	Tubes, Boiler, Steel, Commercial.
45F7	Flanges, Steel, for Steel Pipe and Tubing.
44T13	Tubing, Steel, Seamless, for Oil, Steam, or Water.
44T4	Lapwelded Steel Casing.
44P10	Pipe, Steel, Seamless and Welded, Black and Zinc-Coated (Galvanized).
44P11	Pipe, Iron, Wrought.

Federal Specifications

QQ-S-711	Steel, Structural for Bridges.	
QQ-S-721	Steel, Structural for Buildings.	For Bureau of Yards
QQ-S-731	Steel, Structural for Cars.	and Docks only.
QQ-B-71	Bars, Reinforcement, Concrete.	

Bureau of Construction and Repair Specifications

SPS928   Steel: Plates, Special Treatment, for Protective Hull Plating (see Paragraph 4a14).

SPS1021   Wrought Iron Plates, Structural, Black (Uncoated) and Zinc-Coated (Galvanized).

4a14. The conditions under which production welding may be permitted on the base metals listed in Paragraph 4a13 shall be as set forth by the Bureau.

4b. Grade EB, steel (bare) electrodes.

4b1. Where welding with electrodes, conforming to the requirements of grade EB of Navy Department Specification 22W7, has been authorized, qualification of welders shall be as directed by the Bureau.

4c. Grade ED, and EE, steel (hard-surfacing) electrodes.

4c1. Welders who are qualified to weld with grade EA electrodes will be considered qualified to weld with hard-surfacing electrodes complying with the requirements of grades ED and EE of Navy Department Specification 22W7.

4d. Corrosion-resisting steel electrodes (19 CR.-8 Ni).

4d1. All metal arc welders who are to weld with the corrosion-resisting steel electrodes, shall pass the qualification tests Nos. 1, 2, 3, 4, or 5 as required by Paragraph 3k. The tests shall be carried out as required in Paragraphs 4d2 to 4d10 below. The electrode used in the qualification tests shall be an approved electrode conforming to the requirements of the Bureau of Construction and Repair Specification SPS941.

4d2. The qualification test material shall conform to the requirements of one of the following Navy Department Specifications:

47S20   Steel, Corrosion-Resisting: Plates, Sheets, Strips, and Structural Shapes (Grade 1 only, of 0.07 carbon maximum).

46S18   Steel, Corrosion-Resisting: Bars, Rods, and Forgings (except for Reforging) (grade 1 type A only).

44T27   Tubing, Steel, Corrosion-Resisting (18 percent Chromium and 8 percent Nickel) Seamless-Drawn, Round Structural).

Similar material may be used with the permission of the Bureau.

4d3. If the work contracted for involves piping thinner than

0.120", the minimum required thickness shall be used for the qualification test, but in no case shall the wall thickness be greater than 0.120".

4d4. For Tests Nos. 1 and 5, the thickness of the backing strap shall not be less than ⅛".

4d5. No preheating shall be done.

4d6. The electrode sizes used in the tests shall be as given in Table 25, except that if the work contracted for does not involve electrodes as large as ⁵⁄₃₂" diameter, the maximum diameter to be used on the work may, with the permission of the naval inspector, be used in the qualification test:

TABLE 25

	Test No. 1	Test No. 2	Test No. 3	Test No. 4	Test No. 5
Electrode size.	⁵⁄₃₂ in.	⁵⁄₃₂ in.	Maximum to be used on work.	Maximum to be used on work.	⅛ in.

4d7. No peening shall be done.

4d8. No heat treatment after welding shall be done.

4d9. Test specimens from Tests Nos. 1, 2, and 4 shall be bent to the full capacity of the jig shown in Figure 237. Test specimens from Test No. 5 shall be bent to fracture in the jig shown in Figure 237.

4d10. Test No. 3 shall remain tight under a hydrostatic pressure sufficient to impose a hoop stress of 35,000 lbs. per sq. in.

4d11. The passing of a qualification test with corrosion-resisting steel electrodes on the base metals listed in Paragraph 4d2 above shall qualify a welder to make welds governed by that test with an approved corrosion-resisting steel electrode on any of the base materials conforming to the requirements of the following Navy Department Specifications, or shall qualify him to weld on any combination of these materials or any combination of these with the materials listed in Paragraph 4a12 (except as noted in Par. 4d12):

47S20 Steel, Corrosion-Resisting: Plates, Sheets, Strips, and Structural Shapes. (Grade 1 only, of 0.07 carbon maximum.)

46S26 Steel, Corrosion-Resisting: Bars and Billets (for reforging only). (Grade 1 only.)

46S18 Steel, Corrosion-Resisting: Bars, Rods, and Forgings (except for Reforging). (Grade 1, Type A only.)

44P16 Piping and Tubing, Corrosion-Resisting Steel. (Grade 1 only, of 0.08 carbon maximum.)

44T27 Tubing, Steel, Corrosion-Resisting (18% Chromium and 8% Nickel) Seamless-Drawn, Round Structural.

46S27 Steel, Corrosion-Resisting: Castings. (Grade 1 only, of 0.08 carbon maximum.)

4d12. The conditions under which production welding may be permitted on the base metals listed in Paragraph 4d11, or combinations thereof with those listed in Paragraph 4a13, shall be as set forth by the Bureau, with particular reference to the use of corrosion-resisting steel electrodes on galvanized surfaces.

4e. Nickel-copper alloy electrodes.

4e1. All metal arc welders who are to use nickel-copper alloy electrodes shall pass qualification tests Nos. 1, 2, 3, or 5 as required by paragraph 3k. The tests shall be carried out as required in paragraphs 4e2 and 4e9 below. The electrode used in the qualification tests shall conform to the requirements of Bureau of Engineering Specification 17E4.

4e2. The qualification test material shall conform to the requirements of one of the following specifications:

Navy Department Specification.

46M7 Copper-Nickel Alloy: Bars, Plates, Rods, Shapes, Sheets, Strips, Tubing (Seamless), and Wire.

Bureau of Ordnance Specification.

0S628 Specification for Copper-Nickel Alloy-Monel Metal, Wrought Form.

4e3. No preheating shall be done.

4e4. For Tests Nos. 1 and 5, the thickness of the backing strap shall not be less than the nominal diameter of the filler metal to be used and not less than $\frac{1}{8}''$ in any case.

4e5. The electrode size used in the tests shall be as given in Table 26:

4e6. No peening shall be done in Tests Nos. 1, 3, and 5. Peening may be done on each layer except the first and last layer in Test No. 2.

4e7. No stress-relieving shall be done on Tests Nos. 1, 3, and 5. On Test No. 2, before machining specimens from the joint, the plate shall be stress-relieved by maintaining it at 1,150° F. ($\pm$ 50° F.) for 1½ hrs. followed by slow cooling with the furnace to a temperature below 500° F.

4e8. Test specimens from Tests Nos. 1 and 2 shall be bent to the full capacity of the jig shown in Figure 237, page 415. Test specimens from Test No. 5 shall be bent to fracture in the jig shown in Figure 237.

4e9. Test No. 3 shall remain tight under a hydrostatic pressure sufficient to impose a hoop stress of 25,000 lbs. per sq. in.

4e10. The passing of a qualification test with nickel-copper alloy electrodes on the base metal listed in Paragraph 4e2 above, shall qualify a welder to make welds governed by that test with nickel-copper electrodes on base metal conforming to the requirements of either of the following specifications, or shall qualify him to weld on any combination of these materials with those listed in Paragraph 4a12.

Navy Department Specification.

46M7 Nickel-Copper Alloy: Bars, Plates, Rods, Shapes, Sheets, Strips, Tubing (Seamless) and Wire.

Bureau of Ordnance Specification.

0S628 Specification for Copper-Nickel Alloy-Monel Metal, Wrought Form.

4e11. The conditions under which production welding may be permitted on the base metals listed in Paragraph 4e10, or combinations thereof with those listed in Paragraph 4a12, shall be as set forth by the Bureau.

4f. Carbon-molybdenum steel electrodes.

TABLE 26

	Test No. 1	Test No. 2	Test No. 3	Test No. 5
Electrode size.	5⁄32 in.	Beads 1 to 3 on upper and lower sides may be deposited with 5⁄32 in. electrodes. Remainder shall be deposited with 3⁄16 in. electrodes.	Maximum to be used on work.	1⁄8 in.

4f1. All metal arc welders who are to use carbon-molybdenum steel electrodes shall pass qualification tests Nos. 1, 2, 3, 4, and 5 as required by Paragraph 3k. The tests shall be carried out as required in Paragraphs 4f2 to 4f9 below. The electrode used in the qualification tests shall conform to the requirements of Bureau of Engineering Specification SGS(1)-118.

4f2. The qualification test material shall conform to the requirements of one of the following Navy Department Specifications:

46S33 Steel, Molybdenum-Alloy: Castings

47S23 Steel, Plate, Boiler, Molybdenum-Alloy

44T33 Tubing, Steel, Molybdenum Alloy, Seamless

4f3. Test specimens shall be preheated to a temperature equal to, but not exceeding, the preheat temperature to be used on the work.

4f5. For Tests Nos. 1 and 5 the thickness of the backing strap shall not be less than $\frac{1}{4}''$.

4f6. No peening shall be done in Tests Nos. 1, 3, 4, and 5. Peening may be done on each layer except the first and last in Test No. 2.

4f7. Specimens shall be heated after welding to 1,150° F. (± 50° F.) for 1 hr. for Tests Nos. 1, 3, and 4 and $1\frac{1}{2}$ hrs. for Test No. 2, and allowed to cool with the furnace to below 500° F. Specimens for Test No. 5 shall not be heat-treated.

4f8. Test specimens from Tests Nos. 1, 2, and 4 shall be bent to the full capacity of the jig shown in Figure 237. Test specimens from Test No. 5 shall be bent to fracture in the jig shown in Figure 7.

4f9. Test No. 3 shall remain tight under a hydrostatic pressure sufficient to impose a hoop stress of 40,000 lbs. per sq. in. Microscopic examination of etched transverse weld specimens shall show complete penetration into the root of the weld and freedom from cracks, slag inclusions, porosity or other defects.

4f10. The passing of a qualification test with carbon-molybdenum steel electrodes on the base metals listed in Paragraph 4f2 above, shall qualify a welder to make welds governed by that test with carbon-molybdenum steel electrodes on any of the base materials conforming to the requirements of the following Navy Department specifications, or shall qualify him to weld on any combination of these materials with the materials listed in Paragraph 4a12.

46S33 Steel, Molybdenum-Alloy: Castings.
46S34 Steel, Molybdenum-Alloy: Wrought.
47S23 Steel, Plate, Boiler, Molybdenum-Alloy.
44T33 Tubing, Steel, Molybdenum Alloy, Seamless.

4f11. The conditions under which production welding may be permitted on the base metals listed in Paragraph 4f9 shall be as set forth by the Bureau.

4g. Scale-resisting alloy electrodes (25 Cr.-20Ni).

4g1. All metal arc welders who are to use scale-resisting alloy steel electrodes shall pass qualification Tests Nos. 1 or 5 as required by Paragraph 3k. The tests shall be carried out as required in Paragraphs 4g2 and 4g9 below. The electrode used in the qualification tests shall be an approved electrode conforming to the requirements of Bureau of Engineering Specification SGS-(1)137.

4g2. The qualification test material shall be wrought scale-resisting alloy having the following physical and chemical characteristics:

Physical properties:

Ultimate strength........	80,000 lbs. per sq. in. (min.)
Yield Point.............	35,000 lbs. per sq. in. (min.)
Elongation in 2″.........	30% (min.)

Chemical analysis:

	%
Chromium	23–27
Nickel	17–21
Silicon, max.	1. 5
Manganese, max.	1.10
Carbon, max.	0.20
Phosphorus, max.	0.05
Sulphur, max.	0.05

4g3. For Tests Nos. 1 and 5, the thickness of the backing strap shall be not less than $\frac{1}{8}$ inch.

4g4. No preheating shall be done.

4g5. The electrode sizes used in the tests shall be as given in Table 27, except that if the work contracted for does not involve electrodes as large at $\frac{5}{32}$-inch diameter, the maximum diameter to be used on the work may, with the permission of the Naval Inspector, be used in the qualification test:

TABLE 27

	Test No. 1	Test No. 5
Electrode size	$\frac{5}{32}$ in.	$\frac{1}{8}$ in.

4g6. No peening shall be done.

4g7. No heat treatment after welding shall be done.

4g8. Test specimens from Test No. 1 shall be bent to the full capacity of the jig shown in Figure 237, page 415. Test specimens from Test No. 5 shall be bent to fracture in the jig shown in Figure 237.

4g9. The passing of a qualification test with scale-resisting alloy electrodes on a base metal having the physical and chemical characteristics set forth in Paragraph 4g2 above, shall qualify a welder to make welds governed by that test with an approved scale-resisting alloy electrode on any base metal conforming to the above-mentioned characteristics, or shall qualify him to weld on any combination of this material with the materials listed in Paragraph 4a12 (except as noted in Par. 4g10.)

4g10. The conditions under which production welding may be permitted on the base metal having the physical and chemical characteristics set forth in Paragraph 4g2 above, or combinations thereof with those listed in Paragraph 4a12, shall be as set forth by the Bureau, with particular reference to the use of scale-resisting alloy electrodes on galvanized surfaces.

4h. Aluminum alloy electrodes.

4h1. All metal arc welders who are to use aluminum-alloy electrodes shall pass qualification test No. 6 in the flat position as required by Paragraph 3k. The tests shall be carried out as required in Paragraphs 4h2 to 4h7 below. The electrodes used in the qualification test shall be approved by the Bureau.

4h2. The qualification test material shall be wrought aluminum or aluminum alloy conforming to the requirements of one of the following Navy Department Specifications:

47A2   Aluminum: Plates and Sheets, Class A.

47A4   Aluminum Alloy (Aluminum-Manganese): Plates and Sheets, Class A.

47A12   Aluminum Alloy (Aluminum-Magnesium-Silicon-Chromium) Plates and Sheets, Class A.

4h3. No preheating shall be done.

4h4. The electrode size used in the test shall be the maximum diameter to be used on the work.

4h5. No peening shall be done.

4h6. No heat treatment after welding shall be done.

4h7. Test specimens from Test No. 6 shall be bent to the full capacity of the jig shown in Figure 237.

4h8. The passing of a qualification test with aluminum-alloy electrodes on one of the base metals listed in Paragraph 4h2 above, shall qualify a welder to make welds governed by that test with an approved aluminum-alloy electrode on any of the base metals conforming to the requirements of the following Navy Department Specifications:

47A2   Aluminum: Plates and Sheets.

46A3   Aluminum: Bars, Rods, Shapes, and Wire.

44T19   Tubing, Aluminum, Round, Seamless.

47A4   Aluminum Alloy (Aluminum-Manganese): Plates and Sheets.

46A6   Aluminum Alloy (Aluminum-Manganese): Bars, Rods, Shapes, and Wire.

44T20   Tubing, Aluminum Alloy (Aluminum-Manganese).

47A7   Aluminum Alloy (Aluminum-Manganese), Plate, Floor, Rolled.

44T5   Tubing, Voice: Aluminum Alloy (Aluminum-Manganese.)

47A11   Aluminum Alloy (Aluminum-Magnesium-Chromium): Plates and Sheets.

46A11   Aluminum Alloy (Aluminum-Magnesium-Chromium): Bars, Rods, Shapes, and Wire.

47A12 Aluminum Alloy (Aluminum-Magnesium-Silicon-Chromium): Plates and Sheets.

46A10 Aluminum Alloy (Aluminum-Magnesium-Silicon-Chromium): Bars, Rods, Shapes, and Wire.

46A1 Aluminum Alloy, Light: Castings (Resistant to Salt Water Corrosion) (Classes 2 and 5 only).

44T30 Tubing, Aluminum-Alloy (Aluminum-Magnesium-Silicon-Chromium), Round, Seamless.

4h9. The conditions under which production welding may be permitted on the base metals listed in Paragraph 4h8 above, shall be as set forth by the Bureau.

4i. Qualification of metal arc welders with other electrodes.

4i1. All metal arc welders who are to use electrodes other than those listed herein shall be required to pass qualification tests as required by the Bureau.

STRUCTURAL TESTS

The American Welding Society (A.W.S.) Welders' test qualifications have been or are being adopted for various codes, such as A.P.I., A.S.M.E., A.W.W.A., and are being adopted by the Chicago Bridge and Iron Company for its field welders' test.

The new A.W.S. test is covered in pamphlet "Tentative Standard Qualification Procedure" and in "A.P.I. Specifications on All-Welded Storage Tanks, No. 120, 4th Edition, March, 1941."

Class 1A1 covers welders who pass Tests Nos. 1, 2, 6, 7 and 8. These welders are qualified to weld plates of any thickness in any position.

Class A1 covers welders who pass Tests Nos. 1, 2, 3, 4, and 5. These welders are qualified to weld plates up to and including ¾″ thickness in any position.

Class B1 covers welders who pass Tests Nos. 1, 3 and 4. These welders are qualified to weld plates up to and including ¾″ thickness in a down, vertical or horizontal position for butt or lap joints.

Welders who are not sure of their ability, may start with Test No. 1 and make as many of the eight tests as they can. Their classification will be determined by the number they pass.

Plug Rating. Welders who pass these tests carry conditional ratings until they establish a plug record of 75% or better on eight or more plugs. Welders who cannot maintain an average of 75% or better are automatically dropped to the next lower classification. If in this classification they are unable to maintain 75% or better rating, they drop to the next lower classification. Existing plug records will stand.

Fillet Test. The plates for this test consist of two pieces of ⅜″

TABLE 28

Tests Required for Different Grades			Test No.	Position of Test Plates	Size of Weld Rod
B1	A1	1A1	1	⅜″ Fillet Vertical	³⁄₁₆″
	A1	1A1	2	⅜″ Fillet Overhead	³⁄₁₆″
B1	A1		3	⅜″ Butt Vertical	⁵⁄₃₂″ & ³⁄₁₆″
B1	A1		4	⅜″ Butt Horizontal	⁵⁄₃₂″ & ³⁄₁₆″
	A1		5	⅜″ Butt Overhead	⁵⁄₃₂″ & ³⁄₁₆″
		1A1	6	1″ Butt Vertical	⁵⁄₃₂″ & ³⁄₁₆″
		1A1	7	1″ Butt Horizontal	⁵⁄₃₂″ & ³⁄₁₆″
		1A1	8	1″ Butt Overhead	⁵⁄₃₂″ & ³⁄₁₆″

From butt welds are required only one root bend and one face bend, or two side bends. All welding electrodes used shall be Lincoln Fleetweld No. 5.

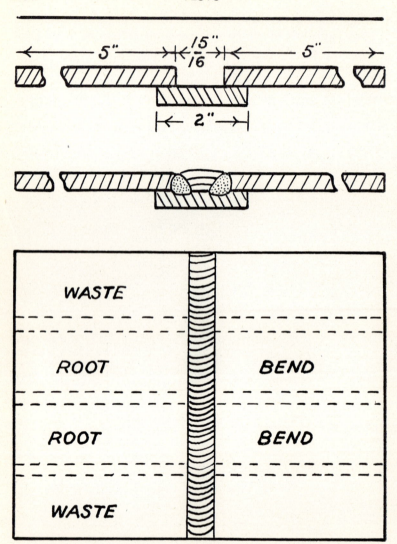

Figure 240: ⅜″ fillet test.

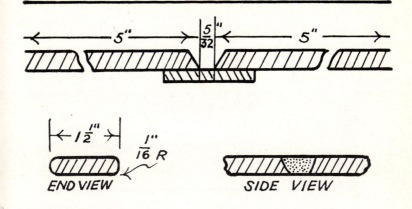

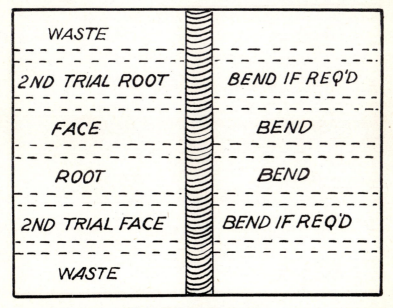

Figure 241: ⅜" butt test.

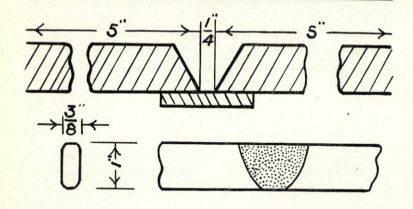

Figure 242: 1″ butt test.

TEST NO.	SKETCH OF TEST PLATE	THICKNESS AND POSITION OF TEST PLATE	TESTS REQUIRED FOR DIFFERENT GRADES		
1		3/8" FILLET VERTICAL	IAI	AI	BI
2	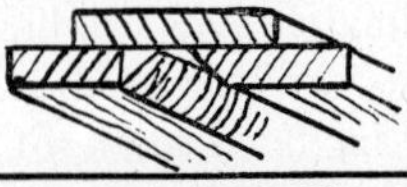	3/8" FILLET OVERHEAD	IAI	AI	
3		3/8" BUTT VERTICAL		AI	BI
4		3/8" BUTT HORIZONTAL		AI	BI
5	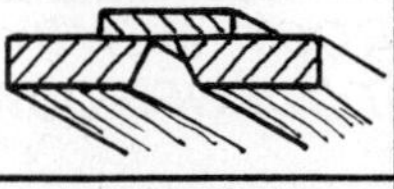	3/8" BUTT OVERHEAD		AI	
6		1" BUTT VERTICAL	IAI		
7		1" BUTT HORIZONTAL	IAI		
8		1" BUTT OVERHEAD	IAI		

Figure 243: Tabulation of tests. 3/8" test plates qualify for 3/4" thickness of work. 1" test plates qualify for any thickness of work.

stock $5'' \times 6\frac{1}{8}''$, spaced $^{15}\!/_{16}''$ apart and a backup strip, $\frac{3}{8}''$ by
$2''$ by $6\frac{1}{8}''$. Two fillet welds are made as shown in Figure 240.
After both of these fillets are completed, the remaining space is filled
in. The fillet test is made in the vertical and overhead positions.
After the welding is completed the weld reinforcement and backup
strip are machined flush with the plate. The complete job is then
cut in four sections as shown; two of these pieces are thrown away
and the other two are tested. Before being tested the corners of the
test specimens are rounded off to approximately $\frac{1}{16}''$ radius.

$\frac{3}{8}''$ **Butt Test.** The plates for this test are bevelled at a $22\frac{1}{2}°$
angle, and spaced $^5\!/_{32}''$ apart, giving an included angle of $45°$ and
a $^5\!/_{32}''$ root opening. The backup strip is $1''$ by $\frac{1}{4}''$. This test is
made in three positions—vertical, horizontal and overhead. After
welding is completed the weld reinforcement and backup strip are
machined flush and test pieces are cut as shown in Figure 241.

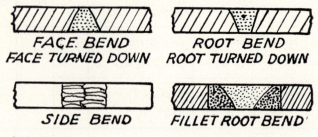

FACE BEND
FACE TURNED DOWN

ROOT BEND
ROOT TURNED DOWN

SIDE BEND

FILLET ROOT BEND

Figure 244: The four types of tests used. Requirements for passing test:
A test plate has failed if there is a crack or hole in the weld more than $\frac{1}{8}''$
in any direction. Cracks starting at corners shall not be considered.

$1''$ **Butt Test.** The plates for this test are $1''$ thick and spaced
$\frac{1}{4}''$ apart. The edges are bevelled at $20°$. The test on this butt
is a side bend rather than a face and root bend. After welding, the
reinforcement and backup strip are machined off as in the previous
cases. The required positions for this test are horizontal, vertical
and overhead. (See Figure 242.)

In order to pass these tests, the specimens being tested must be
bent to the full capacity of the jig without cracking. A specimen

has failed if there is a crack or hole in the weld more than $\frac{1}{8}''$ in any direction. Cracks starting on corners shall not be considered.

Procedure of Testing.

1) Grease shoulders of cradle.

2) Place test plate across cradle with weld centered under plunger.

3) Force plunger down until a $\frac{1}{32}''$ wire cannot be passed between test plate and curved part of plunger.

4) Open jig and remove test plate.

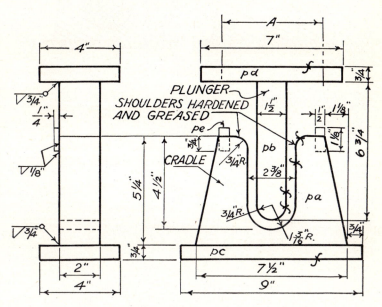

Figure 245: A. W. S. guided-bend test jig. (A): Drill holes to suit for attachment to testing machine.

Bill of material for one test jig:

    1 pa plate, 2" x 7½" x 0'-5¼"

    1 pb plate, 2" x 1¾" (fin. 1½") x 0'-6¾"

    1 pc plate, ¾" x 4" x 0'-9"

    1 pd plate, ¾" x 4" x 0'-7"

    2 pe lugs, ¼" x ½" x 0'-1⅛"

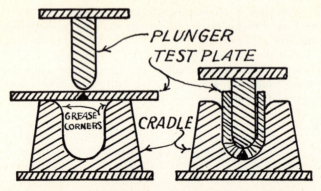

Figure 246: Sketch showing application of test jig.

APPENDICES

APPENDICES

Appendix 1

Thermal Stresses and Shrinkage in Welded Ship Construction[*]

FOREWORD

At a meeting of the Committee on Welding in Marine Construction held in April 1935, it was pointed out that the phenomena of shrinkage in welded joints created a most important problem in welded ship construction: first, as a matter of dimension, and second, with regard to the stresses which would be set up in the structure. In the discussion which followed, it was felt that it might be necessary to develop standard rules of procedure to avoid serious trouble in service. As a result, the Chairman appointed a Subcommittee to assemble available data from previous work and to investigate the general problem of thermal stresses in welded ships.

The members of the Subcommittee are directly involved in this work, each faced with the solution of urgent problems at their individual plants which have been brought about by the rapid expansion of welding. It has been impossible for the Committee as a group to undertake the study of its topic as one for research leading to the development of recommended practice in advance of the application to actual ship construction. Rather, each yard has worked out its own problems and the Committee has served as a clearing house of information springing from practical and service experience.

On October 26, 1939, the Subcommittee presented a complete report in preliminary form to the Committee on Welding in Marine Construction for their general criticism and comment. Following receipt of written comment from practically all members of the Main Committee, the Subcommittee presented its final report, which was approved unanimously by the Main Committee at a meeting held on October 21, 1940.

[*] Report prepared by the Committee on Welding in Marine Construction, American Welding Society, New York. Reprinted by permission.

I—INTRODUCTION

In the field of naval ship construction, the Bureau of Ships (formerly the Bureau of Construction and Repair) has developed, during the past five years, detailed specifications covering the applications of welding, particularly in regard to the procedure to care for the effects of thermal stresses and shrinkage. In merchant ship construction, the regulatory bodies have, speaking generally, been much less specific in regard to this phase in their written rules and specifications, dealing in the results to be obtained rather than in specific methods of procedure. A question of primary importance is, therefore, the necessity for more or less elaborate precautions to prevent or mitigate possible adverse effects of welding shrinkage. If such steps are not required or may be simplified, naval construction will benefit by the elimination of much costly procedure coupled with a reduction in time of building welded ships. Ship welding has had extensive service trial over a period of years with a truly remarkable record of satisfactory performance. More will be said of the matter of service failures later in this report but it may be stated that many ships whose construction in whole or in part violated many principles of stress-free welding procedure have undergone extraordinary sea tests without failure. It is therefore pertinent to reexamine the theory and logic of some of these principles if for no other reason than to account for this excellent record.

The general topic of thermal stresses and shrinkage resolves itself into three main sub-divisions:

I. The loss of original dimensions of welded parts or assemblies, which is reflected in the loss of the principal design dimensions of the ship if no allowance is made.

II. Distortion or the loss of shape of individual parts or assemblies. This includes warping and twist, the appearance of buckles and wrinkles in plane surfaces, or the rise of bow or stern.

III. Residual or "locked-up" stresses, either in the welded joint or in the structure due to shrinkage in proximity to the welded joint.

II—LOSS OF DIMENSION

The most obvious result in welded construction, which does not occur at all or only to an inappreciable degree in other forms of jointing, is loss of dimension due to shrinkage. Further, this loss of dimension is encountered in two different forms. When a joint is made between two individual parts, there is shrinkage of the filler metal, added in the molten state, which tends to draw these parts together. If one part is being attached to the other, that is, when a weld is made to a continuous or passing member, there is also shrinkage in the vicinity of the weld which is reflected in the shortening of the passing member. Applied to ship structure, these two forms can be represented by (a), butts or seams in shell plating, and (b), the attachment of framing to the shell plating. Unless compensation is made for both forms, the completed shell will be less than its original designed length.

The Subcommittee has collected a great deal of test data as well as records of measurement on full-size or actual ship structures. In addition, a very considerable amount of data has been published and a notable collection or summary of these data is available in an A.W.S. Research Supplement.[1] Analysis of all this information reveals so wide a discrepancy in shrinkage between similar joints as to render a summary or tables of predicted shrinkage valueless. The data on record also show wide differences between small and large-scale tests. It must be concluded that too many variables enter this phase of the problem, many beyond the control of the welding operator or shipbuilder.

The problem of dimension is not, however, of primary importance. Where no correction has been made, shrinkage in the length as high as 6 inches in vessels less than 150 feet long has been reported. Such loss is actually of little moment in so far as speed and power are concerned and generally is of concern only in the loss of capacity. In the construction of larger ships, some means of correction has invariably been employed so that the loss in dimension has generally been insignificant.

[1] Shrinkage Distortion in Welding, by W. Spraragen and G. E. Claussen, AMERICAN WELDING SOCIETY JOURNAL, Research Supplement, July 1937.

Among the corrective measures which have been employed in ship construction are (1), the use of expanded scales, (2), the use of excess length or allowance over mold loft or drawing dimension, and (3), "lift from ship" correction.

The use of the expanded scale is borrowed from the pattern shop and foundry. Since a finished casting is smaller than the pattern molded in the sand, an expanded measuring stick is used in the construction of the pattern which makes allowance for the shrinkage per foot of the particular metal being used. The application of this method to a welded ship assumes that welding shrinkage, like that in the casting, is relatively uniform throughout. Unfortunately, this is rarely if ever true. Not only are we faced with wide variations in shrinkage of similar joints as noted above, but there are also wide differences in the application and amount of welding in many different parts of the structure. A deck, for example, may be transversely framed whereas the shell plating in the vicinity of that deck may be largely longitudinally framed. One may consist of considerably heavier plating than the other although the attachment of framing may be made with welds of similar or identical size since the strength of the connection desired is not necessarily a function of plate thickness. It is obvious that the same expanded scales cannot be applied to both structures. Furthermore, in shipbuilding, the use of scales, and the measuring and setting of various parts, is not restricted to any one operation or department. Correlating the proper scales with regard to varying ship structure throughout the progress of material from storage yard to ways has generally proved too complicated a problem for the benefits derived and, although actually tried in practice, this method of correction, as far as the Subcommittee is aware, is generally no longer in use.

A method in common use is to add an arbitrary allowance or excess to the length and width of parts subject to welding shrinkage. As a general rule this allowance is considerably more than the shrinkage actually expected and the excess is then removed after as much shrinkage as possible has taken place. Only where it is impossible to leave such excess is it wise to allow the exact shrinkage predicted. The excess or allowance method may be made on all parts and ships' dimensions corrected at intervals, thus allowing a considerable amount of material to be used without flame cutting or chipping in erection.

A third corrective measure is to leave selected parts of the structure to be measured or "lifted" from the ship after adjacent structures are completely welded and shrunk to the final dimension.

III—DISTORTION

Distortion, particularly when localized in the form of buckles in flat or but slightly curved plates, is an especially troublesome problem to the shipbuilder. While it may be frequently argued that such distortion has little or no effect on the strength or service life of the ship, the unsightliness of such distortion coupled with the complication in the attachment of other parts to warped structure creates a major problem. Where excessive distortion occurs and is unacceptable, the warped part is straightened by the application of heat or mechanical work, usually at great expense. In ships with light scantlings, the cost of straightening has frequently exceeded the cost of fitting and welding the structure. Viewed from the angle of cost, appearance, or utility, prevention of distortion is so much to be preferred to its correction that an extensive study of this particular problem is warranted.

In the field of preventive measures, shipbuilders have experimented with all manner of methods, the principal ones of which may be classified as follows:

(a) Pre-springing or initial distortion

In its simplest application, this method consists of mechanically setting or bending a part in an opposite direction to which warpage is expected so that the effect of welding is to restore the part to its desired shape.

(b) Strong-backs or jig methods

The size and variation of ship structures generally preclude the use of jigs of the type frequently applied to small machine or sheet metal assemblies. A variation which is applicable to large structures is the use of strong-backs and temporary stiffening by which the structure is given increased resistance to distortion but which are removed after the welding has been completed and cooled.

(c) Drum-heading

This classification refers to a method frequently used on large areas where the boundaries have a large degree of permanent or temporary restraint. The effect of the welding operations on this plating tends to shrink it in size and, as a result of the boundary restraint, the plating is kept flat.

(d) Extent of tacking, and wandering sequence

This method is a variation of the drum-head or restraint method. If a considerable section of structure is heavily tacked or if a wandering sequence is employed which involves the virtually simultaneous completion of all welded connections, as opposed to successive completion frame by frame, there may be a considerable reduction in distortion due in part to restraint and part to reduction in local heating.

(e) Design

The importance of design in reducing distortion cannot be over-emphasized. In this classification falls the use of a minimum amount of filler metal, suitable arrangement of joints to avoid localized areas of extensive shrinkage, elimination of shift of butts in all-welded construction, etc. It is not always possible, however, for the designer to obtain such ideal conditions, since many basic specifications require modification and, further, a large proportion of ship draftsmen have not yet had an opportunity to familiarize themselves with the effect of welding shrinkage.

Corrective measures can be roughly classified as follows:

(a) Shrinkage

While varying in detail, this method consists of alternative heating and cooling, frequently accompanied by hammering or mechanical work, thus shrinking excess material in a wrinkle or buckle.

(b) Shrink welding

This is a variation of (a) above, in which the heat is supplied by running beads of weld metal on the convex side of a buckled area.

On cooling, the combined shrinkage of the heated parent metal and the added weld metal removes the distortion. The beads of weld metal may then be ground off if a smooth surface is desired.

(c) Added stiffening

This method, which is applicable only to plate panels, consists of pulling the plate into line by strong-backs and welding additional stiffening to the plate to make it retain its plane. In addition to the stiffness added, there is also benefit from shrinkage in the connecting welds.

It is important to note that certain of the preventive measures, notably drum-heading, extensive tacking, and the wandering sequence as well as the corrective methods of torch shrinking and shrink welding, are directly opposed to the theory that the structure should be free of residual stresses. The success of these measures is due to the fact that opposed and equal stresses are set up. Taken rather broadly, structures tend to relieve themselves by distortion. It follows that its prevention, or correction, means the creation of residual stresses in many instances.

IV—RESIDUAL OR "LOCKED-UP" STRESS

Welding procedure, by which is generally meant the sequence of operations in regard to both erection and welding, has been referred to above in connection with the control of shrinkage and distortion. It also has been closely studied and developed for two other purposes: first, to assure completion of a weld without total or partial failure, i.e. cracking; and second, to leave structures not adaptable to furnace stress relief in a satisfactory condition for service.

The satisfactory behavior of welded structures in service is predicated upon sound welds. The obtaining of sound and properly-fused welds, free of checks and incipient cracks, as well as slag, porosity, blow-holes, and the like, is therefore of major importance. To this end procedure includes much more than sequence of welding; in fact, other factors such as preheat, the continuity of the welding operation, peening, and an endeavor to assure a uniform distribution of stress over the joint are often of equal importance.

Procedure also shares importance with other factors in this matter of obtaining sound welds, namely, adequate inspection, suitable equipment, the proper training and qualification of operators, and not least important, the accessibility of the joint. Even the most carefully developed procedure cannot be depended upon to compensate for deficiencies in the other requisites for sound welds.

The reduction or elimination of residual stresses in the completed structure by means of a definite procedure intended to permit unrestrained shrinkage is the point which is generally given primary importance and on which there are, perhaps, the widest divergence of opinion and elements of controversy. Ship structures generally, with the exception of individual weldments for stern posts, etc., must be placed in service in the as-welded condition. The effect of residual or locked-up stress and the necessity, if any, for its consideration are therefore of primary importance and have received major consideration by the Subcommittee.

"Stress-free" procedure methods, which were referred to at the beginning of this report, are based on two fundamental assumptions:

1) That residual or locked-up stresses can be avoided or minimized by a welding procedure in which no positive external restraint prevents free shrinkage.

2) That these residual stresses are always detrimental and should be avoided at all costs.

Discussing these assumptions in order:

There has been a considerable volume of test data published in recent years on shrinkage stresses in the vicinity of welded joints of various types. Examination of these reports leads to the conclusion that the stress distribution in and near a welded joint is exceedingly complicated and indeterminate. Due to the nature of the process, involving high temperatures, there is plastic flow as well as elastic movement in adjacent parent metal. Time and temperature relations are affected by a large number of variables, some completely beyond the control of the operator, and others which vary widely with different operators. In most shipwelding processes, the filler metal is added literally drop by drop with that first deposited cooling more or less rapidly. Even in the highest speed automatic processes, with the possible exception of flash welding which is not applicable to ship joints in general, a large part of any welded joint has time to cool before completion of that joint and obviously supplies a high degree of restraint. Therefore, we may expect to find, as reliable investigations substantiate, the fact that high residual stresses exist irrespective of any external restraint.

The addition of external restraint may or may not increase the stresses in and near the joint. The lack of restraint probably prevents stressing the member generally, i.e. at a distance from the welded joint. If, however, stresses well beyond the yield point, resulting in permanent set exist in or adjacent to the welded joint, it appears illogical to employ elaborate means to reduce elastic stresses at points between welds.

The second assumption, namely that residual stresses are always detrimental and should be avoided at all costs, may also be seriously questioned both in theory and from a practical standpoint. Residual stresses compose an internal force system which obviously must be in equilibrium. When such a system is subjected to externally applied loads, there is no simple addition to like forces from which to conclude that some local point may be overstressed. For example, externally applied loading in tension cannot be additive to residual stresses of like sign until the balancing compressive stresses of the system in equilibrium are overcome. This principle is well established as in the case of pre-loaded bolts in cylinder head joints and has been demonstrated in a variety of test devices.

A rolled shape, as delivered from the steel mill, is in a similar state of locked-up stress. Investigators have measured residual stresses up to the yield point existing in rolled sections.[2] An indication of these stresses is the warpage of an I-beam when the web is split to form two T-sections, yet these beams are used safely under the assumptions of our beam formulas.

A further consideration which reduces the importance of residual stresses is the property of shipbuilding steels, all of relatively high ductility, to elongate under stress. Although the yield point is reached in comparatively slight extension, considerable elongation is required before such steels reach the point of failure. Before local points reach any appreciable part of this elongation the load has

[2] "Determination of Initial Stresses," Josef Mathar, A.S.M.E. Transactions, 1934; also A.W.S. Journal, July 1934.

been re-distributed with adjacent material assuming a larger proportion. This principle has been used for years in the "stretcher-leveling" of steel plates. In this method, the tendency of a plate to buckle and warp after rolling due to residual rolling stresses is removed by stretching the plate beyond its original elastic limit, thus re-distributing the stresses in a more uniform manner.

There is considerable evidence that residual stresses, whether induced by cold work such as rolling, bending, or flanging, or by hot work, either welding or shrinking, tend to distribute themselves and to reduce peak values particularly when subjected to external loading. I-beams which have been allowed to season do not warp on splitting to the same degree as beams used on receipt from the mill. Castings are frequently allowed to season, at ordinary temperatures, for the same reason. Stress-relieving by furnace treatment is in part an accelerated seasoning process. The critical time, therefore, in a welded structure is a period of somewhat indeterminate length beginning immediately after the welded joint is made. If exposed to sudden changes of temperature which induce highly localized stress before reasonable seasoning can take place, there is the possibility of failure. There have been few such cases in shipbuilding; nevertheless, they are not unknown and appear to account for the majority of plate or joint failures particularly during the winter months in northern yards.

A ship can be regarded, due to its watertight compartmentation, as a series of tanks or pressure vessels. So regarded, however, it would be classed as a thin-walled pressure vessel. In pressure vessel practice, it is well established that the necessity for stress relieving and the avoidance of cumulative residual stress of a probable biaxial nature, is a function of relative wall thickness compared to tank dimension. These ratios in a ship are so low that, by pressure vessel standards, stress relief is wholly unnecessary except in a few heavy weldments forming such items as stern post, rudder post, etc.

The Subcommittee believes that it is impracticable to set a limit on thickness of plating in which the presence of residual stresses is of minor importance. Experience in welded ships indicates that plates up to 1 in. thick may be welded successfully although restrained from free shrinkage. The rigidity of a structure, however, depends not only upon the thickness of plating, but on the relative degree or stiffening, the size and relative dimensions of unsupported panels, and many other factors which make generalization impossible.

From the purely practical standpoint, it may be pointed out that welded joints in large, and frequently complicated ship structures, can rarely be made under conditions which permit the uniformity of shrinkage, irrespective of any external restraint, that has been so frequently assumed. It can also be stated that such structures cannot be erected, regulated, and prepared for welding without an indeterminate degree of restraint. Regardless of the methods employed, it is a matter of practical experience that few structures approach the degree of freedom assumed in theoretical discussions of "stress-free" procedure. To avoid excessive distortion and subsequent straightening, considerable use is made of the step-back, extensive wandering, and berth systems of welding. It cannot be argued that these procedures, especially the latter two, permit the freedom of relative shrinkage which is assumed. The use of tack-welding and bolting, as actually carried out in practical shipbuilding, also denies such freedom of relative movement.

Mention has been made of the use of shrinkage methods to correct distorted structure. It appears highly illogical to take elaborate precautions to prevent or reduce residual stresses only to employ means in fairing the finished structure which depend for their effectiveness upon setting up residual stress.

It is likewise a matter of practical impossibility to complete all operations of welding large structures in perfect sequence. In new construction there are frequent closing or final joints which can be made only after previous work has reduced or entirely eliminated freedom to shrink. Moreover, in repair work as well as in major alterations to existing ships, it is impossible to avoid "locked-up" conditions. The vast number of these jobs, ranging from the replacement of a damaged shell plate to the extensive rebuilding of a ship, which have been accomplished over the past fifteen years and which have successfully stood up under all manner of service conditions is ample evidence that we depend not upon the elimination of residual stresses but upon the ability of the material to accommodate such stresses.

The considerations discussed in the foregoing have been based upon (a), service experience and observation, (b), reference to laboratory and test work by various investigators as published in the technical literature, and (c), tests and experiments made by individual shipyards in the course of their work. Much can be learned from the analysis of failures, perhaps even more than from wholly successful operations. In this phase of its work, however, the Subcommittee has encountered the usual difficulty in that failure of any structure involves the interests of so many individuals or groups that it is rarely possible to make an unbiased analysis of cause and effect, particularly for publication. So far as the Subcommittee is aware, service failures of ship structure in which welding shrinkage has played a possible part have been rare and, in comparison to the extent of work accomplished, insignificant. It is regrettable, nevertheless, that these instances, which might clarify much misunderstanding, have not or cannot be made available for unprejudiced analysis.

Shipbuilders in recent years have demonstrated that the welded ship suffers but little handicap in building cost or time where the structure is not complicated, or where the step by step, stress-free procedure is not rigorously applied. The importance of a reasonable and logical viewpoint toward residual stresses lies in removing these handicaps, so generally claimed in naval vessels and in more complicated types of merchant ship.

V—CONCLUSIONS

The Subcommittee, as individuals, concur in the following:

1) That the phenomenon of shrinkage is complicated by so many factors beyond the control of the shipbuilder that tables of predicted shrinkage are of no value.

2) That the detrimental effects of correcting distortion subsequent to the completion of the structure may be as serious as the residual stresses involved in most methods of prevention.

3) That residual stresses in ships, incident to joints welded under various and indeterminate degrees of restraint, do not appear to affect the strength of the structure in service provided:

a) The filler metal is deposited by electrodes conforming to Grade

E6010 of the filler metal specifications or equivalent process giving a similar degree of ductility.

b) The structural material is of proved welding quality.

c) Due care and diligence is observed in preventing, or detecting, stress cracks during and immediately following the welding operation.

VI—NOTES

The Subcommittee acknowledges with thanks the many comments and suggestions received from the membership of the Society's Technical Committees. Of these, possibly the most pertinent is the criticism that conclusion 3 (b) is not fully defined. So far as the Subcommittee is aware, welding quality has not been accurately or fully defined by any competent authority. A great deal of work has been done and a great deal of material has been published on this subject. In so far as ship construction is concerned, experience indicates that the steels in common use are of welding quality within the meaning of the Subcommittee's conclusions.

Since the comment of Professor Mortimer F. Sayre, of Union College, Schenectady, New York, has direct bearing on this matter of welding quality as well as upon other conclusions of the report, it is given below:

"Probably wisely, the report emphasizes the conditions under which residual stresses are not dangerous, rather than those under which they are dangerous. The reverse side of the picture could possibly tentatively be pictured as follows—and I offer this statement partly in order to elicit criticism with view to modification:

"In absence of defective workmanship residual stresses whether due to thermal or other causes become dangerous only if:

1) The material is brittle, with high resistance to plastic flow as compared to its resistance to cohesive failure.

2) The material is in a notch sensitive state, possibly measurable by unduly low notch impact value.

3) The piece is so thick and so rigid that it maintains its shape even after very high internal stresses have developed. This rigidity prevents plastic flow from occurring, sufficient to relieve these stresses.

4) The stress distribution is such that localized areas of three-dimensional tensile stress can be developed. At these points shearing stress is absent or negligible in amount, and so plastic flow with resulting relief from excessive stress does not occur.

5) Fatigue failures may occur in structures at points of alternating stress. Evidence seems to suggest however that in absence of the stress conditions noted in (3) and (4) above, failure will be due to the presence of stress raisers rather than to the presence of initial stresses."

Appendix 2

Welding Design*

Although welding has been extensively used in the fabrication of engineering structures for a number of years, there is still a decided lack of knowledge among engineers concerning the fundamental factors governing a satisfactory design. In addition, there is a lack of agreement among designers as to the methods of calculating weld stresses and the correct working stresses to employ for different types of joints. This article contains a discussion of a number of variables such as the selection of the proper joint, the calculation of weld stresses, the determination of working stresses and safety factors, and the important features governing a good welded design.

An analysis is made between butt and fillet welds in an effort to assist the designer in the selection of the proper type. Theoretical and practical aspects such as stress concentrations resulting from discontinuities in form, fabrication difficulties, welding costs, and distortion problems are considered.

The calculation of weld stresses in different types of joints is discussed and suitable formulas recommended on the basis of their agreement with test results, and their general applicability and acceptance in present design practice.

Working stresses and safety factors for butt and fillet welds are determined on the basis of static and dynamic tests. A table of recommended working stresses for bare and coated-electrode welds subjected to all types of loading is given to assist the designer. This table is based upon joints made on ordinary low-carbon structural steel.

A number of important design features that are essential in the design of economical welded structures are given. These features include the recommended minimum size of fillet welds for given plate

* By Charles H. Jennings. Reprinted by permission from the American Society of Mechanical Engineers *Transactions* for October 1936.

thicknesses, the application of intermittent welds in design, and the influence of joint design on the economical fabrication of butt joints.

An appendix is attached which contains a number of typical welded-joint designs with the corresponding recommended formulas for calculating the stresses.

The application of welding to the fabrication of engineering structures and equipment presents a great many problems to the designer. Some of these problems are the result of the inherent properties of the deposited metal and the characteristic shape of certain welded joints while others are the result of the designers' efforts to create new and economical designs. Although many of the problems encountered are still unsolved and require a great deal of further research, the vast amount of data and experience which have been accumulated are sufficient to design rationally all types of welded structures and machines.

To design a welded structure properly it is important that the designer be thoroughly familiar with the following items: (1) Methods of calculating weld stresses, (2) allowable working stresses, (3) physical characteristics of parent and weld metals, (4) fabrication problems, and (5) inspection and testing facilities. A welded design may be satisfactory from the standpoint of strength but entirely unsatisfactory from the standpoint of materials and fabrication.

A careful analysis should be made of each structure to insure that it can be fabricated economically. Welds must be designed and located so as to keep distortion of the finished product to a minimum. Rigid joints should be eliminated as much as possible to prevent the development of excessive residual stresses which might cause cracked welds during fabrication or ultimate failure in service.

The choice between butt and fillet welds is subject to much controversy although when properly designed and fabricated each has definite advantages and each is entirely satisfactory. The choice of materials and filler material will vary greatly for different products and will depend largely upon the service conditions, the designer's knowledge of the weldability of materials, and the fabricating facilities available. In many cases two or more materials can be used for a given structure but the selection of the proper one will result in considerable saving in both fabrication and materials costs.

It is the author's intention to discuss how working stresses are determined for welds and to outline briefly the methods of calculating stresses resulting from static and dynamic loadings. In addition, a number of rules covering important points of weld design will be given.

No attempt will be made to discuss the problems of fabrication such as welding procedures, elimination of distortion, and choice of materials, although they are connected closely with the design of a successful structure.

TYPICAL WELDED JOINTS

In the design of welded structures there are two general types of welds used, butt welds and fillet welds (1).* These welds may be used in making many types of joints such as ordinary butt and fillet joints between parallel plates, T joints between plates joining each other at an angle, corner joints, and joggled joints. The proper selection between butt and fillet welds is of importance both from the standpoint of economics and the service life of the structure. Unfortunately, however, no set rule can be applied for selecting the proper weld.

Fillet welds in general require less preparation of the parts preparatory to welding because the parts may be lapped or butted together without the necessity of spending a great deal of time in beveling or preparing the plate edges. If the plates are lapped it is not essential that their dimensions be held to close tolerances. A variation of ⅛ to ¼ in. in the amount of overlap of the plates will have no effect upon the strength of the joint providing the minimum requirements for overlap are maintained. Also if this variation is not the result of abrupt changes it will be impossible to detect it in the appearance of the completed structure.

In joints where the plates are butted at right angles to each other it is only necessary that the edge of the abutting plate be cut at right angles with the plate surface. This requires only a single cutting operation with the shear, cutting torch, or planer. The greatest problem encountered is to insure that the prepared edge is straight so

* Numbers in parentheses refer to Bibliography at the end of the paper.

that it will fit uniformly to the abutting plate. A space or gap between two abutting plates will reduce the effective size of the fillet welds and require that the weld size be increased by the amount of the gap. The increase in the size of a fillet weld caused by a gap between two plates may materially affect the amount of deposited metal required to make a weld of the required size. The percentage increase in the amount of weld metal required will be $[a(2h + a)100]/h^2$ where a represents the gap and h the required size of the weld. When making a $\frac{1}{2}$-in. weld between two plates, a $\frac{1}{16}$-in. gap represents an increase of 26.6 per cent in the amount of weld metal that must be deposited.

Butt welds in general require a better fit of the parts to be joined, and generally at least one of the butting edges is beveled * (thin plates excepted). Beveling of the plate edges is an added operation which must be considered in the cost of the structure.

The presence of a gap larger than necessary between the parts to be welded will also materially increase the amount of metal that must be deposited. Butt welds have an advantage over fillet welds in this respect however, because they are easier to inspect. After a fillet weld is made it is impossible to determine the presence of a gap between the parts by visual inspection; consequently, it is sometimes difficult to determine whether or not the weld is the correct size. This trouble is not encountered with butt welds because their particular design requires that the gap, if any, be entirely filled with weld metal.

The inherent shape of a fillet weld is such that it produces abrupt changes in the contour of the sections and consequently develops points of stress concentration. These stress concentrations are most severe at the root and toe (1) of the weld. Considerable theoretical work has been done on the investigation of fillet welds by photoelastic methods to determine the amount of stress concentrations. Solakian (2) found the stress at the root of a fillet to be six to eight times that of the average stress intensity in the connecting plates while the stress at the toe of the weld was three to five times the average stress intensity in the connecting plates. These stress concentra-

---

* There are a number of welding processes being developed where beveling of the plates is not required. These processes are still under development and cannot be used in all types of structures, consequently, they will not be considered in this paper.

tions varied with the external shape of the fillets and the amount of penetration and undercut present.

Butt welds in general have a more favorable form than fillet welds from the standpoint of irregularities which produce stress concentrations. A butt weld between parallel plates will produce no stress concentration providing it is a sound homogeneous weld and all the reinforcement has been removed. In actual practice, however, this condition is seldom obtained because nearly all butt welds have some reinforcement and a few internal flaws such as minute gas holes. Coker (3) found by photoelastic tests that the reinforcement on butt welds would produce a stress-concentration factor of 2.0. Small drilled holes representing flaws were also found to produce a stress-concentration factor of 2.0.

In cases where T joints are made between plates by using butt welds, there is the possibility of obtaining high stress-concentration factors at the junction of the plates. For fillet sizes of 0.05 in., the theoretical stress-concentration factor (4) will approach 2.5.

Under actual conditions, however, these stress concentrations are not as severe as the theoretical values might indicate. Under static loadings stress concentrations have little or no adverse effect upon the strength of a structure. The ultimate strength of the structure will not be lowered but the ability of the joint to deform plastically will be decreased somewhat, thereby tending to produce a more brittle type of fracture should failure occur. This apparent decrease in ductility does not weaken the structure.

In cases of dynamic loadings stress concentrations are of importance. Although from the data of Peterson and Wahl (4) it is evident that the actual reductions of fatigue strength for such cases of stress concentration as are applicable to welded joints are considerably less than photoelastic values.

This condition is true for holes and for surface irregularities. In the case of very small holes, the type generally obtained in welds, the reduction of fatigue strength was found to be small. Fatigue tests on welded joints, as will be discussed later, have given similar results.

The fact that certain stress concentrations are present in welded joints should not be considered cause for preventing their use on structures subjected to dynamic loads. In the majority of welded structures subjected to dynamic loads, the complete loading consists of a combination of static and dynamic forces. The stress-concentration factor K resulting from the joint characteristics is applied only to the variable portion of the loading as shown in Figure 17 and Equation [39], which will be discussed later. As a result, the increase in stress caused by the stress concentrations usually does not greatly increase the total stress on the joint.

From the standpoint of fabrication problems, two important points must be considered when selecting between butt and fillet welds.

Butt welds in general produce greater residual stresses. This fact has been proved experimentally and in production.

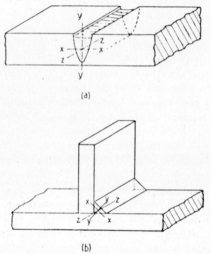

(a)

(b)

Figure 1: Directions of shrinkage when a weld cools.

The reason for higher stresses being developed by butt welds is primarily the result of their characteristic shape. When a section of deposited metal solidifies and cools it tends to shrink uniformly in all directions. Referring to Figure 1a, contraction tends to occur along the xx, yy, and zz axes. The contraction along the yy axis may be disregarded because the deposited metal is free and unrestrained at the top. The contraction along the xx axis tends to pull the plates together while the contraction along the zz axis tends to shorten the joint. Considering the contractions along the zz and xx axes, the latter is the more serious. This fact is readily realized when it is borne in mind that cracks in welds resulting from residual stresses are always parallel with the joint and not transverse as would be the case if the stresses along the zz axis were the more severe.

The degree of residual stress produced by the transverse contraction (along xx axis) is a function of the degree of fixity and the size of the plates. The reason such high stresses can be obtained is because this contraction produces a direct tensile force in the plates.

Considering fillet welds, shown in Figure 1b, it is again possible to confine the discussion to contractions along the xx axis for reasons similar to those previously mentioned. In this case, however, there is generally the possibility of a small movement between the plates resulting from the weld contraction which will greatly reduce the stresses. In addition, this contraction is in such a direction that it tends to bend the parts rather than produce transverse tensile forces in them. As a result some local distortion is apt to be obtained and the presence of this distortion means a reduction in the residual stresses.

The second point in connection with the influence of fabrication problems on the choice between fillet and butt welds is the method of making the welds. In order to increase the speed of welding it is desirable to deposit the weld metal in the down-hand position with large-diameter electrodes. Butt welds are ideal in this connection and are generally preferred. Fillet welds are of such a nature that in the normal horizontal position one fusion zone is in the vertical plane. This necessitates the use of small-diameter electrodes, if welds of the highest quality are desired, unless the parts can be positioned so as to simulate a butt weld and permit down-hand welding. Welding manipulators have been found very helpful under these conditions.

In cases where fillet welds of intermediate quality are satisfactory, special electrodes have been developed which make it possible to use $\frac{1}{4}$ in. diameters. Such cases make fillet welds as economical as butt welds.

Another factor in connection with the selection between butt and fillet welds is that butt welds allow the use of higher design stresses. This point will be discussed in detail later.

Reviewing the foregoing discussion, it is evident that both butt and fillet welds have definite advantages and the proper selection between them depends upon many factors. For a designer to create the most satisfactory and economical structure it is essential that all of these variables be carefully considered.

CALCULATION OF WELD STRESSES

The calculation of stresses in welds is of prime importance in connection with the design of every welded structure. Regardless of this fact, there is a surprising lack of agreement among authorities, particularly with reference to fillet welds, as to the proper methods of analysis. This lack of agreement may be attributed primarily to the characteristic shape of fillet welds and the many attempts to account theoretically for the nonsymmetrical stress distribution and the secondary bending moments encountered.

The object of this paper is not to give a highly theoretical analysis of the stresses in butt and fillet welds, but to discuss the commonly used methods and illustrate their application in the design of all types of structures and joints.

In the analysis of the following joints and connections the following notations will be used:

S = normal stress, lb. per sq. in.

S_s = unit shear, lb. per sq. in.

M = bending moment, in.-lb.

I = moment of inertia, inch units

K = stress-concentration factors

P = external load, lb.

h = size of weld, in. For fillet welds h represents the weld leg and for butt welds h represents the throat of the weld excluding reinforcement

l = length of a weld, in.

L = linear distance, in.

STRESSES IN BUTT WELDS

The calculation of stresses in a butt weld between parallel plates as shown in Figure 2 is a simple matter. The stress is equal to the external load acting on the joint divided by the throat area of the weld.*

$$S = P/hl \dots\dots\dots\dots\dots\dots\dots [1]$$

The stress in a butt weld due to shear loading is

$$S_s = P/hl \dots\dots\dots\dots\dots\dots\dots [2]$$

The values of h (weld throat) in Equations [1] and [2] do not include the reinforcement of the welds. Some authorities take the

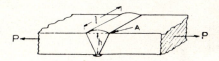

Figure 2: Typical butt joint.

reinforcement into account but this is a questionable practice. The reinforcement of a weld will vary greatly over its length and is a maximum at the throat section. At the junction of the weld and the parent metal, shown as point A in Figure 2, the reinforcement will approach zero, thereby making it the critical section. Also, reinforcement tends to produce stress concentrations which might be objectionable in cases of fatigue loadings.

The purpose of reinforcement on butt welds is to add an additional factor of safety to compensate for flaws which might be obtained when making the welds. As a result it is highly desirable in many cases but it should never be used by the designer as a method of developing the strength required to withstand the applied loads.

* The weld throat is defined as the minimum thickness of a fusion weld along a straight line passing through its root (1).

STRESSES IN FILLET WELDS

The stress distribution in fillet welds has been proved by photo-elastic methods to be nonuniform (2, 3). In addition, their particular shape causes certain secondary bending moments which can-

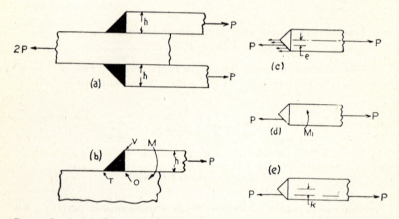

Figure 3: (a-b) Transverse fillet weld. (c-e) Equilibrium of forces in a transverse fillet weld.

not be determined accurately and which tend to increase or decrease the stresses at different points in the weld. Because of these facts many attempts have been made to calculate fillet-weld stresses with the result that numerous formulas have been derived (5, 6, 7, 8). These formulas are all based upon arbitrary assumptions, consequently, none are strictly correct. For this reason only the generally accepted formulas will be considered.

Transverse Fillet Welds. In the generally accepted method of computing stresses in transverse fillet welds it is assumed that the stress at the throat section * is principally a normal tensile stress. (Photoelastic tests by Dustin (9) tend to justify this assumption.)

* The throat section of a weld is considered to be the critical section.

The stress on the throat section of a fillet weld shown in Figures 3a and b transmitting a load P is therefore taken as

$$S = \frac{P}{\text{weld throat}} = \frac{P}{0.707hl} = \frac{1.414P}{hl} \dots \dots [3]$$

where 0.707 = cosine of 45 deg.

If the force P acts through the center of the welded bar as shown in Figure 3b, it will produce a bending moment M on the weld and the stress given by Equation [3] will not be the complete stress. On a joint of the type shown in Figure 3a, however, a transverse force acts between the overlapping surfaces of the joint and this force produces some bending moment M_1 as indicated in Figure 3d which acts in the opposite direction to the bending moment M caused by the force P. A shearing force also results from this reaction but it is probably small in comparison to the other forces and will be neglected. The force P and the moment M_1 shown in Figure 3d can be represented by a force P eccentrically applied to the welded member as shown in Figure 3e. The condition of equilibrium will be obtained when the bending moment M_1 is of such a value that the eccentricity k causes the load P to act along the center line of the weld throat. This is possibly the condition that occurs in a fillet weld at the point of failure. Consequently, the stress values obtained by this method are comparable to what would be expected from tests on all weld-metal test specimens.

There are certain cases in design when fillet welds are used on only one side of a plate as shown in Figures 4a and b. In joints of this type there is no counteracting bending moment present as the result of the overlapping plates pressing against each other. Consequently, a bending moment resulting from the joint eccentricity must be considered.

Referring to Figure 4c, it is seen that the weld throat is subjected to a tensile force P and a bending moment resulting from the eccentricity of the force P acting along the fusion zone OH. This bending moment M is equal to Ph/4.

The stress resulting from the direct load P is

$$S = \frac{1.414P}{hl} \dots \dots [4]$$

In determining the stress resulting from the bending moment M a rectangular stress distribution is assumed. (This is the type of stress distribution that is obtained before the weld fails in tension.) Here

$$S = \frac{4M}{(0.707h)^2 l} = \frac{4Ph}{4(0.5)h^2 l} = \frac{2P}{hl} \dots \dots \dots \dots [5]$$

This bending stress increases the stress at the root O and decreases the stress at the outer edge of the throat. As a result the root stress is the critical stress and the total stress is obtained by adding Equations [4] and [5]

$$S = \frac{1.414P}{hl} + \frac{2P}{hl} = \frac{3.414P}{hl} \dots \dots \dots \dots [6]$$

It is seen that for a given load P the stress obtained by Equation [6] is about 2.4 times the stress obtained by Equation [3].

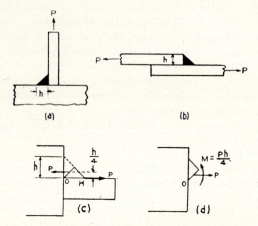

Figure 4: (a-b) Non-symmetrical fillet welds. (c-d) Forces in non-symmetrical transverse fillet weld.

Ultimate stresses in joints of the type shown in Figure 4a as calculated by Equation [6] agree fairly well with results that would be expected from the tensile strength of the weld metal.

Parallel Fillet Welds. Parallel fillet welds are assumed to be subjected only to shearing stresses. The stress distribution along the weld is not uniform, although it is generally considered as such when calculating the stress. Smith (10) has shown experimentally that the stress at the ends of the welds is considerably higher than the average stress. (The exact value of the end stresses depends upon the length and size of weld and the size of the parts welded.) Weiskopf and Male (11) and Hovgaard (12) obtained similar results analytically.

Regardless of this fact, however, tensile tests made by Vogel (13), the U. S. Navy, and the Structural Steel Welding Committee of the American Bureau of Welding (14) indicate that the strength of such welds is directly proportional to the weld size and the weld length. As a result, the assumption that the stress is uniformly distributed over the entire length of the weld appears justified for normal design practice.

The shear stress in parallel fillet welds is calculated by dividing the load transmitted by the weld throat. This shear stress is

$$S_s = \frac{P}{\text{weld throat}} = \frac{1.414P}{hl} \quad \ldots\ldots\ldots\ldots\ldots\ldots\ldots\ldots [7]$$

In cases where extremely long parallel welds are used, a formula based upon experimental constants has been derived by Rossell (15) which takes into account the stress distribution in the weld. In general welding design, however, there is no requirement for this formula, consequently, it will not be included.

STRESS CALCULATIONS FOR TYPICAL CONNECTIONS

Equations [1] to [7], inclusive were derived for simple butt and fillet welds in tension and shear. In the following, typical joints subject to bending, tension, and shearing loads will be considered by applying these same equations.

When considering lap or T fillet-welded joints containing two parallel or transverse welds loaded in tension or compression as shown in Figure 5, the load should be considered uniformly distributed between the welds. The weld stress is

$$S = \left(\frac{P}{2}\right)\frac{1.414}{hl} = \frac{0.707P}{hl} \quad \dots \dots \dots \dots \dots \dots [8]$$

If plates of unequal thickness are used in combination with transverse fillet welds as shown in Figure 6a, the load distribution be-

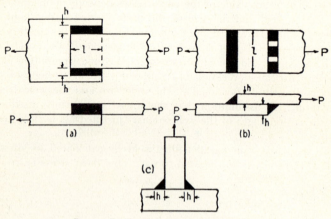

Figure 5: Typical fillet-welded joints.

tween the welds is proportional to the thickness of the plates because the plate sections between the welds do not distribute the load uniformly. Referring to Figure 6a, the stress in weld A is

$$S = \frac{a}{(b+a)}\frac{1.414P}{hl} \quad \dots \dots \dots \dots \dots \dots [9]$$

and stress in weld B is

$$S = \frac{b}{(b+a)}\frac{1.414P}{hl} \quad \dots \dots \dots \dots \dots [10]$$

If side welds are used in making a lap joint between plates of unequal thickness, the load is considered uniformly distributed between the welds because the load distribution between the plates does not affect the load distribution on the welds. In this case Equation [8] applies.

Stresses in lap joints containing combinations of parallel and transverse fillet welds as shown in Figure 6b and c are computed by assuming the load uniformly distributed between the welds. Although

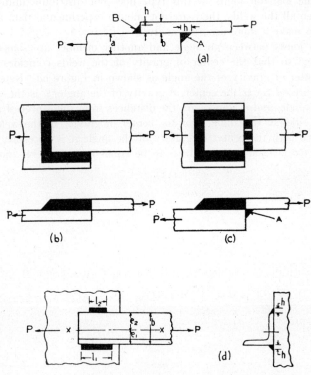

Figure 6: (a) Fillet-welded joint between plates of unequal thickness. (b-c) Fillet-welded joints containing both transverse and parallel welds. (d) Joint between an angle and a plate.

this is the generally accepted method of calculating the stresses in joints of this type the load is actually not uniformly distributed between the welds. Tests have shown that parallel (side) welds deform more under load than transverse (end) welds. As a result the transverse welds will take more than their normal share of the load and will fail first. If the plates are of unequal thickness as shown in Figure 6c, weld A will be the highest stressed. Although it is known that the load on joints of this type does not distribute uniformly between all the welds, there are not enough experimental data available to make a more accurate analysis.

Lap joints between an angle and another member are sometimes designed so that the center of gravity of the welds coincides with the center of gravity of the angle as shown in Figure 6d. Referring to Figure 6d, xx is the center of gravity of the angle, b is the width of the angle, and e_1 and e_2 are the distances from the center of gravity to sides of the angle. For the center of gravity of the welds to coincide with the center of gravity of the angle it is necessary that $l_1e_1 = l_2e_2$. Assuming the stress to be equal in both welds then

$$S = \frac{1.414P}{h(l_1 + l_2)} \dots\dots\dots\dots\dots\dots\dots [11]$$

also

$$l_2 = \frac{l_1e_1}{e_2} \dots\dots\dots\dots\dots\dots [12]$$

Substituting the value of l_2 in Equation [11] and simplifying

$$S = \frac{1.414Pe_2}{hl_1(e_2 + e_1)} = \frac{1.414Pe_2}{hl_1b} \dots\dots\dots\dots\dots\dots [13]$$

Similarly

$$S = \frac{1.414Pe_1}{hl_2b} \dots\dots\dots\dots\dots\dots [14]$$

The value of distributing the welds so that their center of gravity coincides with the center of gravity of the angle is open to question. Griffith (16) made comparative tests between joints of this design and joints having the weld uniformly divided, and proved one is equally as good as the other. Initial yielding occurred at approximately the same loads and the ultimate strength was approximately the same. On the basis of Griffith's tests and experience obtained on many structures, the author is of the opinion that it is unnecessary to design a joint on angle bars so that the centers of gravity of the angle and welds coincide.

Transverse fillet-welded joints subjected to bending as shown in Figure 7a and b are often found in machines. The weld stresses in

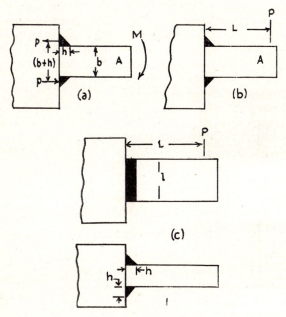

Figure 7: (a-b) Transverse fillet welds loaded in bending. (c) Longitudinal fillet welds loaded in bending.

this type of joint are computed by assuming the bending moment M to be counteracted by a couple composed of forces p acting at the center of the vertical fusion zones of the welds as shown in Figure 7a. Therefore, $M = p(b + h)$, or

$$p = \frac{M}{(b + h)} \quad \dots \dots \dots \dots \dots \dots \dots [15]$$

The weld stress is

$$S = \frac{1.414p}{hl} = \frac{1.414M}{hl(b+h)} \quad \cdots\cdots\cdots\cdots\cdots [16]$$

If a transverse load is applied to the member A as shown in Figure 7b in place of a bending moment, the weld will be subjected to stresses resulting from the shearing force of the load P and the bending moment PL. Several methods have been suggested for combining these forces to determine the weld stress. The simplest and most commonly used method is given in the following paragraphs. This method is admittedly only an approximation but tests made on joints having a wide ratio of shearing and bending forces indicate that it gives satisfactory results (17).

Assuming both welds to be of equal length l, the shearing force on each weld will be $(P/2)$. From Equation [15], the force on each weld resulting from the bending moment PL will be

$$p = \frac{PL}{(b+h)}$$

The weld stress is computed by dividing the resultant of these two forces by the weld throat. Therefore, the weld stress is

$$S = \frac{1.414 \sqrt{\left[\left(\frac{P}{2}\right)^2 + \left(\frac{PL}{b+h}\right)^2\right]}}{hl} \quad \cdots\cdots\cdots\cdots [17]$$

$$S = \frac{P}{hl(b+h)} \sqrt{\left[2L^2 + \frac{(b+h)^2}{2}\right]} \quad \cdots\cdots\cdots\cdots [18]$$

If the term $(b+h)$ is small in comparison to L, Equation [18] approaches Equation [16] for pure bending.

Parallel fillet-welded joints subjected to bending as shown in Figure 7c are also commonly used. Stresses in this type of joint are calculated on the basis of the weld-throat sections' being subjected to the bending moment. The same formula is used in calculating the weld stress regardless of whether the bending is caused by a pure bending moment or a cantilever load. This, of course, is the result of the shearing stress being zero at the ends of the weld where the bending stresses are a maximum.

Referring to Figure 7c the bending moment acting on each weld is

$$M = PL/2 \dots \dots \dots \dots [19]$$

The section modulus of a weld throat is

$$\frac{0.707hl^2}{6} \dots \dots \dots \dots [20]$$

Therefore, the stress resulting from the bending moment is

$$S = \frac{6PL}{2(0.707)hl^2} = \frac{4.24PL}{hl^2} \dots \dots \dots \dots \dots [21]$$

If a bar is fillet-welded to another member by welds on all sides as shown in Figure 8a and subjected to a bending moment, the stress is calculated as follows:

The bending moment M_1 which is resisted by the transverse welds A can be calculated by Equation [16] where

$$S_1 = \frac{1.414M_1}{hl(b+h)} \quad \text{or} \quad M_1 = \frac{S_1hl(b+h)}{1.414} \dots \dots \dots \dots [22]$$

The bending moment M_2 which is resisted by the longitudinal welds B can be calculated by Equation [21] where

$$S_2 = \frac{4.24\,M_2}{hb^2} \quad \text{or} \quad M_2 = \frac{S_2hb^2}{4.24} \dots \dots \dots \dots [23]$$

If the maximum stress in all welds is the same, then $S_1 = S_2$ or $\dfrac{1.414\,M_1}{hl(b+h)} = \dfrac{4.24\,M_2}{hb^2}$

$$M_1 = M_2 \frac{3l(b+h)}{b^2} \dots \dots \dots \dots [24]$$

but $M = M_1 + M_2$. Therefore, by substituting in Equation [24],

$$M = M_2 \frac{3l(b+h)}{b^2} + M_2$$

$$M = M_2 \left[1 + \frac{3l(b+h)}{b^2} \right] \dots \dots \dots \dots [25]$$

Substituting Equation [23] in Equation [25] and solving for S

$$S = \frac{4.24\,M}{h[b^2 + 3l(b+h)]} \quad \ldots\ldots\ldots\ldots\ldots\ldots [26]$$

The stress in a round bar, fillet-welded to another part and subjected to a bending moment as shown in Figure 8b, is calculated by

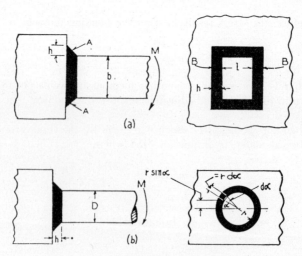

Figure 8: (a) Fillet-welded bar subjected to bending. (b) Fillet-welded shaft subjected to bending.

assuming the stress in each weld element to be proportional to its distance from the neutral axis. It is also important in the derivation of the weld stress in this joint to bear in mind that the stress in the weld throat is (1/0.707) times the shear stress in the fusion zone of the weld, where 0.707 is the cosine of 45 deg.

Assuming an elementary area of the fusion zone $hr\,da$, shown in Figure 8b, on the periphery of the round bar at an angle a with the neutral axis subjected to a shearing force, df, the stress will be

$$ds = \frac{df}{hr\,da} \quad \ldots\ldots\ldots\ldots\ldots\ldots [27]$$

Also, if S_s is the maximum shearing stress then

$$\frac{S_s}{r} = \frac{ds}{r \sin \alpha} \text{ or } ds = S_s \sin \alpha \ldots \ldots \ldots \ldots [28]$$

Therefore, by substituting the value of ds in Equation [27]

$$df = S_s \sin \alpha \, hr \, d\alpha \ldots \ldots \ldots \ldots \ldots [29]$$

The bending moment developed by the force df is

$$dm = S_s hr^2 \sin^2 \alpha \, d\alpha \ldots \ldots \ldots \ldots [30]$$

By integrating Equation [30], the shearing stress S_s is obtained in terms of the bending moment M acting on the joint, or

$$S_s = \frac{M}{hr^2 \pi} \ldots \ldots \ldots \ldots \ldots \ldots [31]$$

The stress in the weld throat as a function of the bending moment and the diameter of the welded bar will be

$$S = \frac{4M}{0.707 h D^2 \pi} = \frac{5.66 \, M}{\pi h D^2} \ldots \ldots \ldots \ldots [32]$$

where 0.707 is the cosine of 45 deg.

If a welded joint of a design similar to that shown in Figure 8b is subjected to torsion the weld stress is obtained as follows:

The torque M is resisted by the shearing force in the weld throat acting at a distance $D/2$ from the center of the joint

$$M = \text{shearing force} \times D/2 \ldots \ldots \ldots \ldots [33]$$

The shearing stress resulting from this shearing force is equal to the force divided by the weld throat. Therefore

$$S_s = \frac{2M}{0.707 \pi D^2 h} = \frac{2.83 \, M}{h D^2 \pi} \ldots \ldots \ldots \ldots [34]$$

When making a butt joint in a tension member it is often found necessary to reinforce the joint by an additional butt strap fillet-welded across the joint. This condition arises because the allowable design stress in a butt weld is not as high as the design stress for the parent material. If the parent material is stressed at 18,000 lb. per sq. in., and only 13,000 lb. per sq. in. is allowed on the butt weld, the entire member must be increased in size to bring the stress down to 13,000 lb. per sq. in., or a reinforcing bar must be added to carry the excess load. The latter of the two methods is usually the more economical.

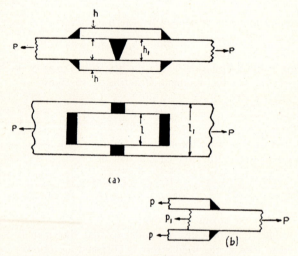

Figure 9: Reinforced butt joint.

When designing a joint of this type it is desirable to place a butt strap on both sides of the joint in order to eliminate secondary bending moments. This procedure, however, is not always practical. In such cases a bending moment is present which tends to increase the stress on the side of the butt weld away from the strap. If the butt weld is of the single V type it is desirable to have the root of the weld next to the strap.

The total elongation of all the plates that comprise the joint must be the same, assuming that the fillet welds do not deform. Consequently, the stresses in all the plates must be equal because the stress is directly proportional to the elongation. Also, if the stresses in the various plates are equal, the loads transmitted by the plates must be proportional to their cross-sectional areas.

If the load transmitted by each butt strap is p and the load transmitted by the butt-welded plate is p_1 as shown in Figure 9b, then, because the load is proportional to the cross-sectional area of the plates

$$p = \frac{Phl}{(2hl + h_1l_1)} \dotfill [35]$$

and

$$p_1 = \frac{Ph_1l_1}{(2hl + h_1l_1)} \dotfill [36]$$

The stress in the fillet welds by using Equation [3] is

$$S = \frac{1.414Phl}{(2hl + h_1l_1)hl} = \frac{1.414P}{(2hl + h_1l_1)} \dotfill [37]$$

The stress in the butt weld by using Equation [1] is

$$S = \frac{Ph_1l_1}{(2hl + h_1l_1)h_1l_1} = \frac{P}{(2hl + h_1l_1)} \dotfill [38]$$

The welded joints that have been considered do not comprise all the joints that are used on welded structures. They do, however, cover the joints most commonly used, and the methods used in calculating the stresses can be applied in a similar manner to other types of joints.

Figures 12–15 show a number of typical welded joints with the corresponding formulas for calculating the stresses. These formulas are based upon the methods of stress calculation discussed.

DETERMINATION OF WORKING STRESSES

In the design of any welded joint it is important to know what safe working stresses can be used. The allowable working stresses are obtained from experimental tests by reducing the ultimate strengths or endurance limits obtained by a suitable factor of safety.

Many tests have been made on both fillet and butt welds. Consequently, it is not a difficult matter to obtain sufficient test data from which satisfactory design stresses may be determined.

There are two general types of welding electrodes used in the fabrication of welded structure; bare electrodes and coated or shielded arc electrodes. Typical physical properties of weld metal deposited by bare and coated electrodes are given in Table 1.

Extensive tests on butt-welded joints indicate that the physical properties of butt welds are comparable to the physical properties of all weld metal. This condition is true regardless of the joint design, providing the weld is sound and homogeneous.

The working stresses for butt welds made with bare electrodes as recommended by the American Welding Society in the Structural Steel Welding Committee (18) and machinery construction codes (19) are given in Table 2.

Comparing the allowable stresses for static tension and compression given in Table 2 with the minimum ultimate strength of weld metal deposited with bare electrodes given in Table 1, it is seen that a safety factor of 3.4 is used in tension and 2.5 in compression. It is the author's opinion that the safety factor in compression is too small. The design stress for bare-electrode welds subjected to compression should be 15,000 lb. per sq. in. This represents a safety factor of 3.

The working stress for butt welds in static shear is 11,300 lb. per

---

TABLE 1

PHYSICAL PROPERTIES OF METAL DEPOSITED BY BARE AND
COATED ELECTRODES

Property	Bare electrode		Coated electrode	
	Min.	Max.	Min.	Max.
Yield point, lb. per sq. in.	35000	40000	42000	55000
Ultimate strength, lb. per sq. in.	45000	55000	60000	70000
Elongation in 2 in., per cent.	8	15	25	35
Reduction of area, per cent.	15	20	45	65
Endurance limit, lb. per sq. in.	16000	20000	26000	30000
Impact strength, Izod, ft.-lb.	5	15	40	50
Density, g. per cc.	7.5	7.6	7.81	7.85

sq. in. This is 87 per cent of the working stress for static tension and may be questioned.

Tests made on butt welds in shear by the Westinghouse Electric and Manufacturing Company, the Structural Steel Welding Committee of the American Bureau of Welding (14) and the U. S. Navy indicate that the shearing strength of butt welds is about 65 per cent of the tensile strength. This ratio of shearing strength to tensile agrees closely to the theoretical ratio of 58 per cent as obtained by the shear-energy theory (20, 21).

In order to have the working stress in shear in agreement with the other values it should be approximately 60 per cent of the working stress in tension or 8000 lb. per sq. in. (8000 lb. per sq. in. is 61.8 per cent of 13,000 lb. per sq. in.).

The allowable working stress for butt welds subjected to dynamic loads should be the same for both tension and compression. For complete reversal of load, the design stress can be obtained from the endurance limit of butt joints or weld metal. Using 16,000 lb. per sq. in., which is a typical fatigue value for butt welds, and a safety factor 3.2, a working stress of 5000 lb. per sq. in. is obtained. This is the value used by the Westinghouse Electric and Manufacturing Company and agrees very well with that recommended by the A.W.S. machinery code (19). For dynamic shearing stresses a value about 60 per cent of 5000 should be used, or 3000 lb. per sq. in. This value is about 12 per cent lower than that recommended by the A.W.S. machinery code (19).

Considering coated or shielded-arc electrode welds, it is seen from

---

TABLE 2

RECOMMENDED WORKING STRESSES FOR BUTT WELDS MADE WITH BARE ELECTRODES

	Structural code	Machinery code
Static tension, lb. per sq. in.	13000	13000
Static compression, lb. per sq. in.	18000	18000
Static shear, lb. per sq. in.	11300	11300
Dynamic tension, lb. per sq. in.	...	5100
Dynamic compression, lb. per sq. in.	...	7000
Dynamic shear, lb. per sq. in.	...	3400

Table 1 that the tensile strength is from 27 to 30 per cent greater than the tensile strength of bare-electrode welds. Therefore, it is satisfactory to increase the working stresses for static tension, compression, and shear to 16,000, 18,000, and 10,000 lb. per sq. in., respectively. The percentage increase in all cases is 25 per cent or less.

For dynamic loadings with this type of electrode using the minimum value of 26,000 lb. per sq. in. and a safety factor of 3.25, a working stress of 8000 lb. per sq. in. is obtained for tension and compression. The working stress for shear loadings can be established at 5000 lb. per sq. in. (62.5 per cent of 8000 lb. per sq. in.).

The tensile strength of fillet welds varies depending upon the design of the joint because of the type of loading, secondary bending moments and the approximate formulas used in calculating the weld stresses. In a report published by the Structural Steel Welding Committee of the American Bureau of Welding (14) it was found that side (parallel) fillet welds were approximately 25 per cent weaker than end (transverse) fillet welds. This is, of course, what would be expected because side welds are stressed in shear while end welds are stressed principally in tension. Also joints containing some eccentricity were found to be weaker than symmetrical joints.

In determining the working stress it has been the practice to use the weaker joints as the criterion, thereby having only one working stress for all types of fillet welds.

The working stress recommended by the Structural Steel Welding Committee (14) and the A.W.S. machinery code (19) is 11,300 lb. per sq. in. This value is derived on the basis of a tensile strength of 42,000 lb. per sq. in. and a safety factor of 3.7 (the stress of 42,000 lb. per sq. in. is the weighted average of some 761 specimens tested by the Structural Steel Welding Committee of the American Bureau of Welding).

This working stress appears to be entirely satisfactory and has been used for several years with good success. It is also very convenient because it represents a load-carrying capacity of 1000 lb. per linear in. per $\frac{1}{8}$ in. of weld. In other words, a $\frac{1}{8}$-in. weld 1 in. long will carry a 1000-lb. load; a $\frac{3}{8}$-in. weld 1 in. long will carry a 3000-lb. load and so on.

The fact that welds made with coated electrodes are from 27 to 30 per cent stronger than those made with bare electrodes makes it possible to increase their working stress to 14,000 lb. per sq. in. (This value is 24 per cent greater than 11,300 lb. per sq. in.) This working stress is also convenient to employ because it is approximately equivalent to the decimal equivalent of the weld times a factor of 10,000. A ⅛-in. weld 1 in. long will carry 1250 lb.; ½-in. weld 1 in. long will carry 5000 lb., and so on.

The establishment of working stresses for fillet welds subjected to dynamic loadings is a difficult problem because of the large variation in the results which have been obtained. Also, in many cases the results given are based upon failure in the parent metal at the end of the weld and not in the weld metal. As a result they do not give fatigue values of the weld. Fatigue data on parent-metal failures at the ends of welds are important, however, in determining the stress-concentration factor at that point in the joint.

Fatigue tests made by the author and R. E. Peterson (22) on transverse fillet welds (bare electrodes) by means of rotating specimens, gave endurance limits of the 13,000 to 17,000 lb. per sq. in. for the weld. These tests also gave endurance limits for the parent metal at the weld toe of 18,000 lb. per sq. in. Kommerell (23) obtained endurance limits of 9200 to 14,600 lb. per sq. in. Hankins (24) obtained endurance limits of 9000 lb. per sq. in. for bare-electrode welds and 16,000 lb. per sq. in. for coated-electrode welds, while Roberts (25) obtained endurance limits of 17,900 lb. per sq. in. for bare electrodes. Ros and Eichinger (26) obtained values of about 18,000 lb. per sq. in. (computed by the author on the basis of recommended formulas) on coated electrodes.

On the basis of these data a working stress of 3000 lb. per sq. in. for transverse fillet welds made with bare electrodes and 5000 lb. per sq. in. for transverse fillet welds made with coated electrodes appears satisfactory. The fatigue strengths of parallel fillet welds are slightly lower than those of transverse fillet welds. Hankins (24) found them to be about 13 per cent less, Ros and Eichinger (26) about 19 per cent less and Roberts (25) about 25 per cent less. Kommerell (23), however, found parallel welds to be about 20 per cent stronger than transverse welds. Because of the large safety factor used for transverse fillet welds it is satisfactory to use the same design stress for longitudinal fillet welds. This greatly simplifies the design of fillet-welded joints and is in agreement with the method employed in selecting the static working stress for fillet welds.

Because the parent metal is weakened at the end or toe of a weld as a result of metallurgical changes and stress concentrations, it is desirable to determine the stress-concentration factor at these points. The stress-concentration factors given are based upon mild-steel parent metal. In cases where medium carbon or alloy steels are used, these stress-concentration factors may be greater because of more serious metallurgical changes.

Fatigue tests made by the author and the authorities mentioned indicate that the endurance limit of mild steel is reduced to about 18,000 lb. per sq. in. (22) at the toe of a transverse fillet weld. This corresponds to a stress-concentration factor of 1.5 (the endurance limit of mild steel is approximately 27,000 lb. per sq. in.). This fac-

---

TABLE 3

WORKING STRESSES AND STRESS-CONCENTRATION FACTORS FOR WELDS ON LOW-CARBON STEELS

| | Working stresses bare electrodes | | Coated electrodes | |
| | Static loads, lb. per sq. in. | Dynamic loads, lb. per sq. in. | Static loads, lb. per sq. in. | Dynamic loads, lb. per sq. in. |
Type of weld				
Butt welds:				
Tension	13000	5000	16000	8000
Compression	15000	5000	18000	8000
Shear	8000	3000	10000	5000
Fillet welds:				
Transverse and parallel welds	11300	3000	14000	5000

Stress-concentration factors

Location	Stress-concentration factor, K
Reinforced butt welds	1.2
Toe of transverse fillet weld	1.5
End of parallel fillet weld	2.7
T butt joint with sharp corners	2.0

tor appears to be the same for welds made with both bare and coated electrodes.

The endurance limit at the end of parallel fillet welds is 10,000 to 13,000 lb. per sq. in. This corresponds to a stress-concentration factor of 2.7.

On reinforced butt welds Roberts (25) obtained stress-concentration factors of 1.2 as compared to machined butt welds.

For T joints made with butt welds and having a right-angle corner, a stress-concentration factor of 2.0 will be found satisfactory.

The working stresses and stress-concentration factors that have been derived are given in Table 3. The stress-concentration factors given are applicable for welds made with both bare and coated electrodes, and need only be used in cases where dynamic loads are encountered.

COMBINED STATIC AND DYNAMIC LOADS

The design of structural members subjected to simple static or dynamic (complete reversal of stress) loadings is an easy matter on the basis of the previous design stresses given. In most structures this simple condition is seldom encountered, however, because most members are subjected to various combinations of static and dynamic loadings.

The accumulation of experimental data obtained on specimens under various combinations of static and dynamic loadings has made it possible to determine certain relationships. If the steady stress is plotted as abscissas against the variable stress as ordinates, the experimental curve will take the shape shown by the dotted line in Figure 10. Gerber approximated this curve as a parabola while Goodman approximated it as a straight line between the endurance limit and the ultimate stress. It will be noted, however, that the curve dips toward the yield point. Therefore, it is more simple and conservative to connect the endurance limit with the yield point as shown by the dot-and-dash line in Figure 10 (27).

The line connecting the yield point and the endurance limit is assumed to represent the combinations of steady and variable stresses that will cause failure. It is necessary in design practice, however, to employ a suitable factor of safety. Consequently, the working stresses for variable and steady loads are used in place of the endurance limit and yield point, respectively. This confines the permissible stresses within the shaded area of Figure 10.

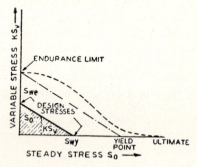

Figure 10: Relation between steady and variable stress.

The relation between the steady stress S_o and the variable stress S_v as defined by the straight line joining the variable working stress S_{we} and the steady working stress S_{wy} (28) is

$$\frac{KS_v}{S_{we}} + \frac{S_o}{S_{wy}} = 1 \quad \dots\dots\dots\dots\dots [39]$$

The steady stress S_o is equal to one half the algebraic sum of the maximum and minimum stresses applied to the member or joint. The variable stress S_v is equal to one half the algebraic difference between the maximum and minimum stresses and the factor K is the stress-concentration factor for dynamic loads. If the maximum stress is S_{max} and the minimum stress is S_{min} then

$$\frac{K(S_{max} - S_{min})}{2S_{we}} + \frac{(S_{max} + S_{min})}{2S_{wy}} = 1$$

and

$$S_{max}(S_{we} + KS_{wy}) + S_{min}(S_{we} - KS_{wy}) = 2S_{we}S_{wy} \quad \dots\dots\dots\dots [40]$$

If the loading of a joint is known, the weld size can be calculated by substituting in Equation [40] the proper expressions for S_{max} and S_{min} in terms of the loads and the weld size.

To illustrate the application of Equation [40], consider a butt weld between 1-in. plates. This weld is made with coated electrodes, the reinforcement is not removed, and the tensile load on the joint varies from 10,000 to 40,000 lb. The required length of the weld is determined as follows:

From Equation [1], $S = (P/hl)$. Therefore, by substituting the value of S in Equation [40]

$$\frac{P_{max}}{hl}(S_{we} + KS_{wy}) + \frac{P_{min}}{hl}(S_{we} - KS_{wy}) = 2S_{we}S_{wy}$$

$$l = \frac{P_{max}(S_{we} + KS_{wy})}{2h\,S_{we}S_{wy}} + \frac{P_{min}(S_{we} - KS_{wy})}{2h\,S_{we}S_{wy}}$$

From Table 3, $S_{we} = 8000$ lb. per sq. in., $S_{wy} = 16,000$ lb. per sq. in., and $K = 1.2$. Solving for l

$$l = \frac{40,000\,[8000 + (1.2 \times 16,000)]}{2 \times 1 \times 16,000 \times 8000}$$
$$+ \frac{10,000\,[8000 - (1.2 \times 16,000)]}{2 \times 1 \times 16,000 \times 8000}$$

$l = 4.2 - 0.44 = 3.76$ or 3.75 in.

If the load on this joint varied from 40,000 lb. tension to 40,000 lb. compression (complete reversal of load) the required length would be

$$l = \frac{40,000\,[8000 + (1.2 \times 16,000)]}{2 \times 1 \times 16,000 \times 8000}$$
$$- \frac{40,000\,[8000 - (1.2 \times 16,000)]}{2 \times 1 \times 16,000 \times 8000}$$

$l = 4.25 + 1.75 = 6$ in.

If a welded joint were subjected to shearing stresses, Equation [40] still applies but the working stresses for shear are used.

GENERAL DESIGN NOTES

The design of a welded structure does not consist of simply designing the many joints to withstand the necessary loads. There are many economic and fabrication problems which must be considered in order to make the most satisfactory structure. In some cases these problems may be of sufficient importance to make the fabrication of the structure entirely impractical.

The ideal welded structure is composed of the fewest parts possible joined with the minimum amount of weld metal that is adequate for fabrication and service requirements. Whenever possible flanges and adjacent members should be bent from the same plate to eliminate corner welds. Structural steel plates and shapes cost about 2¢ a pound while deposited weld metal costs about $0.50 to $1 a pound. Consequently, the advantage of reducing the amount of welding is readily recognized.

When butt welds are used, the plate edges need not be beveled for thicknesses $\frac{1}{4}$ in. or less. The edges of heavier plates however should be beveled to form some type of V joint. The best design of the joint; that is, whether it is a single or double bevel, single or double V, single or double U, or single or double J will depend upon a number of factors.

Oxyacetylene and oxyhydrogen cutting, is, in general, the cheapest method of preparing bevels for butt joints. It is adaptable to complicated shapes and suitable only for cutting plane kerf surfaces. Machining is particularly adapted for U-type joints, for cases where an excellent fit is required, and for parts of such a nature that they can be machined at a relatively low cost.

Double U- and V-type joints are recommended for plates $\frac{3}{4}$ in. thick and over if it is possible to weld from both sides of the plate. This type of joint produces less distortion of the welded parts and reduces the amount of weld metal necessary to weld a plate of a given thickness.

TABLE 4. MINIMUM-SIZE FILLET WELDS FOR DIFFERENT THICKNESSES OF PLATE

Plate thickness, in.	Minimum weld size, in.
$\frac{1}{8}$ to $\frac{3}{16}$, inclusive	$\frac{1}{8}$
$\frac{1}{4}$ to $\frac{5}{16}$, inclusive	$\frac{3}{16}$
$\frac{3}{8}$ to $\frac{5}{8}$, inclusive	$\frac{1}{4}$
$\frac{3}{4}$ to 1, inclusive	$\frac{3}{8}$
$1\frac{1}{8}$ to $1\frac{3}{8}$, inclusive	$\frac{1}{2}$
Above $1\frac{1}{2}$	$\frac{3}{4}$

The U-type joint with its rounded bottom makes it possible to make the first passes with an electrode of any desired diameter. The V-type joint is generally narrow at the bottom, consequently, the first passes must be made with small-diameter electrodes. Regardless of this fact, however, experience indicates that on plate thicknesses up to 1 in. there is little or no difference between the welding speeds obtained on the two types of joints.

The width of the bottom of a U-type joint greatly influences the welding cost. On plates up to 1 in. in thickness, it is advantageous to design the joint so that the first passes can be made with large-diameter electrodes. On plates over 1 in. in thickness, it is advantageous to design the joint for small-diameter electrodes on the first passes.

When using fillet welds in any design it is important to remember that to double the size of a weld it is necessary to deposit four times as much weld metal. This fact often has an important influence in determining whether to use continuous or intermittent welding.

If a weld is designed on the basis of stress only, it is often possible that very small welds will be satisfactory. Experience has shown, however, that there is a minimum-size fillet weld that should be applied to a given plate thickness, if a sound strong weld is to be obtained. Recommended minimum-size fillet welds for different plate thicknesses, are given in Table 4.

When a continuous weld of the minimum size exceeds the required strength, and the weld is not required to be leakproof, intermittent welds may often be used. The minimum length of an intermittent weld should be at least four times the size of the fillet and never shorter than 1 in. A certain amount of time is required for a welder to start and stop a weld; consequently, it is recommended that welds longer than 1 in. be used whenever possible in order to reduce their cost.

Two types of intermittent welding are used, staggered and chain welding, as shown in Figure 11. The choice between the two types is open to controversy. The staggered welding, however, has the advantage of producing a joint stiffness approximately equivalent to that of chain welding by using only half as much welding.

Recommended spacings for intermittent welds limit the maximum center-to-center spacing between increments to 16 times the thickness of the thinner member for compression, and 32 times the thickness of the thinner member for other loadings. In no case, however, should the spacing be greater than 12 in. between adjacent welds. (This spacing is somewhat greater than that permitted by the U. S. Navy on ship construction but it is entirely satisfactory for machinery and structures.)

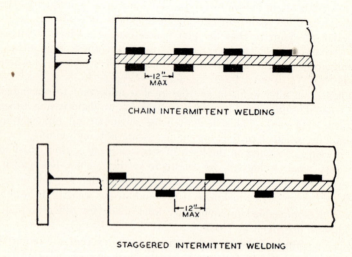

CHAIN INTERMITTENT WELDING

STAGGERED INTERMITTENT WELDING

Figure 11: Types of intermittent welding.

In cases where two parts are lapped together and it is possible to use either parallel or transverse fillet welds, it is recommended that parallel welds be used because the load is generally more evenly distributed between the welds.

When fabricating such items as frames and bed plates from bars, plates, angles, or channels, it is generally preferred to use straight cut-off pieces rather than mitered ends to form the corners.

Bearing pads and other parts that require subsequent machining should have the welds designed strong enough to withstand the machining forces which may be larger than the service loads. Pads that have a width of over 12 times their thickness should be plug-welded at the center to prevent the center from bulging. The diameter of plug welds should be made from 2 to 4 times the thickness of the plate.

The general design of all structures should be such as to eliminate rigid and fixed joints as much as possible. Such joints tend to develop high internal stresses which will cause difficulty in fabrication and may impair the service life of the structure.

Equipment that requires close machining tolerances, and that will be subjected to dynamic service loads, should be stress-relieved after welding whenever possible. This stress-relieving process should consist of heating slowly to 1100 or 1200° F., soaking for 1 hour per inch of thickness and cooling slowly to at least 300° F. before removing from the furnace.

CONCLUSION

It has been the aim of this paper to discuss briefly the essential factors of welding design. Many of the equations derived for computing the weld stresses are admitted to be approximate but experience has proved them to be adequate in all respects.

Figures 12–15 on the following pages show a number of typical welded joints with the corresponding formulas for calculating the stresses. The formulas are based upon the methods of calculating stresses discussed in the paper.

The working stresses and stress-concentration factors given are for welds made on mild low-carbon steels. When welding steels or materials of other types, other working stresses must be used. These values may be obtained from experimental tests in a similar manner.

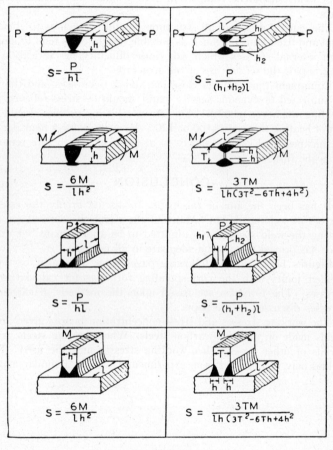

Figure 12.

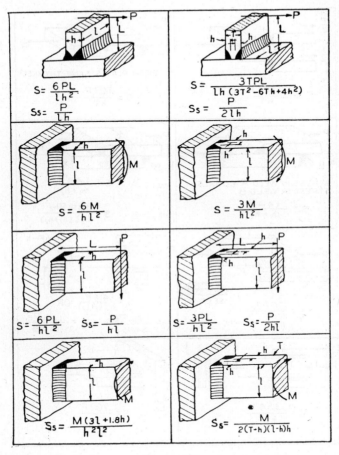

Figure 13.

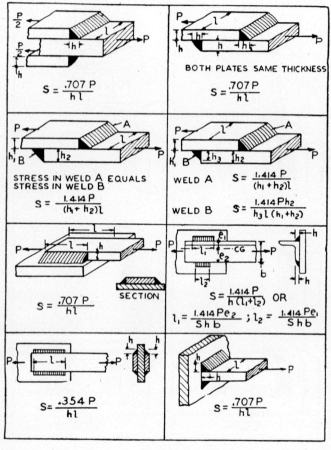

Figure 14.

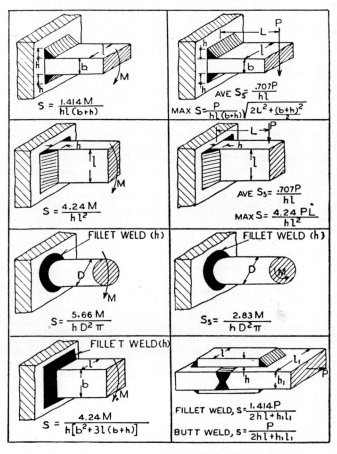

$$S = \frac{1.414\,M}{hl\,(b+h)}$$

$$\text{AVE } S_{\overline{s}} = \frac{.707P}{hl}$$

$$\text{MAX } S = \frac{P}{hl\,(b+h)}\sqrt{2L^2+\frac{(b+h)^2}{2}}$$

$$S = \frac{4.24\,M}{h\,l^2}$$

$$\text{AVE } S_s = \frac{.707P}{hl}$$

$$\text{MAX } S = \frac{4.24\,PL}{h\,l^2}$$

FILLET WELD (h)

$$S = \frac{5.66\,M}{h\,D^2\,\pi}$$

FILLET WELD (h)

$$S_s = \frac{2.83\,M}{h\,D^2\,\pi}$$

FILLET WELD (h)

$$S = \frac{4.24\,M}{h\,[b^2+3l\,(b+h)]}$$

FILLET WELD, $S = \dfrac{1.414\,P}{2hl+h_1 l_1}$

BUTT WELD, $S = \dfrac{P}{2hl+h_1 l_1}$

Figure 15.

ACKNOWLEDGMENT

The writer is indebted to R. E. Peterson, manager, mechanics division, Westinghouse Research Laboratories, for his interest and assistance in the preparation of this article.

BIBLIOGRAPHY

1 "Welding and Cutting Nomenclature, Definitions and Symbols," The American Welding Society, 33 West 39th Street, New York, N. Y.

2 "Stress in Transverse Fillet Welds by Photoelastic Methods," by A. G. Solakian, *The American Welding Society Journal*, vol. 13, 1934, pp. 22–29.

3 "Stress Analysis of Fusion Joints," by E. G. Coker, Symposium on the Welding of Iron and Steel, The Iron and Steel Institute, London, England, vol. 2, 1935, p. 703.

4 "Two- and Three-Dimensional Cases of Stress Concentration, and Comparison With Fatigue Tests," by R. E. Peterson and A. M. Wahl, *Journal of Applied Mechanics*, vol. 3, March, 1936, p. A-15 (Trans. A.S.M.E., vol. 58, 1936).

5 "Fusion-Welded Pressure Vessels," Technical Report, British Engine Boiler and Insurance Company, Ltd., 1928, pp. 26–28.

6 "The Theory of Stresses in Welds," by L. C. Bibber, *The American Welding Society Journal*, vol. 9, 1930, p. 104.

7 "A Review of Stresses in Welded Joints," by A. Jaeger, *Here's How It's Welded*, vol. 2, January, 1934, p. 25.

8 "Riveting and Arc Welding in Ship Construction," by H. E. Rossell, Simmons-Boardman Publishing Company, New York, N. Y., 1934.

9 "Fundamental Principles of Arc Welding," by H. Dustin, Lincoln prize paper in "Arc Welding," McGraw-Hill Book Company, New York, N. Y., 1929, p. 193.

10 "Stress-Strain Characteristics of Welded Joints," by J. H. Smith, *The American Welding Society Journal*, vol. 8, September, 1929, p. 79.

11 "Stress Distribution in Side-Welded Joints," by W. H. Weiskopf and M. Male, *The American Welding Society Journal*, vol. 9, September, 1930, p. 43.

12 "Stress Distribution in Longitudinal Welds and Adjoining Structures," by W. Hovgaard, *Journal of Mathematics and Physics*, vol. 13, May, 1934, p. 195.

13 "Design of Joints for Welded Steel Structures," by A. Vogel, *The American Welding Society Journal*, vol. 8, April, 1929, p. 68.

14 "Report of the Structural Steel Welding Committee of the American Bureau of Welding," The American Welding Society, 33 West 39th Street, New York, N. Y., 1931.

15 "Riveting and Arc Welding in Ship Construction," by H. E. Rossell, Simmons-Boardman Publishing Company, New York, N. Y., 1934, p. 158.

16 "Effect of Fillet Welds on Eccentricity," by J. R. Griffith, *Welding,* vol. 4, January, 1933, p. 11.

17 "Combined Stresses in Fillet Welds," by C. D. Jensen, *The American Welding Society Journal,* vol. 13, February, 1934, p. 17.

18 Code for "Fusion Welding and Gas Cutting in Building Construction," The American Welding Society, 33 West 39th Street, New York, N. Y., 1934.

19 Tentative code for "Fusion Welding and Flame Cutting in Machinery Construction," The American Welding Society, 33 West 39th Street, New York, N. Y., March, 1935.

20 "Strength of Materials," by S. Timoshenko, D. Van Nostrand Company, Inc., New York, N. Y., vol. 2, 1930, p. 711.

21 "Plasticity," by A. Nadai, McGraw-Hill Book Company, New York, N. Y., 1931, p. 72.

22 "Fatigue Tests on Fillet Welds," by R. E. Peterson and C. H. Jennings, Proceedings, American Society for Testing Materials, vol. 30, part 2, 1930, p. 384.

23 "Results of Fatigue Strength Tests on Welded Connections," by Dr. Ing. O. Kommerell, The American Institute of Steel Construction, New York, N. Y., 1936.

24 "Fatigue Tests and Non-Destructive Tests of Welds," by G. A. Hankins, Symposium on the Welding of Iron and Steel, Iron and Steel Institute, New York, N. Y., vol. 2, 1935, p. 811.

25 "Fatigue of Welds," by A. M. Roberts, Symposium on the Welding of Iron and Steel, Iron and Steel Institute, London, England, vol. 2, 1935, p. 831.

26 "The Strength of Welded Connections," by M. Ros and A. Eichinger, Symposium on the Welding of Iron and Steel, Iron and Steel Institute, London, England, vol. 2, 1935, p. 843.

27 "Electrically Welded Structures Under Dynamic Stress," by M. Stone and J. G. Ritter, *Journal of the American Institute of Electrical Engineers,* vol. 49, March, 1930, p. 202.

28 "Working Stresses," by C. R. Soderberg, *The Journal of Applied Mechanics,* vol. 2, September, 1935, p. A-106 (Trans. A.S.M.E., vol. 57, 1935).

Index